A Guide to

Sound Ship Structures

A GUIDE TO
SOUND SHIP STRUCTURES

By

AMELIO M. D'ARCANGELO

Professor of Naval Architecture and Marine Engineering, University of Michigan

Prepared for the Ship Structure Committee
under the general direction of the Ship
Structure Subcommittee National Academy
of Sciences–National Research Council.

CORNELL MARITIME PRESS, INC.

Cambridge   **Maryland**
1964

Contents

Foreword

The wealth of information developed through ship structural research is not always reduced to a form usable by the naval architect. Even less often is technical data made available for practical use by shipyard production personnel.

The extent and complexity of the ship's structure make it impossible for the designer to show on his plans each of the infinite number of details in the construction of the vessel. No matter how good the basic ship design, some imperfection in a minor detail can easily reduce—and sometimes almost completely destroy—the strength of the hull structure. Recognizing the important part that shipyard workmen play in many details of shipbuilding, the Ship Structure Committee* authorized the preparation and publication of *A Guide to Sound Ship Structures*.

The *Guide* is not a design manual. It is primarily intended for use by draftsmen, loftsmen, shipfitters, riveters, welders, and other ship craftsmen in understanding the "why" and "how" of good workmanship in the construction of the ship, and particularly in those areas over which they exercise some degree of control.

Originally meant to be only a working handbook, the *Guide* was considerably expanded during its development to include the many good reasons for careful attention to quality of construction in structural details. The usefulness and effectiveness of the *Guide* should be correspondingly increased through greater understanding on the part of its users.

The author, Professor A. M. D'Arcangelo, was selected because of his unique combination of technical knowledge in ship design and his practical experience in shipbuilding. The Project Advisory Committee has thoroughly enjoyed working with Professor D'Arcangelo in the preparation of the *Guide*. His patience and understanding in the face of sometimes supercritical comment was admirable, and the committee congratulates him on the end result of his labors.

The assistance of the Subcommittee on Hull Construction, Committee on Welding in Marine Construction, American Welding Society, in coordinating this publication with their *Hull Welding Manual* (AWS D3.5-62) is gratefully acknowledged.

---

* The Ship Structure Committee is composed of the following member agencies: Bureau of Ships, Department of the Navy; Military Sea Transportation Service, Department of the Navy; United States Coast Guard, Treasury Department; Maritime Administration, Department of Commerce; American Bureau of Shipping.

This handbook was prepared under the terms of Contract NObs-74584, Index No. NS-021-201 between the Bureau of Ships, Department of the Navy, and the National Academy of Sciences–National Research Council. The work was carried out as Subproject SR-148 of the Ship Structure Subcommittee.

The opinions expressed herein do not necessarily represent those of the Ship Structure Committee or of its member agencies. The data included herein likewise should not be interpreted as the rules or requirements of the several regulatory bodies.

The manuscript was periodically reviewed during its preparation and finally in its finished form and has been approved for publication.

The Project Advisory Committee

MEMBERS OF THE PROJECT ADVISORY COMMITTEE

M. Mack Earle, P.E., Chairman
Consulting Naval Architect

D. B. Bannerman, Jr.
Vice President—Technical
American Bureau of Shipping

Ralph D. Bradway
Welding Engineer
New York Shipbuilding Corp.

Daniel Costello, Jr.
Chief Draftsman
Friede and Goldman, Inc.

Grayson B. Hanes
Preliminary Design Branch
U. S. Maritime Administration

Meredith Johnson
Supervisor, Structure and Form Sections
Bureau of Ships, Navy Department

Wiley E. Magee
Merchant Marine Technical Division
United States Coast Guard

Robert H. Miller
Naval Architect and Chief Engineer
Manitowoc Shipbuilding, Inc.

Frank L. Pavlik
Naval Architect
Sun Shipbuilding and Drydock Co.

Preface

The purpose of this *Guide,* as implied in the title, is to promote sounder ship structures.

In recent years significant progress has been achieved in the understanding of conditions leading to ship structural failures, particularly those of a catastrophic nature. This better understanding has resulted in the adoption of design and building practices which have reduced substantially the number and magnitude of failures.

A broad and intensive research program during the last two decades has resulted in many enlightening and valuable publications on the subject of ship structures.

It has been felt for some time, however, that the useful information obtained through research and service experience has not in all cases reached the man in the shipyard or drafting room who can best put this knowledge to practical use. One of the principal aims of this publication is to correct this situation. The *Guide* contains also valuable and useful material for practicing engineers and for students in ship structures.

The first section of this *Guide* presents fundamentals of mechanics of materials and of ship strength. This material makes the publication a self-contained unit.

The remaining sections of the *Guide* include numerous examples of objectionable engineering practice in ship structures and suggest remedies and improvements. The good and bad engineering features in these examples are explained rationally, enabling the reader to analyze situations other than those presented in the publication.

Finally, the *Guide* introduces and refers the reader to an extensive and valuable bibliography in the field of ship structures.

This *Guide* was written under the supervision of an authoritative group of specialists in the field of ship structures. These highly-qualified professionals who served on the Advisory Committee for this project are listed in the Foreword. I am greatly indebted to the committee members for their help, guidance and encouragement throughout the writing of this book. In particular, I want to thank Mr. M. Mack Earle for his enthusiastic and effective chairmanship, and Mr. Wiley E. Magee for his many contributions to this publication quite beyond his role of advisor. Any merit this publication may have is due to the Advisory Committee.

Sources for this publication have been acknowledged in general throughout the text, and we are most grateful for this help. We would like to thank also the following firms and organizations which contributed valuable material not acknowledged elsewhere: American Bureau of Shipping, Kawasaki Dockyard Co. Ltd., Manitowoc Shipbuilding, Inc., and Maryland Shipbuilding and Drydock Co.

A group of professionals to whom I am particularly indebted for their encouragement and inspiration are those who during the writing of this book occupied the following positions: Chairman, Ship Structure Sub-committee; Secretary, Ship Structure Committee; Director and Executive Secretary, National Research Council of the National Academy of Sciences.

In addition, there would be a long list of individuals who worked on the typing of the several drafts of the *Guide* and who prepared the illustrations. To all of them my sincere appreciation, for without their help this book would not have been possible.

Finally, my deepest gratitude to my wife for her help in editing the several drafts and for her patience and understanding throughout the long and arduous period of preparation of the manuscript.

Amelio M. D'Arcangelo

Ann Arbor, Michigan

A Guide to

Sound Ship Structures

SECTION I

Stresses and Strains on Ships

INTRODUCTION

Before studying the design and fabrication of structural details in ships, a thorough understanding of some of the basic principles of ship's strength is necessary.

The structure of the completed ship, under all possible conditions of loading, must be able to withstand the most violent sea states to be experienced, without structural failure which would endanger the vessel.

This section explains the basic types of ship loading which may result in tension, compression, shear and bending stresses.

Ship areas and specific locations where stresses and strains may be significant are indicated in as much detail as the scope of this publication permits.

Definitions and explanations are given for some of the most important and frequently used expressions in ship structures, such as brittle fracture, section modulus, strength deck, stress concentration, etc.

The problem of ship's strength is treated fully in several books which the reader may consult if a more complete or advanced treatment of the subject is desired (see refs. 1 and 21).*

TENSION AND COMPRESSION STRESSES

In Fig. 1-1 we have two solid metal bars, and in each case two equal and opposite longitudinal forces, P, applied along their centers. The effect of the applied forces, P, at any cross section of area A is shown apart from the bars in insets B and C. We have the forces P applied to the section under consideration, but they can be replaced by a group of forces s each corresponding to a unit of area. The total of the s forces is the force P. Applied forces per unit area (per square inch, for example) of the type of s forces are called *stresses* and we will refer to them as such from now on. Stresses are usually expressed in pounds per square inch (psi).

By looking at Fig. 1-1(a), we see that in this case the stresses s tend to "extend" or "stretch" the metal. This action is called *tension* and results in *tension stresses*, $s = s_t$. The opposite is shown in Fig. 1-1(b) where the stresses s tend to "contract" or "shrink" the material by an action called *compression* which produces *compression stresses*, $s = s_c$.

---

* References listed at the end of this publication.

1-1

TENSION AND COMPRESSION STRAINS

As a result of the application of the *tension forces* P to the metal bar of Fig. 1-1(a), any original length such as *ab* has stretched to a value *ac*. In the metal bar of Fig. 1-1(b), the *compressive force* P has shortened the original length *ab* to the *ac* value. The differences between the original lengths *ab* and the final lengths *ac* are called *deformations*. The deformation per unit length of the bar is called *strain*. Therefore, we have *tension strains* in Fig. 1-1(a) and *compression strains* in Fig. 1-1(b). Within usual load limits in ship structures (where the behavior is elastic), strain is proportional to stress. For example, by doubling the stress, the strain is also doubled.

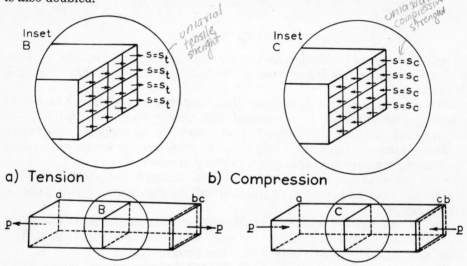

Inset B

Inset C

uniaxial tensile strenght

uniaxial compressive strenght

a) Tension

b) Compression

FIG. 1-1.   Bars in tension and compression.

BODY OF UNIFORM WEIGHT AND CROSS SECTION FLOATING IN STILL WATER

Figure 1-2 represents a piece of timber floating in still water. If the timber is solid all the way through and has a constant cross section, the weight and the volume per foot of length will be constant from one end to the other. Because the volume is constant all along the length, the *buoyancy* (support received from the water) will also be constant and will balance the weight at any point. Under these conditions the timber, when considered as a beam or a girder, is not stressed or deformed by the acting forces of weight and buoyancy.

LOCAL VARIATIONS OF WEIGHT AND BUOYANCY IN A SHIP IN STILL WATER, SHEAR AND BENDING

A ship floating in still water is subject to upward or buoyancy forces and downward or weight forces. These forces are represented in Fig. 1-3, which shows a ship divided in five sections by means of watertight bulkheads numbered from one to five, starting from the bow. Within each one of these sections, we have considered the weight (shown by the arrows on deck) and buoyancy (shown by the arrows on the bottom) to be evenly distributed. Downward forces were assigned the negative sign and upward forces the plus sign. The difference between weight and buoyancy for each section is represented by a heavy central arrow, with a quantity in tons at the arrowhead. The plus sign indicates an excess of buoyancy for the section and a minus sign indicates an excess of weight.

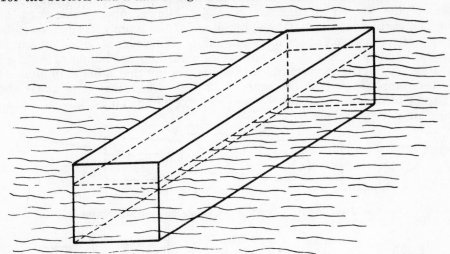

FIG. 1-2.　Body of uniform weight and cross section floating in still water.

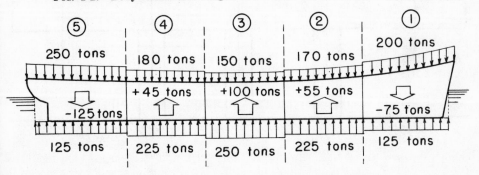

FIG. 1-3.　Forces acting on a ship in still water.

Although the buoyancy and weight forces balance each other for the ship as a whole, there is no longer a point-to-point balance as was the case with the floating timber of uniform weight and cross section. This is clearly shown by Fig. 1-3, and if we were to cut the ship at the four transverse watertight bulkheads, each one of the sections would float at a different draft, as indicated by Fig. 1-4, where the dashes indicate the original waterline.

It is evident, then, that in the intact ship all along its length there are upward and downward vertical forces, as shown by the arrows in Fig. 1-3, which tend to change its longitudinal shape (*see also* Fig. 1-4). These vertical forces are called *shearing forces* because they tend to cut or shear the ship into vertical slices.

The loading condition of the ship in Fig. 1-3 can also be represented by Fig. 1-5, where the ship has been replaced by a solid horizontal beam. Each upward force represents the excess of buoyancy for one of the original ship sections, and each downward force represents an excess of weight. Looking at Fig. 1-5, it is obvious that the actual loading will bend the ends of the beam downwards. As a result of this action, the upper fibers of the beam will be stretched and the lower fibers contracted, or adopting earlier definitions, the upper fibers of the beam will be stressed in tension and the lower fibers in compression. Whenever a beam similar to the one illustrated in Fig. 1-5 undergoes a loading producing stresses of opposite type in the upper and lower fibers, we say that a *bending moment* has been applied, or that the beam is in *bending*, or that it is under the influence of *bending stresses*. By analogy, the same can be said of a ship under similar conditions.

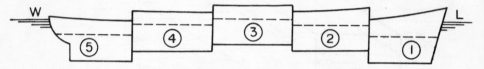

Fig. 1-4. Relative draft of five ship's slices in still water.

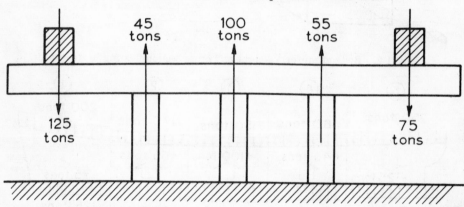

Fig. 1-5. Beam-ship loading analogy.

Ship's Hogging and Sagging Conditions

With the aid of Figs. 1-3, 1-4, and 1-5, we saw how bending stresses can be developed in a ship floating in still water, as a result of the unequal distribution of the buoyancy and weight.

When the ship is in a seaway, the waves with their crests and hollows produce greater differences between weight and buoyancy, and, as a result, generally greater bending moments and correspondingly greater bending stresses are generated. Dynamic effects due to the movement of the ship at sea can further increase these stresses. Figure 1-6 represents the ship centered on the crest of a wave, producing tension on deck and compression on the bottom, as illustrated (hogging condition). Figure 1-7 represents the ship centered on the hollow of a wave, producing compression on deck and tension on the bottom, as illustrated (sagging condition).

LONGITUDINAL SHEAR

We have already seen how vertical shear forces were developed on a ship floating in still water, Figs. 1-3 and 1-4. Forces of the same type but of greater magnitude are present when the ship experiences the hogging and sagging conditions, such as indicated in Figs. 1-6 and 1-7.

Let us now consider a composite beam made up of several layers of flat bars kept pressed together but free to slide at the contact or bearing surfaces, Fig. 1-8(a). When we apply a bending moment to this beam, as shown in Fig. 1-8(b), the contact surfaces of the individual bars will slide with respect to each other and produce a staggered end surface as indicated. In this function, each flat bar will act as an independent member and, for the bending condition shown in Fig. 1-8(b), the result will be compression at the top of any individual bar and tension at the bottom.

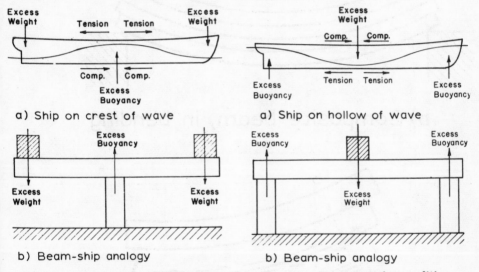

a) Ship on crest of wave

b) Beam-ship analogy

FIG. 1-6. Ship in hogging condition.

a) Ship on hollow of wave

b) Beam-ship analogy

FIG. 1-7. Ship in sagging condition.

If, however, there is a (metallic) bond between the layers to eliminate their sliding, an end configuration such as line *ab* in Fig. 1-8(c) would result in place of a staggered end surface. This straight line configuration is the same as if the beam were solid instead of in layers. To achieve this condition, the stress pictured in Fig. 1-8(c) must develop in the bonding material to prevent slippage along the horizontal plane surfaces. (For brevity only, the stresses at the lower contact surfaces are shown.) The same tendency will be present at any horizontal plane in a solid bar or in a ship in bending. This tendency to cut or shear the ship in longitudinal slices is called *longitudinal shear* and is resisted by the horizontal layers of bonding metal, whether in the parent plate material or in horizontal joint material.

LONGITUDINAL STRESS DISTRIBUTION

Let us first consider a beam of rectangular cross section subject to bending. This is represented by Fig. 1-9, where the forces P and 2P cause the beam to deform in the manner illustrated, due to bending.

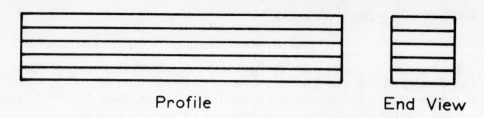

Profile   End View

a) Composite beam, unstressed

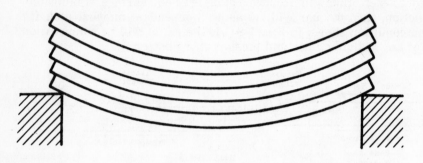

b) Composite beam, in bending

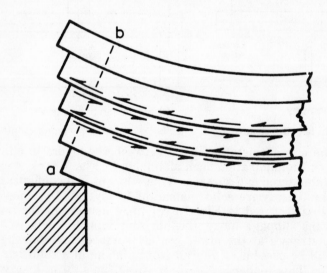

c) Fragment of composite beam showing stresses at the contact surfaces

FIG. 1-8. Composite beam showing longitudinal shear.

The same figure shows a cross section, FF, of the beam. It also demonstrates clearly that the upper fibers of the beam must stretch (in tension) while the lower ones shrink (in compression) and, therefore, somewhere in between, the fibers will neither stretch nor shrink. The position of the unstrained fibers is called the *neutral axis;* for the rectangular beam under consideration, it is at the middle of its depth. The line NA is the neutral axis.

In Fig. 1-10, the portion BCDE of the beam of Fig. 1-9 is shown at a larger scale. The bending moment, produced by the forces P and 2P, results in the stresses shown in Fig. 1-10. It will be seen that there are no stresses at the neutral axis, while stresses increase gradually, from zero at the neutral axis to a maximum at the outside fibers of the beam. For the loading under consideration, the tension stresses reach a maximum value at the uppermost fibers, while compression stresses reach theirs at the lowermost fibers. The reverse would be true if the loading were similar to that of Fig. 1-7, as then compression would reach a maximum at the top and tension a maximum at the bottom of the beam. At various points in the depth of the beam, the nearer the points are to the neutral axis, the smaller the tension or compression is for the same amount of bending.

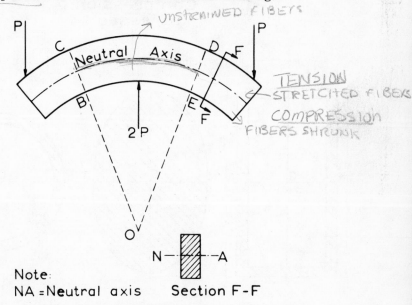

Note:
NA = Neutral axis   Section F-F

FIG. 1-9.   Rectangular beam in bending.

GEOMETRIC PROPERTIES OF A STRUCTURAL MEMBER

There are three geometric properties of structural members which are of special interest when considering the longitudinal stress distribution in a beam in bending. These are the neutral axis of a beam, the moment of inertia, and the section modulus of its cross section.

The *neutral axis* of the beam, as illustrated in Figs. 1-9 and 1-10, corresponds to the position of its unstrained fibers when in longitudinal bending. To find the position of the neutral axis, it is necessary to consider the

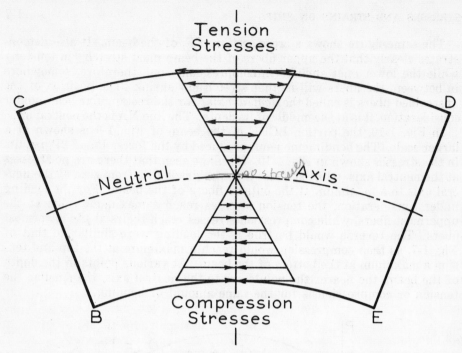

FIG. 1-10. Longitudinal stress distribution in a beam in bending.

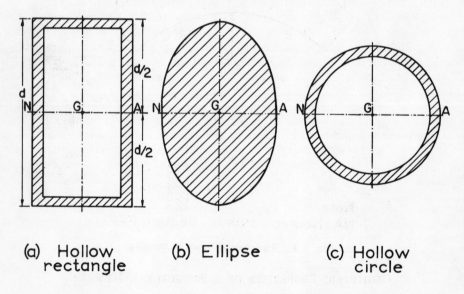

(a) Hollow rectangle   (b) Ellipse   (c) Hollow circle

Notes: (1) "NA" is the neutral axis of the figure, which is a cross section of a beam in longitudinal bending.

(2) "G" is the center of gravity of the figure, as well as the center of symmetry, in the figure shown above.

FIG. 1-11. Location of the neutral axis for three symmetrical geometric figures.

cross section of the beam (section FF in Fig. 1-9). When the beam cross section is vertically symmetrical, the location of the neutral axis will be a horizontal straight line located at mid-depth of the section. Figure 1-11 shows the location of the neutral axis for three such symmetrical geometric figures.

When the cross section of the beam is not a symmetrical geometric figure, the location of the neutral axis is more complicated. Since the neutral axis always contains the center of gravity of the cross section, G, determination of this G point also will locate the neutral axis. There are mathematical and arithmetical methods to determine the location of the center of gravity of composite geometric figures which the reader will find in any applied mechanics textbook. An elementary, practical method to determine the center of gravity of an irregular plane figure is explained in Fig. 1-12 (the cross section of an I-beam is illustrated).

The *moment of inertia* of the cross section is another geometric property of the beam. From a practical standpoint, this property is a measure of a beam's ability to resist deflection. When this property is doubled, a beam under a given condition of loading will deflect (in hog or sag) only half as much as before. However, it will be noted from the following paragraph, that while a doubled moment of inertia may result from doubling of horizontal dimensions of a beam cross section, this is not so where vertical dimensions are concerned.

With the I-beam cross section of Fig. 1-12, we can explain (as shown in Fig. 1-13) how its moment of inertia, with respect to the neutral axis, N.A., may be determined. Let us imagine that the area of the I-beam cross section is divided into very small areas, a, and each such small area is multiplied by the square of its distance, d, from the neutral axis. The sum of all these products (for both sides of the neutral axis) is what we call the moment of inertia of the I-beam.

In explaining the method of obtaining the moment of inertia, we have used an I-beam as an example. The determination of the moment of inertia will be done in similar fashion for any other type of beam cross section.

Another geometric property of a beam is that of the *section modulus* of its cross section. Section modulus is a measure of the structural bending strength of the section involved.

The value of the section modulus for each flange of a beam allows us to obtain the maximum bending stress imposed upon them, when the value of the longitudinal bending moment is known. The value of the stress is obtained from the expression indicated below:

$$\text{Stress} = \frac{\text{bending moment}}{\text{section modulus}}$$

If the bending moment is expressed in pound-foot (lb-ft), and the section modulus is in.^{2} ft, then the resulting stress is given in pounds per square inch (psi).

Each material is associated with a particular value of allowable stress. If the stress level, as determined by the above equation, is too high for a definite bending moment, the section modulus must be increased to lower the stress level. Section modulus may be increased by redistribution as well as increase of area of the section. Also, it is seen that by using the

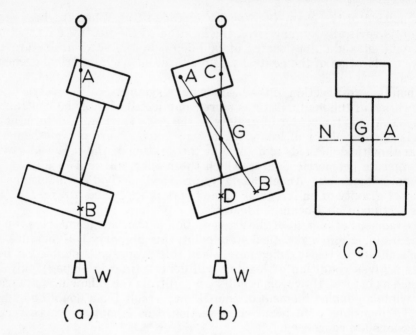

(a)   (b)   (c)

Procedure

(1) Draw out the figure on a piece of cardboard and cut out the shape.

(2) Hang the cardboard cut-out at A from a string with a small weight, W, suspended at its end, as shown in (a).

(3) Mark on the piece of cardboard two points in line with the string, such as A and B. Remove the cut-out and draw line AB on the cut-out. The center of gravity must lie on AB.

(4) Suspend the cardboard by C, as in (b), and draw the line CD, which will also contain the center of gravity. It is evident, then, that the intersection of lines AB and CD must be G (the center of gravity).

(5) Once G has been determined, the neutral axis, NA, can be drawn as shown in (c).

FIG. 1-12.   Practical method to determine the neutral axis of an irregular plane figure.

above equation with a specified, allowable, bending stress, and with a given bending moment and given type of material in a section, one may compute the necessary section modulus. As in the case of the other geometric properties mentioned before, section modulus is independent of the type of material used.

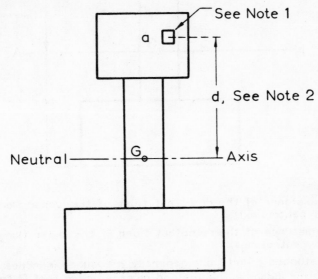

Notes:
1) a=one of the very small areas into which the total I-beam cross-section area is divided (generally measured in square inches, sq in.).

2) d = distance of each one of the very small areas to the neutral axis (generally measured in inches, in., for individual beams and girders and in feet, ft, for each element when considered as a part of the ship's girder as defined later in this section).

3) Multiply the area a (sq in.) times the square of the distance d^2 (sq in.) or (sq ft). This product will be expressed as follows: $a \times d^2$, sq in. $\times$ sq in. $=$ in.^{4}, or sq in. $\times$ sq ft.

4) Add all these products together. The sum total will be expressed in in.^{4} or sq in. $\times$ sq ft and will be called moment of inertia.

FIG. 1-13.   Determination of the moment of inertia, I, of the cross section of a beam.

The section modulus (assuming a horizontal N.A.) is found by dividing the previously discussed moment of inerta of the section about the neutral axis by the distance of the neutral axis from the face of the upper or lower flange. So a section has two section moduli. The smaller of the two is generally critical relative to stress level. Figure 1-14 shows how the two moduli are obtained.

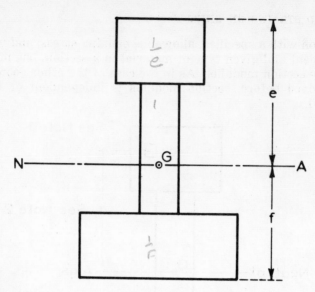

Notes:

1) e=distance of the remotest fiber of the upper flange to neutral axis.

f=distance of the remotest fiber of the lower flange to neutral axis.

Distances e and f are generally measured in inches, in., for individual beams and girders and in feet,ft,for each element when considered as a part of the ship's girder as defined later in this section.

2) Each section modulus is found by dividing the moment of inertia of the total section by the distance from the neutral axis to the remotest fiber of the flange. The two moduli for the figure above are as follows:

$$\text{Upper flange section modulus} = \frac{I}{e}$$

$$\text{Lower flange section modulus} = \frac{I}{f}$$

3) The units for the section modulus are expressed as indicated below:

Moment of inertia I in.^4, or   sq in. x sq ft

Section modulus $\frac{\text{in.}^4}{\text{in.}} = \text{in.}^3$, or $\frac{\text{sq in. x sq ft.}}{\text{ft}} = \text{sq in. x ft.}$

Therefore, the section modulus is generally expressed in in.^3 for individual beams and girders and in sq in. x ft for the ship's girder.

FIG. 1-14. Determination of the section modulus of the cross section of a beam.

	Per Cent of Maximum Value Included in the Table		
	Moment of Inertia, I	Section Modulus	Stress
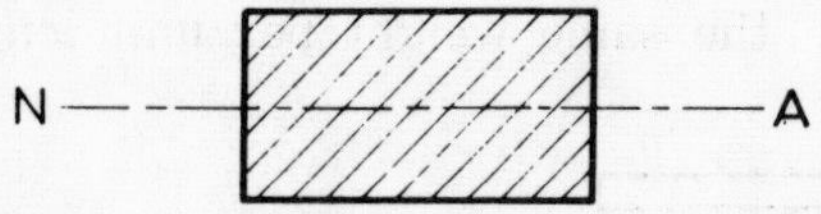 (a) **Rectangle.** (Height = 1/2 × length)	5.4	17.1	100
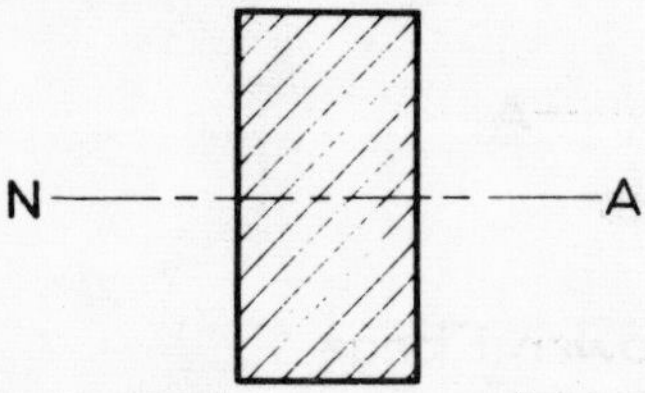 (b) **Rectangle.** (Height = 2 × length)	21.6	34.1	50
 (c) **I-beam cross section.**	50	50 (Upper flange)	34.2
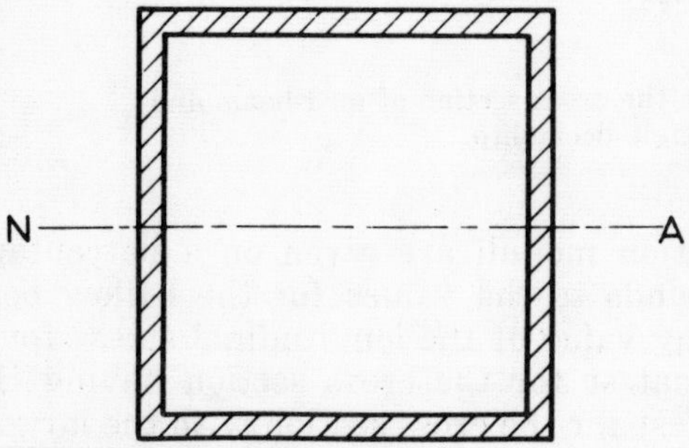 (d) **Hollow box girder.**	100	100	17.1

FIG. 1-15. Properties of sections.

In Fig. 1-15 four cross sections of the following different forms and proportions are shown: a) a rectangle of a height half as large as the length, b) a rectangle of a height twice as large as the length, c) an I-beam cross section, and d) a hollow box-girder. These four plane figures have the same area, corresponding to beams having the same weight per unit length.

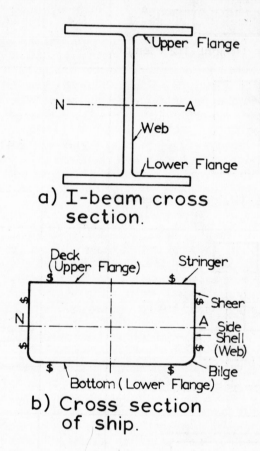

a) I-beam cross section.

b) Cross section of ship.

FIG. 1-16.   Comparison between the cross section of an I-beam and that of a single-deck ship.

Their moments of inertia and section moduli are given on a percentage basis, where 100 per cent corresponds to the values for the hollow box-girder. Of course, the corresponding value of the longitudinal stress for a given bending moment will be greatest for the cross section having the smallest section modulus, and smallest for the cross section with the largest section modulus. The relative values of the stress are also given in Fig. 1-15 on a percentage basis, where 100 per cent corresponds to the stress for the (a) rectangle. (It is to be noted that only the smaller section modulus for the I-beam has been considered, because this is the critical one relative to stress.)

THE SHIP AS A BOX GIRDER

We have analyzed the longitudinal stress distribution in a rectangular beam in bending. The meaning of moment of inertia and of the section modulus of a beam cross section also has been explained.

Let us consider again the cross section of an I-beam and compare it with a cross section of a ship. The I-beam, Fig. 1-16(a), consists of two flanges, upper and lower, joined by a web. The main hull of a ship is, in its simplest form, a box girder, Fig. 1-16(b), where the deck and bottom are the flanges and the side shell is the web. It differs from the I-beam of Fig. 1-16(a) only in that, instead of having a single central web, it has two side webs.

The description in Fig. 1-13, showing how the moment of inertia of a cross section is obtained, indicates clearly that material at a great distance from the neutral axis is particularly important in strengthening the structure (its area is multiplied by the square of the distance to the neutral axis when computing the moment of inertia). This is illustrated further in Fig. 1-15, where four plane figures and their relative moments of inertia are shown. For this reason, in a ship's hull the upper deck and the bottom material are far more important to longitudinal strength than, say, the steel in a 'tween deck.

It stands to reason then that, for the same weight, an I-beam will be more effective in resisting bending than the solid rectangular beam, because a large percentage of its material is well removed from the neutral axis. It is easy to appreciate, also, that the main hull of a ship is very efficient in resisting bending moment because a large proportion of its material is placed at a relatively great distance from the neutral axis of the section.

In general, we may conclude that, as far as bending stresses are concerned, the most efficient distribution of the material of the ship's girder is that which places it at the greatest distance from the neutral axis. However, if we take a second look at the expression for stress given previously, we find that for a given bending moment, the stress increases as the section modulus decreases. Now, we may have a large value for the moment of inertia of the ship's cross section, and yet in some particular location, because of its specially large distance from the neutral axis, we may obtain, at that point, an undesirable low value for the section modulus (a low value of the section modulus results in a high stress). This condition is known to have caused trouble in superstructures, bulwarks and other structures placed at a large distance from the neutral axis. Remedies for these particular cases will be treated elsewhere.

In the previous paragraph, it was stated that the most efficient distribution of ship's girder material is that which places it at the greatest distance from the neutral axis. This is true, provided the upper and lower flanges are balanced; that is, the material is distributed symmetrically with respect to the neutral axis. That this is so will be proved by considering the I-beam of Fig. 1-15 when adding and subtracting material, as shown in Fig. 1-17. For each case, Fig. 1-17 gives the area, the moment of inertia, the section modulus and the stress for a given, constant, bending moment on a percentage basis, where the 100 per cent value corresponds to the original I-beam of Fig. 1-17(a). The position of the neutral axis is indicated also. In Fig. 1-17(b), values correspond to the case where 20 per cent

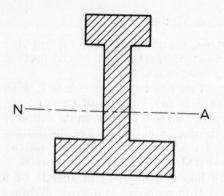

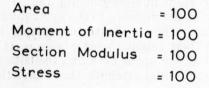

Area   = 100
Moment of Inertia = 100
Section Modulus   = 100
Stress   = 100

(a) Original I-beam.

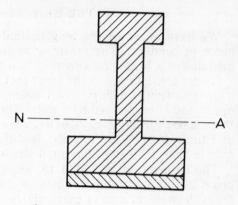

Area   = 120
Moment of Inertia = 133
Section Modulus   = 115
Stress   = 87

(b) Original I-beam with reinforced lower flange.

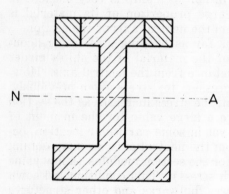

Area   = 120
Moment of Inertia = 130
Section Modulus   = 150
Stress   = 67

(c) Original I-beam with reinforced upper flange.

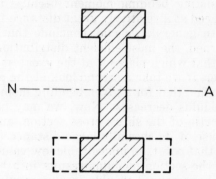

Area   = 80
Moment of Inertia = 80
Section Modulus   = 91
Stress   = 110

(d) Original I-beam with cut lower flange.

FIG. 1-17. Geometric properties of modified I-beams.

of the original area is added to the lower flange, with a corresponding 13 per cent reduction in stress. The same amount of area is added in the case of Fig. 1-17(c), but the resulting composite I-beam is now symmetrical with respect to the neutral axis, and the corresponding reduction in stress is 33 per cent instead of 13 per cent. Figure 1-17(d) shows a case where the original area has been decreased by 20 per cent, making the I-beam symmetrical with respect to the neutral axis. In the latter case, a reduction of 20 per cent in the area corresponds to a stress increase of only 10 per cent. Extreme cases will be found where a reduction in material in the direction of geometric symmetry will actually result in lower bending stress and vice versa. The examples are especially valid with respect to the ship's hull girder. The cross section of a ship, however, is not symmetrical with respect to the neutral axis. The ship's bottom is made heavier mainly to take care of the local additional load due to water pressure. Also, decks may have considerable loss in effective material due to hatch openings. Figure 1-16(b) shows the cross section of a single-deck ship and the relative position of its neutral axis. The I-beam of Fig. 1-15 corresponds more closely, then, to the actual ship's hull girder condition than does the I-beam of Fig. 1-16(a).

When the ship girder is loaded by the forces of the sea and the weight of the ship, it bends as a beam, and the upper and lower flanges are stressed in tension and compression, respectively, when the vessel hogs. These stresses are reversed when the vessel sags.

The buoyant forces of the sea acting on the ship are continuously changing, subjecting the deck and bottom structure to successive stress reversal (from tension to compression) as the vessel passes from crest to hollow of waves. At any given instant, the resultant stress across each flange (deck or bottom) is fairly uniform, while the stress in the side shell varies uniformly from zero at the neutral axis to the value existing at the flanges, as illustrated in Fig. 1-18 (this assumes the vessel remains continually upright in the water although actually the vessel is subject to roll).

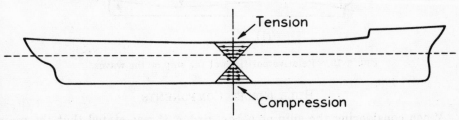

FIG. 1-18. Ship-girder bending stress distribution in the side shell.

When the vessel is heeled, the position of the neutral axis changes, and the distance between the material at the corners of the ship box girder and the neutral axis increases. This increase may result in a smaller section modulus and correspondingly higher longitudinal stresses in plating, such as the deck stringer and the sheer and bilge strakes. Since this material is quite often heavier than the rest of the hull plating, the section modulus for the heeled vessel occasionally may be greater than the one for the upright vessel, in which case the stresses for the heeled condition will be smaller than those for the upright ship.

Figure 1-19(a) and (b) illustrate the hogging and sagging conditions when bending moments and stresses are likely to reach maximum values. Figure 1-19(c) and (d) represent intermediate conditions when the acting buoyancy and weight forces produce generally smaller stresses on the ship considered as a box girder. In either case, (a) or (b), the bending stresses usually will be greater at the middle portion of the length. It is due to this variation of the bending moment that the ship's scantlings in the middle portion of the length are made heavier than at the ends. Classification societies require that the midship thickness of the shell plating and the sectional area of the effective decks be maintained for 40 per cent to 60 per cent of the length amidships.

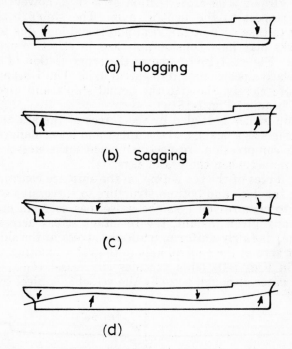

(a) Hogging

(b) Sagging

(c)

(d)

Fig. 1-19.   Relative positions of the ship on the waves.

HULL GIRDER COMPONENTS

When considering the ship as a box girder, it was stated that the main components were the side shell, acting as the web of the girder, and the bottom and deck plating, acting as the flanges. Together these members form what is often referred to as the *strength* envelope. Of these, the more highly stressed members are, as mentioned before, the stringer plate and the sheer and bilge strakes.

When a ship with more than one deck has a long superstructure, or has stepped decks, it is not always evident at first which is the *strength deck* (the deck that is built to work as the upper flange of the ship box girder). Figure 1-20 shows several types of ships and the strength deck of these is indicated by the heavy line in the sketches. It is important to realize that, although generally the whole strength deck is at one level, there are cases, like that of Fig. 1-20(b), where it is in two levels, forming steps. Since the thick side plating is generally terminated at the strength deck, the thickness of the side shell is a good indication of the position of the strength deck.

Having considered the primary components of the hull girder, let us now look at the secondary components of the ship's box girder. Among the latter, we have all continuous decks, other than the strength deck, longitudinal bulkheads of sufficient length, inner bottom, vertical keel, side keelsons and continuous longitudinal framing associated with the structure. In recent years, actual tests on ships subjected to controlled and accurately estab-

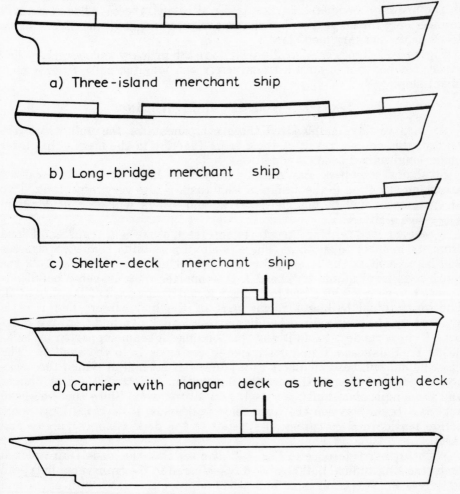

a) Three-island   merchant   ship

b) Long-bridge   merchant   ship

c) Shelter-deck   merchant   ship

d) Carrier   with   hangar   deck   as   the   strength   deck

e) Carrier   with   flight   deck   as   the   strength   deck

Note: The   heavy   line   indicates   the   ship's   strength   deck

FIG. 1-20.   The strength deck in different types of ships.

lished conditions of longitudinal bending have shown that most of these members act as effective ship's girder components. In this function, their stresses under longitudinal bending are roughly proportional to their distance from the neutral axis of the cross section.

Whenever we design or fabricate structural details in ships, we should aim, with due regard to cost, at obtaining the best quality of design and workmanship. This is particularly important in the case of the more highly stressed ship's structural members. A clear knowledge of which members comprise the primary and secondary hull girder is necessary. While the primary members should receive the closest attention with respect to structural details, most of the secondary members are important enough also to be carefully considered, especially when they are immediately adjacent to the primary members. In this latter situation, the so-called secondary members are for all practical purposes subject to the same maximum stress levels as the primary members.

Figure 1-21 shows graphically which are the primary and secondary hull girder components in both a transversely and longitudinally framed merchant ship.

LOCALIZED STRESSES OF SIGNIFICANCE

So far, we have emphasized those components of the hull which are highly stressed as a result of their beam function in the main ship girder under longitudinal bending conditions.

Structural members may also be subject to high stresses in localized areas and attention to the design in such cases is also very important. Two of these cases will be described below, and others will be considered in successive sections.

Whenever load-bearing structures intersect, there is a transfer of load from one member to another. There is also a possibility that high stresses will be present at the intersection and bordering areas. In Fig. 1-22 the continuous longitudinal bulkhead L is supported by transverse bulkheads T, which in turn are attached to and supported by the shell of the ship at H. The longitudinal bulkhead forms part of the hull girder, and thus is stressed by the longitudinal bending-stress load P. In addition, the bulkhead L supports deck loads D and thus becomes a beam supported by bulkheads T. Bulkheads T in turn transfer the loads D to the shell H. The longitudinal bulkhead also acts as a portion of a beam of which the decks above and below (omitted from the illustration for clarity) act as flanges and the longitudinal bulkhead itself acts as the web. Since this bulkhead acts as a beam between the transverse bulkheads, it develops local beam action tension and compression stresses at the deck (flanges) above and below.

With further reference to Fig. 1-22, we see that the loads D are picked up by the longitudinal bulkhead and transferred to the transverse bulkhead by forces S. The transverse bulkheads support this load with equal and opposite reactions S_1. This load transfer from one structure to another by equal but opposed reactive forces is referred to as shear. This same type of load transfer is present throughout the longitudinal bulkhead in varying amounts due to the succession of imposed loads, D. Each load D is transferred progressively and accumulatively through the longitudinal bulkhead

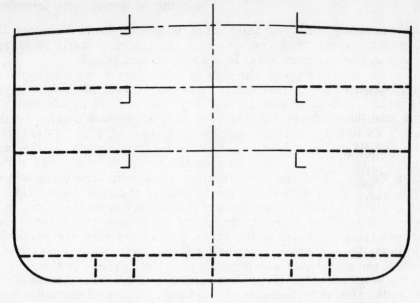

a) Transversely framed general-cargo ship.

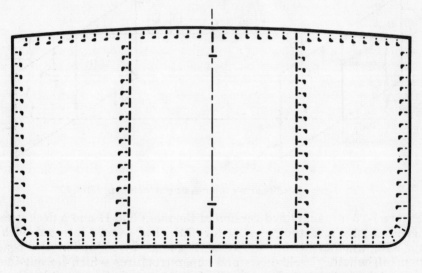

b) Longitudinally framed tanker.

Note : 1) Heavy solid lines indicate primary hull girder components.
2) Heavy dash lines indicate secondary hull girder components.

FIG. 1-21.   Midship sections of typical merchant ships showing the primary and secondary hull girder components.

to the supporting transverse bulkhead at its ends by shear. Therefore, there is increasing shear from the center of the system toward the support points, and the maximum shear is at these support points.

When we first dealt with the ship as a box girder, we considered it a simple box structure. A real ship is never that simple. Most ships have, in addition to the so-called primary and secondary structural members previously mentioned, structural additions such as superstructures or deckhouses. These may be relatively short, as those of Fig. 1-20(a) (forecastle, bridge and poop) or may be of substantial length, as the bridge shown in Fig. 1-20(b). Depending on their relative length and stiffness and on the details of their construction, these ship structures will contribute to the ship's girder strength in smaller or larger degree (i.e., will share a smaller or larger proportion of the load acting on the ship). In this function, the ends of superstructures and deckhouses which form abrupt changes of configuration in the ship's girder structure are particularly important. These changes, commonly called *structural discontinuities*, are generally associated with exceptionally high local stresses in their vicinity, and, therefore, should be given most careful consideration. Actually, wherever practicable, it is desirable to avoid such *structural discontinuities*.

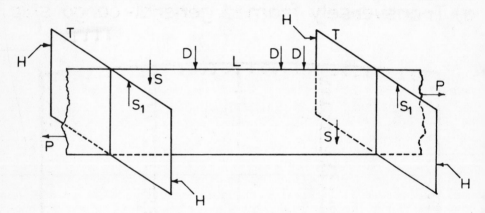

FIG. 1-22.   Load-bearing intersecting structures.   (Ref. 2)

Figure 1-23 is a simplified version of the main hull H and a deckhouse D. In general, any longitudinal structure attached to and integral with the main hull, whether within or without, adopts by induction the bending action in the hull. Deckhouses and superstructures which lie outside the main hull are induced to bend to the deflection curve assumed by the hull. However, these structures would tend to retain their original shape, if they were not integrally attached along their lower boundary to the primary strength flange of the hull girder. Were the deckhouse of Fig. 1-23 not attached at the end portions to the main hull, it would retain its shape and not bend with the hull. Therefore, in general, there are forces F_1, acting downward at the ends, and F_2, acting upward in the center portion of the deckhouse, to force it to assume the hull deflection. These forces act through the attachment of the deckhouse to the hull. The more rigid the deckhouse itself, the higher the force will be.

When the hull girder bends, the upper flange elongates in tension when hogging or shortens in compression when sagging. If the deckhouse were not attached at the end portions, its length would not change to correspond to the lengthening or shortening of the upper flange. Since it is attached, there are boundary forces F_3 which act to pull the deckhouse ends.

These forces F_1, F_2, and F_3, acting on the deckhouse, are resisted by equal and opposite forces acting on the main hull. The F_1 and F_2 forces, which will be analyzed in more detail in Section II, are highly localized in nature and may produce excessive stresses in the ship in way of the discontinuities involved.

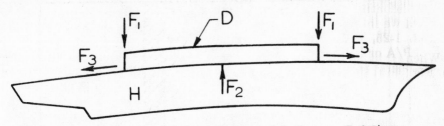

FIG. 1-23. Interaction between hull and deckhouse. (Ref. 3)

LOCATIONS OF SIGNIFICANT SHEAR

The existence of shear forces in ships was explained on pages 2 to 3, and shear stress, in connection with longitudinal shear in a bar in bending, was defined on page 5.

The value of shear stresses in ship structures may be important enough so that special provisions may have to be made in some special cases which will be discussed later. It is difficult to point out all cases where shear becomes an important load consideration. However, shear stresses may be significant in the two areas indicated below:

a) At support points (as indicated in connection with Fig. 1-22).

b) At the vessel's neutral axis (approximately mid-depth) in the vicinity of one-quarter of the length from the ends (a position which is commonly referred to as the *quarter points*).

STRESS CONCENTRATION

If the uniform-section plate of Fig. 1-24 is loaded by an axial force P, this force exists and is equal across each section of the plate as shown. The stress on each such section is the load divided by the cross-section area, or P/A, and is uniform across the width of the plate. (Earlier in this section and in agreement with this definition, we defined stress as the force per unit area.)

If a rectangular hole with square corners is cut in the center of the plate of Fig. 1-24, as shown in Fig. 1-25(a), it might be assumed that the stress is still the load divided by the area, P/A, at the uncut portion, and P/2a at the cut portion. Such an assumption might be true, if it were not for the influence of the abrupt change in section shape in the transition zone between the intact and the cut portions of the plate. This abrupt change of section is called a *discontinuity*. Figure 1-25 (b) shows another plate with a rectangular hole with rounded corners. The rounding of the corners makes for a more gradual change of section and lessens the adverse effect of the discontinuity.

When we introduce a sharp corner or discontinuity in a plate, as shown in Fig. 1-25, the stress in the vicinity of the discontinuity no longer equals P/A or P/2a, but varies widely in value depending upon the location of the fibers; those fibers closest to the abrupt change in the section being

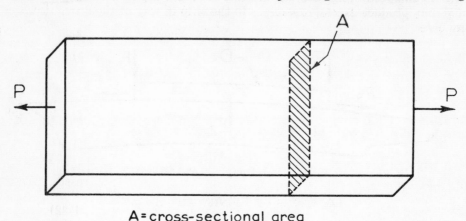

A = cross-sectional area

FIG. 1-24.   Intact rectangular plate under stress.

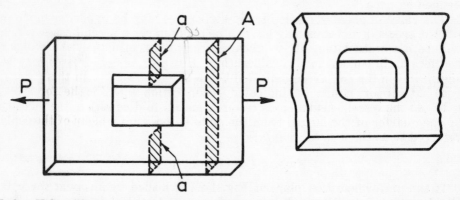

Left: Hole with square corners; poor practice. Right: Hole with rounded corners; better practice. 2a = cross-sectional area of the plate in way of the opening; A = cross-sectional area of the intact plate.

FIG. 1-25.   Holes in a plate under stress.   (Ref. 4)

affected more than those that are farther away. This variation in stress has been calculated theoretically for various plate-hole configurations, and the results of some experimental tests have agreed quite closely with them.

Some of the fibers close to the discontinuities of Fig. 1-25 are subject to stresses which have a magnitude several times that of P/2a or P/A. The ratio of the local stress to the average stress in the minimum section (stress in the net section across the hole, P/2a) is called the *stress concentration factor* and is denoted by K. This factor can be expressed by the following fraction:

$$K = \frac{\text{Local Stress}}{\text{P/2a}}$$

For a plate under tension stress, as that shown in Fig. 1-25, a value of K greater than unity means that the local stress is greater than the average stress in the minimum section, P/2a. A positive value of K smaller than one indicates that the local stress is smaller than P/2a. A negative value of K means that the plate is stressed in compression rather than in tension. In general, in this publication the stress concentration factor will be as defined above.

Sometimes the stress concentration factor is defined as the ratio of the local stress to the uniaxial stress applied at infinity, i.e., the uniform stress which would exist if no opening were present. The symbol k will be used to represent the stress concentration factor defined in this manner. This can be expressed by the following fraction:

$$k = \frac{\text{Local Stress}}{\text{P/A}}$$

The relationship between the two stress concentration factors is as follows:

$$K\,\frac{P}{2a} = k\,\frac{P}{A},$$

or

$$K = k\,\frac{2a}{A}$$

For a plate of finite width with an opening, the fraction $\frac{2a}{A}$ will always be smaller than unity and, therefore, the factor K will be smaller than k. The two factors K and k will be equal only when the width of the plate which has the opening is infinitely large.

Numerical values of K and k in plates with openings are given in Section II.

Figure 1-26 illustrates one type of notch in a structure under load. The load in the structure produces a bending moment in the material from A to B, and the resultant nominal stress at any point including point A can be calculated. Theory and experimentation show that the stress at the base of a notch (point A) is higher than the nominal value calculated by usual methods. As a rough approximation, the stress at the base of a notch may be two or three times the nominal stress expected or higher. The precise stress value depends upon the shape of the notch; the sharper the notch, the higher the stress concentration.

Figures 1-27 and 1-28 show plates under stress with notches of different types and ways to reduce their severity by rounding off the sharp corners. By using care and proper practices, the structural notch effect and the value of the stress concentration factor K can be substantially reduced.

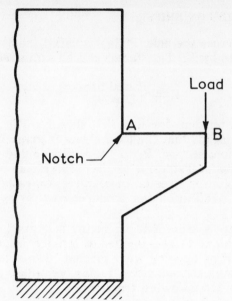

FIG. 1-26.   Notch in structure under load.

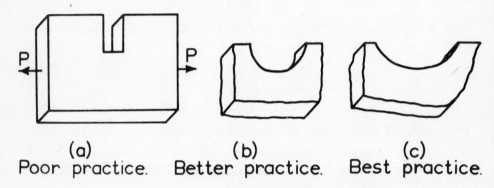

(a)
Poor practice.

(b)
Better practice.

(c)
Best practice.

FIG. 1-27.   Slots in plates under stress. (Ref. 4)

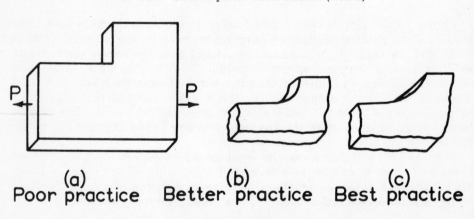

(a)
Poor practice

(b)
Better practice

(c)
Best practice

FIG. 1-28.   Recessed in plates under stress. (Ref. 4)

BRITTLE FRACTURE

In the early 1940's, a large number of welded ships were built. At that time, the behavior of all welded large steel structures under stress (including aggravating details) was not understood sufficiently.

As a result of some spectacular fractures, a number of those ships broke in two. Also, a large number had their structural integrity seriously impaired by somewhat lesser fractures. Each fracture was a threat to the safety of the ship itself, and thus to the lives aboard. As a result, national interest was stimulated in the subject, and special studies and research programs initiated to promote understanding of the causes of fracture and to explore possible remedies.

Virtually all of these fractures in ship's plating were of the brittle variety known as cracks. Such fractures develop suddenly, produce practically no local material deformation, and spread instantaneously. Such fractures are always caused by tensile stresses.

The properties of the steel and the service temperature are important factors in the occurrence of brittle fracture. The condition of stress of the structure has a marked influence on the occurrence of brittle fracture. The avoidance of conditions favoring brittle fracture is the main objective of this publication.

It has been found that almost all cracks start at a notch of some kind in the structure, produced by an improper square-cornered cut in the plating or by defective welding, either of which can result from poor design or fabrication. A structural notch creates the condition of *multiaxial tensile stress* necessary to initiate brittle fracture. This multiaxial stress condition and the circumstances associated with its development are described in the following paragraphs.

If the metal bar of Fig. 1-1 is loaded within moderate limits by a simple load such as P, the resulting effect is called a *uniaxial stress*. This stress will be a *uniaxial tensile stress*, s_t, or a *uniaxial compressive stress*, s_c, depending on whether the applied load is as shown on Figs. 1-1 (a) or 1-1 (b), respectively.

Under simple multiaxial tension, steel elongates elastically until the yield point is reached (at a stress of about 30,000 lb per sq in. for mild steel). At this level, and while maintaining this stress bearing ability, the steel undergoes a relatively large extension (plastic deformation or flow) most of which is permanent. Upon release of load and successive reloading, the steel again behaves elastically as it did originally. It is this property of steel (i.e., its ductility) which, in the absence of special fracturing circumstances, permits structural readjustment without fracture, when the yield point of the steel is locally exceeded in way of stress concentration.

A simplified illustration of the mechanism of plastic flow is given in Fig. 1-29. Figure 1-29(a) shows a bar under uniaxial tensile stress s_t. This stress s_t produces the shear stresses s_s in the bar, which are a maximum along the 45° directions shown. The development of these shear stresses s_s is responsible for and necessary to production of plastic flow, as mentioned above.

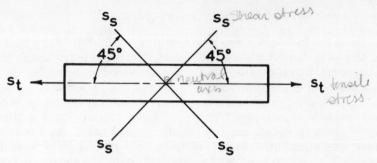

a) Bar under uniaxial tensile stress s_t.

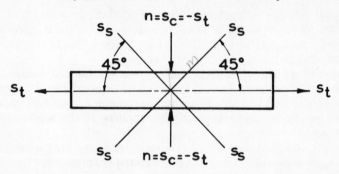

b) Bar under biaxial state of stress s_t and s_t.

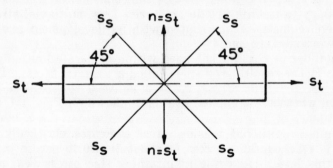

c) Bar under biaxial state of stress s_t and s_c.

Notes:

1) s_t = tensile stress, s_c = compressive stress
   s_s = shear stress, n = stress normal to bar.

2) Maximum value of shear stress $s_s = 1/2(s_t - n)$.

3) When n varies from zero to degrees of compression, the stresses s_s are adequate to promote ductility.

4) When $n = s_t$, as in b), plastic flow is restricted

FIG. 1-29. Simplified mechanism of plastic flow.

Under the biaxial states of stress shown in Figs. 1-29(b) and (c) which involve an additional tensile or compressive stress, $n = s_t$ or $n = s_c$, perpendicular to the original uniaxial tension, the maximum shear stresses still develop in the 45° directions. The magnitude of these maximum shear stresses is equal to one-half the algebraic difference between the mutually perpendicular stresses. When such stresses are equal, $s_s = \frac{1}{2}(s_t - s_t) = 0$. Conversely, when n is a compressive stress, i.e., $s_c = -s_t$, of the same magnitude but opposite sign as the tensile stress, the maximum shear stress is equal to the stress s_t, i.e., $s_s = \frac{1}{2}(s_t + s_t) = s_t$. For the intermediate condition where n is zero, the maximum shear stress is equal to one-half the tensile stress, $s_s = \frac{1}{2}(s_t - 0) = \frac{1}{2}s_t$.

When the perpendicular stress varies from zero to degrees of compression, as shown in Figs. 1-29(a) and (c), the shear stresses are adequate to promote ductility. However, when a perpendicular tensile stress builds up as shown in Fig. 1-29(b), shear stresses, and attendant ability of the material to flow plastically, diminish in the biaxial state of stress indicated.

When three-dimensional stressing exists, such as by introducing a stress perpendicular to the plane of the paper for Figs. 1-29(b) and (c), the general discussion above applies to development of shear stresses in the triaxial state of stress which now exists. Considering the three mutually perpendicular principal stresses (tension and compression) which now exist, and taking these stresses two at a time, there are three biaxial states of stress. When maximum shear stresses of the magnitude indicated can be developed in any one of the three biaxial states, the material is subject to plastic flow. For cases where the three principal stresses are all tension, shear stresses diminish (and vanish when these tensile stresses are equal). With diminishing shear stresses, the ductile behavior of the steel, leading to eventual but long delayed ductile fracture, vanishes and the steel is subject to an entirely different mode of fracture. This is the *cleavage* mode, i.e., cracking, where relatively little plastic deformation occurs in way of the fracture, even though the yield stress of the material may have been exceeded locally (due to stress concentration).

In the presence of ship openings and similar situations, a biaxial state of tensile stress is developed in the plane of a ship's plate (under tension), due to stress flow around the opening. When structural notches are present in such a stress field, a triaxial state of tensile stress is created, due to the additional tensile stress created locally in a direction perpendicular to the plane of the plate, as mentioned in the following.

A clear illustration of biaxial tensile stress fields is that corresponding to the pressure vessel of Fig. 1-30. Figure 1-30(a) shows a closed pressure vessel under internal pressure. As a result of internal pressure, there is a tendency for the ends of the pressure vessel to be pushed out of the cylindrical shell, as illustrated in Fig. 1-30(b). The steel in the shell reacts to this pressure and, as a consequence, it is subjected to the tensile stress $s_1 - s_1$. The other tendency to failure is that of the cylinder being split longitudinally in two halves, as a result of the internal pressure, Fig. 1-30(c). The reaction of the shell results in the tensile stress $s_2 - s_2$. The condition of stress corresponding to a spot such as A of Fig. 1-30(c) is called a *tensile biaxial stress* state. Biaxial tensile stress fields are also created in pressure-loaded bulkhead diaphragms which involve bending restraint on longitudinal and transverse boundaries. When structure under tensile loading is attached perpendicularly to the plating of these structures, triaxial stress fields are also created locally.

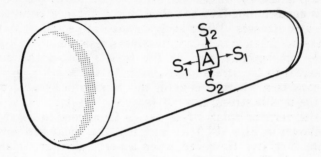

a) Closed vessel under internal pressure.

 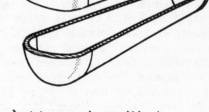

b) Vessel with ends   c) Vessel split in
   pushed out.   two, longitudinally.

Note:
   The tendencies of the internal pressure shown in b)
   and c) produce a biaxial stress condition at A.

FIG. 1-30.   Biaxial stress condition in a pressure vessel.

To explain the creation of the additional tensile stress (locally at a notch) in a direction perpendicular to the plane of the plate, it is necessary to realize that when a steel fiber is uniaxially stressed in tension, either elastically or plastically, the cross section of the fibers contract dimensionally. This property, in conjunction with the stress concentration in the intact material at the base of a notch (in a plate subject to tensile stress), is responsible for the creation of the tensile stress perpendicular to the plane of the plate. Figure 1-31 illustrates a notched plate under tension and the stress distribution across the intact plate in way of the notch.

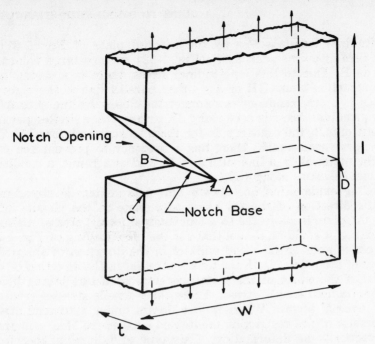

Notch Opening

B

A

C

Notch Base

l

D

W

t

Note: l, indicates direction of length
        t, indicates direction of thickness
        w, indicates direction of width

a) Notched plate under tension load.

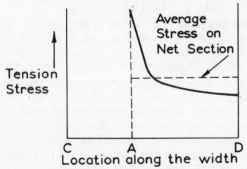

Average
Stress on
Net Section

Tension
Stress

C   A   D
Location along the width

Note: A, C, and D, correspond to the points equally
        labeled in a).

b) Longitudinal stress distribution.

FIG. 1-31.   Notched plate under longitudinal tension stress.

1-31

The longitudinal tensile stress of the notched plate of Fig. 1-31(a) varies from zero at points such as F (Fig. 1-32) to very large values at points such as E. Due to this longitudinal stress, there is a strong tendency for contraction along GH or any other parallel line to the right of AB on Section L-L (the tendency is stronger the closer the line is to AB). Since the longitudinal stress is zero along JK or any other similar parallel line to the left of AB, the tendency is for these to stay undeformed. The material on a line such as JK, then, has a tendency to prevent the contraction of the material on a line such as GH, and as a result, a condition of tensile stress develops along GH.

The preceding explanation has shown how a large tensile stress may develop in the direction of the thickness of a plate in the vicinity of a notch, when the plate is subjected to a longitudinal tensile stress. Using a similar reasoning, it could be shown that for the plate loading of Fig. 1-31, a tensile stress of substantial value will act in the direction of the width in the vicinity of the notch. Both the tensile stresses in the direction of the thickness and of the width of the plate prevent contraction taking place, due to the longitudinal tensile stress. These three tensile stresses create a condition of *triaxial stress*. When failure occurs under a triaxial stress condition, because of the restriction mentioned earlier, the steel will fracture with practically no deformation. This type of failure is, therefore, called brittle fracture, and its appearance is characteristically *bright* and *granular*.*

The same metal that behaves as a brittle material under the effect of triaxial stresses may undergo considerable deformation before failure under a uniaxial or biaxial stress condition. In addition to the triaxial states of stress mentioned, there are structural details in ships which may create such a comparable state and lead to cracking.

It should be mentioned here that rounding of the corners of openings in ship plate subject to high tensile stress does not eliminate the stress concentration and biaxial state of stress in the plane of the plate. However, it does spread out the effect of unstressed material upon the contiguous, highly-stressed material at the opening, and thereby reduces the magnitude of the tensile stress normal to the plate surface which develops. With reduction of this tensile stress, shear stresses are allowed to develop and the material at the rounded corners then behaves ductilely. In this case, eventual failure at the notched section would be a shear tear across the plate. This shear fracture edge would be set at 45° to the plane of the plate, and the fracture would appear dull and silky. Also considerable necking-down of the metal would occur in way of the fracture.

---

* It should be pointed out here that shear stresses such as result from shear forces F_3 in Fig. 1-23 in way of a longitudinal deckhouse discontinuity, or such as exist in section x-x of Fig. 1-32, for other notch discontinuities, are of high order and might be expected to promote ductility at the notch. However, they are sufficiently removed from the critical notch zone which promotes brittle fracture (even though the distance is small), that they do not help appreciably. These high shear stresses do perform another very significant function, the details of which are not developed in this publication. This function is to bend or direct the tensile or compressive stresses travelling past the notch into the otherwise discontinuous, longitudinal, inert material on one or both sides of the notch, and thus create a biaxial state of stress in the plane of the plate, at the notch and just beneath the notch root.

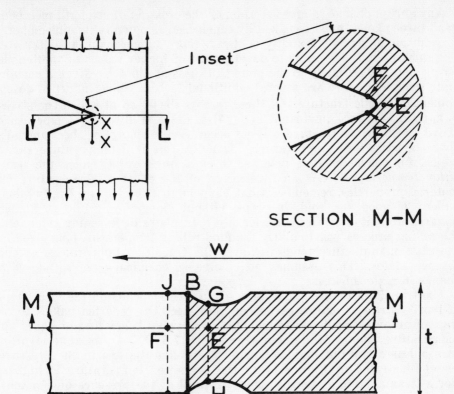

SECTION M-M

SECTION L-L

Notes:
1) t, indicates direction of thickness
   w, indicates direction of width

2) Longitudinal tensile stress values:
   a) Zero at points such as F (between J and K).
   b) Several times larger than average for net section
      at points such as E between G and H (see
      Fig. 1.31, b).

3) Due to stresses in 2 (b) there is a strong tendency
   for contraction along GH and none along JK. Material along JK restricts contraction along GH and
   this results in tensile stress along GH.

FIG. 1-32.   Stresses in the direction of thickness.

Any abrupt change in cross section, or the crossing of strength members in all three planes, must be carefully considered as potential troublemakers. A condition of stress triaxiality is always more dangerous in a thick plate. The thick plate is favorable to development of higher values of the tensile stress disposed normally to the plate thickness at a notch. Given a certain plate thickness, there are several additional factors which influence development of brittle fracture. Of these factors the speed at which the stress is applied is a very important one. Also, there is always a temperature above which brittle fracture will not occur, due to change of the material's characteristics with temperature. Actually, this is a temperature range which, for convenience, is referred to as a single value, called the *transition temperature*. (As an illustration of the effect of temperature on material properties, remember what happens to a piece of cold taffy when pulled. If good and cold, it snaps without elongation, while at higher temperatures, it elongates considerably.) In plates of lessening thickness, the rolling process (particularly the final rolling temperature) involved in the plate manufacture tends to lower the transition temperature of the thinner plates. This assumes no change in chemical composition with change in plate thickness.

The transition temperature for a given steel depends on the local state of tensile stress. For low carbon or mild steel, the reported values for a state of uniaxial tensile stress have been somewhat below that of liquid air temperature (liquid air temperature is -317.6 F. at atmospheric pressure). For a state of biaxial tensile stress, like the one in the pressure vessel illustrated in Figure 1-30, the transition temperature is higher. For a triaxial state of tensile stress (typical of the presence of a notch) in mild steel, the transition temperature may be high enough to reach the range of ship's structure service temperatures, particularly in winter, and become critically dangerous.

The chemical composition of steel has a definite influence on its transition temperature. In plain carbon steels, an increase in carbon will raise the transition temperature appreciably. Manganese is the most helpful alloying element in lowering the transition temperature of structural steels. For these steels, the ideal composition is relatively low carbon with relatively high manganese. Since carbon cannot be reduced below a certain point without adversely affecting the necessary properties, desirable crack-resistant quality is obtained by control of the manganese-carbon ratio. A ratio of three or four to one is considered necessary in present day ship steel.

The manufacturing practice also has a great effect on the transition temperature of carbon structural steels. An adequate control of the oxidation of the molten steel in the ingot will result in a lower transition temperature. Steels with finer grain size, other things being equal, have lower transition temperatures than coarser grained steels.

At service temperature and in the absence of notches, a failure in tension is ordinarily accompanied by a large deformation of the metal in its dimensional directions. In ship plate, this is usually the thickness direction, particularly where the onset of failure happens to occur in way of a stress concentration which does not involve a notch. This type of failure, which has been mentioned briefly in previous pages, is called a ductile fracture and is entirely unlike that of brittle fracture. A ductile fracture, as opposed to the bright, granular appearance of the brittle fracture, has a *dull, gray, velvet* appearance.

The photograph of an actual fractured, hull, steel strake on Fig. 1-33 shows the characteristic appearance of two types of failure:

a) Typical ductile fracture (dull, gray and velvety) on both sides of each rivet hole.

b) Typical brittle fracture (bright and granular) on the right portion of the plate.

FIG. 1-33. View of an actual fractured, hull, steel strake with arrows on top of the portion which failed by cleavage. The arrows, as well as the chevrons on this portion of the fracture, aim toward the point of initiation of the crack. On both sides of the rivet holes the failure was by shear.

Another distinguishing feature of a brittle fracture is the herringbone structure which can be seen in Fig. 1-33 and which is schematically shown in Fig. 6-31. The vertices of the herringbone structure in all cases aim toward the point of initiation of the crack, as indicated by the arrows in Fig. 1-31.

FATIGUE FRACTURE

Brittle fracture has been discussed previously. A basically different type of failure also may occur in structures and this is called *fatigue fracture.*

It should be mentioned that except in one or two isolated instances, fatigue fracture has not been identified with sudden, catastrophic cracking of ship hull girders. Fatigue fracture is more properly associated with fracture of notched structural details in secondary or in lower stressed primary structures.

While brittle fracture happens suddenly and propagates rapidly, an initial fatigue fracture may progress very slowly and take years before final failure. Brittle failure may be produced by tension stresses due to a single high tensile loading, while fatigue failure may be caused by repeated but much lower tensile or compressive stresses, or a combination of both.

For fatigue fracture, time plays a definite part since, in general, stresses must be changed in magnitude, or sense, or both, a large number of times before the beginning of failure. A fatigue failure starts with a small crack. Before complete failure, this crack has to increase its size until the remaining intact cross-sectional area is insufficient to carry the applied load.

Figure 1-34 shows, in schematic form, the appearance of a typical fatigue fracture in a cylindrical metal bar. Failure starts at the more highly stressed points, generally where a stress concentration is present (in the figure these are points P and Q). Failure is started in the form of

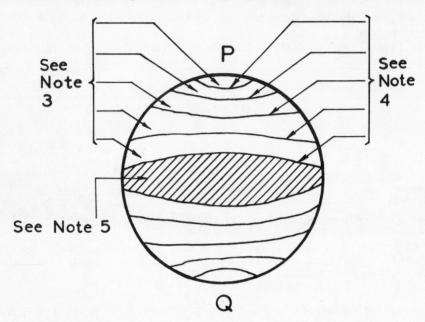

Notes:
1) The figure shows a cross section of a cylindrical bar.

2) Crack starts at the more highly stressed points such as P and Q.

3) These areas, and the ones below corresponding to Q, are the smooth polished surfaces of the original crack.

4) These lines show the gradual progress of the original crack.

5) This is the granular area of final fracture.

FIG. 1-34.   Fatigue fracture in cylindrical bar.

a minute crack resulting from repeated service loads of varying magnitude. Since the initial crack is in itself a stress raiser, further applications of load extend the crack. While the crack is growing, the adjoining faces rub against each other, producing the following characteristic features of a fatigue fracture, illustrated in Fig. 1-34: a) the smooth, polished surfaces, and b) the lines showing the gradual progress of the crack. Eventually, the remaining intact portion of the member cross section can no longer withstand the load and the bar breaks. There is practically no deformation in the vicinity of a fatigue fracture, whether the metal is ductile or brittle. The final failure (*see* note 5 of Fig. 1-34) has a granular appearance somewhat resembling that of a brittle fracture. For a fine-grained metal, the granular character of the final failure tends to be *silkier* than for a coarse-grained metal.

Fatigue failures are quite likely to occur in ship structures if precautions to avoid them are not taken.* Localized or low order stressing of the fluctuating and reversing types favor fatigue fractures. *Hard spots*, as defined in Section VI, are the causes of most fatigue fractures in ship structures.

SUMMARY

In a structural member, applied force per unit area is called *stress*. Stresses are usually expressed in pounds per square inch (psi). The corresponding deformation per unit length is called *strain*. In the steel's elastic range, strain is proportional to stress. For example, by doubling the stress, the strain is also doubled. When stress tends to extend or stretch the metal, it is called *tension stress*, and it produces a *tension strain*. When stress tends to contract or shrink the metal, it is called a *compression stress*, and it results in a *compression strain*.

A ship floating in still water or on waves is subjected to upward and downward forces along its length. These vertical forces are called *shearing forces*, or simply *shear forces*, because they tend to cut or shear the ship into vertical slices.

Tension or compression stresses in a ship in bending vary gradually from a maximum at the deck, or bottom, to a minimum or zero value at a height at, or close to, mid-depth. The position of zero bending stress is called the *neutral axis*.

The *moment of inertia* of the ship cross section relative to longitudinal loading is the sum of the products of every "effective" element of its area (both sides of the neutral axis) multiplied by the square of the distance of every "effective" element of its area to the neutral axis.

The *section modulus* for any longitudinal fiber of the ship's girder cross section is equal to the moment of inertia of the total cross section, divided by the distance of the fiber from the neutral axis. The bending stress at that particular fiber is equal to the hull bending moment, divided by the corresponding section modulus. If the neutral axis of the ship's cross section is not at mid-depth, neither the section moduli, nor the bending stresses for the deck and bottom, will be equal. For a given bending moment, the bending stress depends upon the location of the stressed fiber in question and upon the value of the corresponding section modulus; the smaller the section modulus, the higher the stress and vice versa.

----

* Although fatigue failures are neither as spectacular nor as catastrophic as brittle failures, they are numerous enough to require special consideration in ship structural detail design and fabrication to avoid fatigue fractures. Shipbuilding steel has been improved considerably with regard to its crack-resistant quality because of the urgency and importance of improvement in that direction. No comparable effort has been made to improve the fatigue resistant quality of shipbuilding steel, and until this takes place, great care should be taken to avoid fatigue failure.

The ship can be compared with a hollow box girder where the side shell (both sides) is the web and the deck and bottom are the flanges of the girder. When the ship has more than one deck, generally one of them, called the strength deck, is designed so it will work as the upper flange of the box girder. The strength deck, the bottom and sides of the ship, also known as the *primary hull girder components*, make up what is known as the *strength envelope*. The hull girder has, in addition, other members which are called *secondary hull girder components*. Both the primary and secondary hull girder components are shown in Fig. 1-21.

Due to the nature of the forces normally acting on the ship, the longitudinal bending moment is greater in the middle portion of its length. The bending moment decreases in value towards the ends of the ship, and is practically negligible at the extreme ends.

Some faired and carefully controlled discontinuities such as occur in way of openings, bilge keel ends, etc., and their attendant stress concentrations, are unavoidable in ship design. Except for such unavoidable instances, stress concentrations, particularly those involving unfaired discontinuities, or notches (including ragged plate cuts or edges, potential weld voids, etc., due to poor fabrication), are dangerous and should be eliminated.

Stress concentration in way of a discontinuity is defined commonly as the ratio (K) of the local stress at a point to the average stress in the net material of the minimum section (the latter, for instance, is the stress in the net section across the hole, $P/2a$ in Fig. 1-25). Sometimes the stress concentration factor is defined as the ratio of the local stress at a point to the uniaxial stress prevalent at a point far distant from the area of stress magnification (this position is generally considered to be at infinity). The latter would be the uniform stress which would exist if no opening or other stress raiser were present. This factor is denoted by k. These ratios, K and k, are larger than unity in the general vicinity of a discontinuity and may reach values of three, and even larger, at the immediate point of discontinuity.

A notch produces a local *triaxial state* of *stress* in a structure. Since in virtually all cases a stress concentration also will be present at the notch, the resulting magnified stress condition is particularly severe and susceptible to cracking failure. These stresses are especially serious in thick steel plates, due to the higher transition temperature of such plates, plus the increased ability of the thicker plates to develop triaxiality of stress. A condition of stress triaxiality means that failure will occur with little or no deformation. This type of failure, called *brittle fracture*, is produced by tensile stresses only and results in a fracture surface perpendicular to the plate surface as contrasted to the ductile fracture surface which is set 45° to the plane of the plate. Also the brittle fracture appearance is *bright* and *granular* with typical herringbone pattern, as opposed to the characteristic appearance of a ductile fracture which is that of dull gray velvet.

Brittle fractures, i.e., cracks, are subject to catastrophic suddenness in their initiation and propagation. The most serious feature of brittle fracture is that this phenomenon is a separate characteristic from the normal, expected, ductile characteristic of ship steel plate. Under this separate characteristic, which involves a state of triaxial tensile stress, brittle fracture failure properties take over entirely from the ductile failure properties when the operating temperature of the steel plate (such as occurs in winter) is below the transition temperature of the steel. Under such circumstances, failure occurs with a great reduction in applied stress (also reduction in resultant material deformation), as compared to desired or expected ductile behavior.

The chemical composition of steels and their manufacturing process can be adjusted to lower the *transition temperature*, which, for a given set of circumstances, is the temperature above which brittle fracture will not occur.

Fatigue fracture, which is a slowly progressing failure over a long time period, may be produced by tensile or compressive stresses, or a combination of stresses. This failure is the result of varying or cyclic stresses applied over a long period, as mentioned. Fatigue fractures may be caused by stresses which are much lower than the static stresses necessary to produce sudden catastrophic failure.

Hard spots, i.e., points or areas of high rigidity in highly stressed structural members which otherwise may be considered relatively soft (or low in rigidity), are generally the cause of fatigue failure under cyclic stressing. The attachment of a rigid bracket directly to the non-rigid plating of a bulkhead forming a tank boundary is a good hardspot example.

A fatigue fracture, as illustrated in Fig. 1-34, shows the following characteristic features: a) a series of smooth, polished surfaces, produced by their rubbing against each other, and b) the lines showing the gradual progress of the crack. The final fracture is granular in texture and its appearance is similar to that of a brittle fracture.

As mentioned above, good design and fabrication of structural details in ships should avoid, as far as it is possible, discontinuities or stress concentrations. The greatest care should be exercised to this effect in the primary hull girder components and in some localized areas which are mentioned below. The secondary hull girder components also require adequate attention, insofar as they play an important role in the overall strength of the ship and are directly attached to the primary hull girder components.

Following are some general rules regarding the design and fabrication of structural details:

1) Avoid whenever possible discontinuities in high stress regions of the longitudinal strength envelope and in similar highly stressed regions in longitudinal members attached thereto.

2) Exercise the utmost care regarding the design and fabrication of unavoidable discontinuities in the highly stressed flanges of the ship hull girder; namely, the bottom and strength deck.

3) The ends of longitudinal deckhouse structure are discontinuities and also regions of high stress concentration. This applies both to the longitudinal house structure (in the vicinity of the deck level) and the hull structure to which it is attached. Any additional discontinuity or imperfection is especially dangerous in these areas and should, if possible, be avoided. Local reinforcement of longitudinal house structure and deck, as well as other discontinuities in the area, is usually necessary in these

regions. (*Deckhouses*, as used here, includes superstructures where the house side is an upward extension of the shell.)

4) When the vessel is heeled, the corners of the ship box girder contain the furthest fibers from the neutral axis. As a consequence, the highest longitudinal bending stresses may occur at the stringer plate, and sheer and bilge strakes, which make up these corners. They should, therefore, be carefully designed and fabricated.

5) The longitudinal bending moment and the corresponding bending stresses are higher in the mid-length of the ship. The preceding rules, therefore, should be carefully enforced in this portion of the hull.

6) Whenever load-bearing structures intersect, there is a transfer of load from one member to another. There is also a possibility that high shear stresses will be present at the intersection and bordering areas. These stresses are in addition to local bending stresses (which may be *high* or *low*) resulting from local beam girder action. Special care in the design and fabrication of structural details is required.

7) Shear stress values may be significant in the vicinity of mid-depth of the hull girder in way of one-quarter of the length from the ends (a position which is commonly referred to as the *quarter points*). This area should be carefully considered with regard to structural details.

Minor Openings in Ship Steel Structures

INTRODUCTION

The material here presented applies in general to any size opening in ship structures. However, special large openings, such as cargo hatches and side cargo ports, are treated separately because of their special nature.

Openings in ship structures are made for access, cargo handling, passage of pipes, ducts and cables, lightening of the structure, drainage and air escape, weld relief, etc.

Any opening in a stressed structural member, no matter how small or how well designed and fabricated, always causes a stress concentration.*

Ship openings that are improperly designed, poorly located, or involve bad workmanship in cutting and welding may lead to serious structural failures. To serve as a guide, some simple rules resulting from experience and experimentation will follow. These rules will deal with opening control, opening location and workmanship, rounding-of-the-corners, relative size, shape, proportions and reinforcements.

OPENING CONTROL

The greater complexity of modern ships requires a larger number of openings in decks and bulkheads than in the past. This is particularly true relative to the passage of piping and ducts. In an effort to get direct leads for some of these systems, openings are sometimes poorly located as far as structural strength is concerned. For this reason, in some larger passenger ships, trunks are especially provided for the passage of cables, pipes, vents, etc. Although use of trunks necessitates larger openings, the following overall advantages result from the reduction in number of openings: a) their position can be more effectively established and controlled to insure structural adequacy, b) compensation for weakening of the ship girder can be more easily provided, and, c) improved fabrication and workmanship are more readily obtained in cutting, fit-up and welding.

In any ship work, whether repair, alteration, conversion or new construction, special attention must be given to the matter of openings. At times "opening" plans may be helpful in giving specific instructions for the common cases. However, it is understood that the solution of the more unusual or complex situations must be referred to the structural division of the Engineering Department.

---

* For a definition of stress concentration refer to Section I.

OPENING LOCATION AND WORKMANSHIP

In Section I, *Stresses and Strains on Ships,* we considered the ship's hull as a hollow box girder (Fig. 1-16) whose webs are the side plating and whose upper and lower flanges are, respectively, the uppermost strength deck and the bottom plating.

Bending stresses in the strength deck and the bottom generally are higher than those on the side plating, as shown in Fig. 1-18.

The plating at the corners of the ship box girder is more highly stressed, as seen previously (Fig. 1-16).

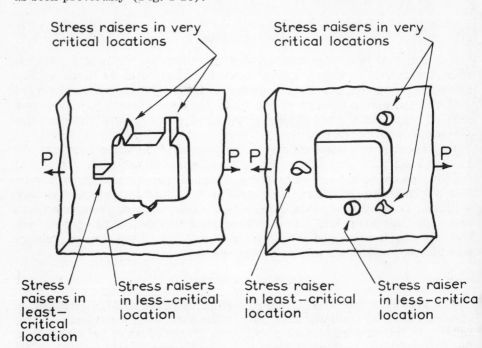

Stress raisers in very critical locations

Stress raisers in very critical locations

Stress raisers in least-critical location

Stress raisers in less-critical location

Stress raiser in least-critical location

Stress raiser in less-critical location

Note: Most critical stress raiser locations are in lateral vicinity of opening corners.

FIG. 2-1. Stress raisers at or in the vicinity of an opening.

Because of the variation of the ship's bending moment, explained in Section I, the stresses mentioned above are more severe in the portion of the ship that we call the *middle 2/5L to 3/5L* (40 per cent to 60 per cent of the length amidships).

The foregoing facts about bending stresses become more significant when we consider the effect of openings in the main hull. We saw in Section I that openings are the cause of appreciable stress concentration. When these concentrations are applied to hull bending stress levels that are already high, critical stress situations can develop.

In accordance with our comments on Figs. 1-25 to 1-28, it is evident that any slot with sharp corners, and also any notch or edge irregularity n the vicinity of the opening (and its concentration), will produce an additional stress concentration. The same will be true of any hole near he opening. All the defects shown in Fig. 2-1, with some exaggeration, will be particularly dangerous if they occur close to a point of high stress concentration of the opening.

Figure 2-1 and the foregoing comments indicate the importance of good workmanship in connection with hull openings. It should be evident, then, that an opening whose edges look like the ones of Fig. 2-2 should never be allowed in structural members where stresses might be significant.

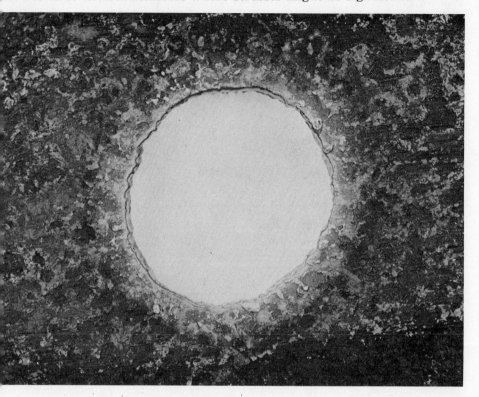

FIG. 2-2. Opening in a structural member showing poor workmanship.

The hatching of Fig. 2-3 indicates the portions of the strength envelope where we have to be particularly careful with opening design and workmanship. In these regions it would be very desirable to avoid the presence of any opening whatsoever. This ideal situation is seldom realized. Whenever possible, the structural division of the Engineering Department should be consulted before cutting any holes in these areas.

In Fig. 2-3 (a) (top view), the upper deck is shown intact. In most ships, however, especially merchant vessels, the decks have large openings n the centerline, as shown in Fig. 2-4.

Since not located at section of minimum strength (i.e., in way of hatches), the deck material within the line of hatches is not included when he moment of inertia or section modulus of the ship girder is calculated.

This is indicated graphically in Fig. 1-21 (a), where the primary and secondary hull girder components are shown. In Fig. 2-4, the hatched areas at both sides of the hatches are the deck portions that are considered effective in the overall longitudinal bending strength of the ship. Although this is a sound procedure, we have to be careful in avoiding stress raisers in the areas considered ineffective, since some portions may actually be as highly stressed as those areas considered fully effective. The areas of reduced stress in these so-called ineffective areas are as mentioned in the following.

Theory and experimentation (*see* Fig. 2-14 and ref. 10) have proven that a rectangular opening in a plate under tensile stress results in a re-

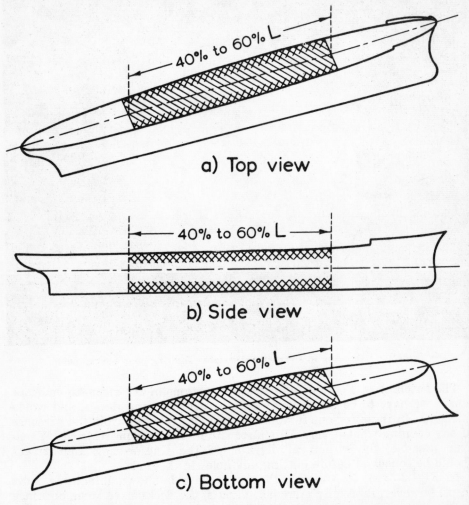

a) Top view

b) Side view

c) Bottom view

Note: 1) ⬛⬛⬛⬛ indicates areas of high bending stresses.
2) ⬛⬛⬛⬛ indicates critical areas in bending.

Fig. 2-3. Hull portions where openings are most dangerous.

duced stress area in the plate immediately adjacent to both ends of the opening in the direction of stress (except at corners). These areas are shown cross-hatched on Fig. 2-5. It will be noted that the outer boundary of these reduced stress areas is given as extending a distance from the opening equal to twice the breadth of the opening (i.e., $l = 2b$ in Fig. 2-5). Bureau of Ships Design Data Sheet DDS 9290–2–n, paragraph 3, specifies this distance. Outside this distance, the plate should be regarded as fully stressed. Within these areas, as the opening is approached, the stress level decreases progressively so that at the 45° line, corresponding to $l = \dfrac{b}{2}$ (also shown in Fig. 2-5), the stress is about one-third of full stress value.

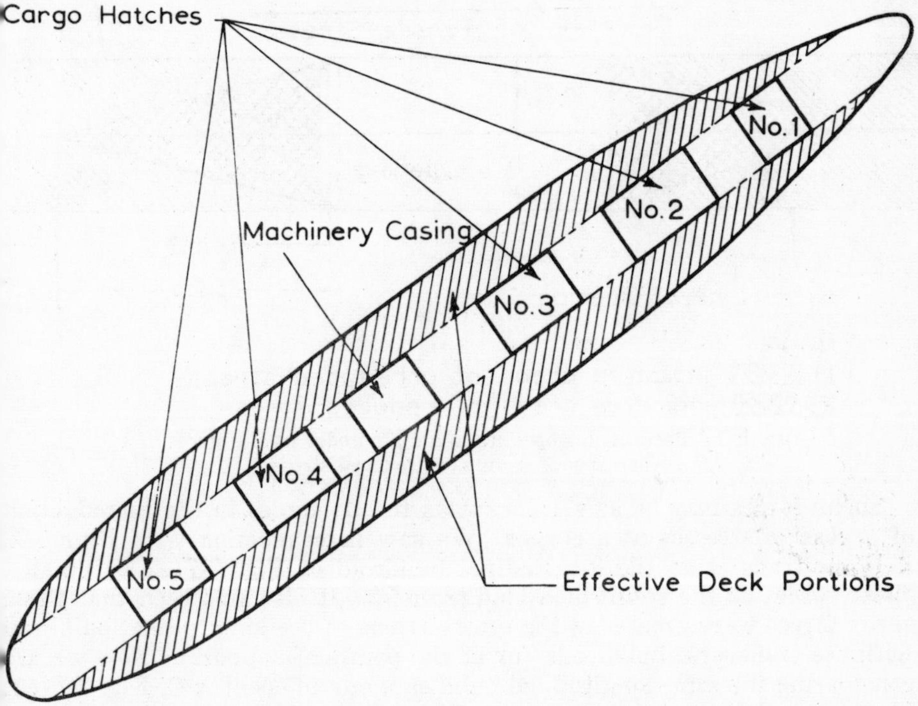

Fig. 2-4. Deck plan view of general cargo ship showing openings.

As a practical matter affecting design, it may be said that minor or secondary openings near the outer limit ($l = 2b$) should be designed as if they were primary openings, subject to full stress value of primary structure. Secondary openings within or near the 45° line are not critical and only require small corner rounding. Secondary openings in the zone between the 45° line and the $l = 2b$ line should receive design attention commensurate with stress magnitude at their location.

When two or more rectangular openings are arranged in line in the direction of stress, the conditions shown in Fig. 2-6 result. Figure 2-6(a) shows widely spaced openings, as found in destroyer decks; Fig. 2-6(b) shows closely spaced openings, like the cargo hatches in a general cargo

ship; and the very closely spaced openings of Fig. 2-6(c) would correspond to the cargo hatches in an ore carrier.

Figure 2-6 illustrates the effect of the superposition of the areas of reduced stress between major openings, aligned in the direction of a tensile
stress, when the distance between openings is changed. The cross-hatched
areas of Fig. 2-6 are areas of reduced stress, where necessary secondary
openings may be located to avoid dangerous superposition of stress concentrations. The location and characteristics of these secondary openings
within the areas of reduced stress, whenever possible, should follow the
recommendations given previously with regard to Fig. 2-5.

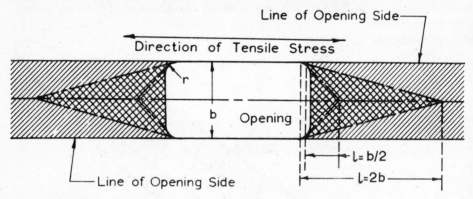

Notes:
1) ▨▨▨ indicates areas of unreduced stress.
2) ▨▨▨ indicates areas of reduced stress.

FIG. 2-5.   Rectangular opening in a plate under tensile stress and
corresponding areas of reduced stress.

Shear forces may be as significant as tensile forces in the introduction
of excessive stresses at a corner. We saw in connection with Fig. 1-22
how the loads D on the longitudinal bulkhead of Fig. 2-7(a) originated
shear forces as the result of a load transfer. It also was seen that these
shear forces were greater at the intersections of the longitudinal bulkhead
with the transverse bulkheads (or at the points of support). Now we are
considering the same longitudinal bulkhead, but an opening O, Fig. 2-7(a),
has been included.

Figure 2-7(b) is a diagram of the direction of forces in the longitudinal
bulkhead near the support points. S and S_1 are the same forces shown in
Figs. 1-22 and 2-7(a). If these were the only forces in the system, this
would be unbalanced and would rotate counterclockwise. Therefore, there
is a built-in restraint S_h and S_{1h}, provided by the decks, which is equal and
opposite to S and S_1. Any two equal forces at right angles to each other
can be resolved into single forces R, which act at 45° and act in compression or tension, depending upon their direction. This fact can be demon-
strated by grasping a piece of paper along parallel edges and moving one
edge in the opposite direction to the other. The result is a shear force,
and the fact that the paper wrinkles shows that the shear force induces
forces in the plane of the paper that are tensile in the direction of the
wrinkles on the diagonals and compressive across the wrinkles.

Figure 2-7(c) shows a hole similar to O of Fig. 2-7(a). The action of the shear force is such that it tends to compress the hole across two opposite corners and elongate it across the other corners. This action intro-

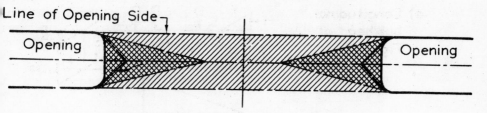

a) Widely spaced openings.

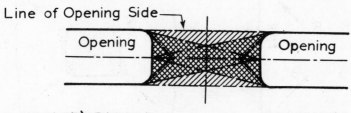

b) Closely spaced openings.

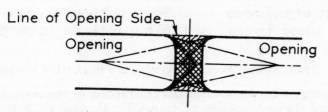

c) Very closely spaced openings.

Notes:

1) ▨▨▨ indicates areas of unreduced stress

2) ▧▧▧ indicates areas of reduced stress.

3) The best location for minor openings in the vicinity of the large openings shown in (a),(b) and (c) is within the cross-hatched areas. However, minor openings should be placed well removed from the corners of the large openings.

FIG. 2-6.   In-line rectangular openings in a plate under tensile stress and corresponding areas of reduced stress.

duces high tensile forces at the corner that is being opened and the opening itself causes stress concentration in these corners (*see also* Fig. 2-21). It is obvious from this analysis that openings should be located well away from regions of high shear, such as the intersections of load-carrying members.

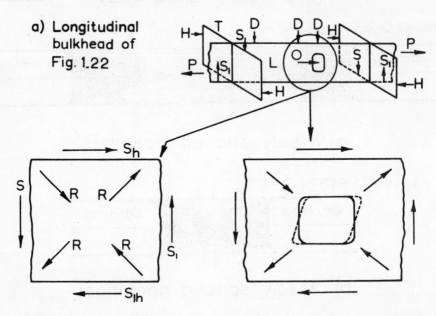

a) Longitudinal bulkhead of Fig. 1.22

b) Fragment of bulkhead showing shear forces.

c) Same bulkhead fragment as (b) but with an opening.

FIG. 2-7.   Effect of shear forces on an opening in a longitudinal bulkhead.

In Section I, Fig. 1-23, we studied the interaction of the main hull and a deckhouse, and the development of forces F_1, F_2, and F_3, Fig. 2-8(a), was explained. In Fig. 2-8(b), the forces which act on the ends of the deckhouse are more clearly defined. The deckhouse is forced to move because of its rigid attachment at the hull, which provide forces F_1 and F_3. It resists change of shape by forces R_1 and R_3 to counterbalance the external forces. Thus, couples* *ff* and *rr* are established and a shear condition results. These couples resolve into tension and compression forces which may overstress the structure, especially if a discontinuity, such as an opening, is present in this highly stressed field. The structural action in way of such an opening is similar to that described relative to Fig. 2-7(c).

Figure 2-9 reminds us of the areas in the strength envelope where shear may become significant, as seen in Section I.

---

* We call a *couple* a system of two equal and opposite forces such as *f* and *f*, or *r* and *r*. The distance between the forces is termed the *arm* of the couple. The *moment* of the couple is the product of one of the forces times the distance between them.

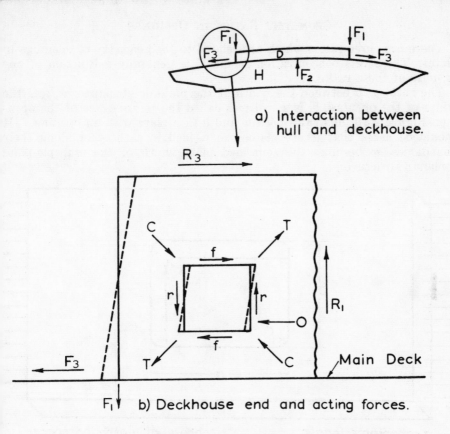

a) Interaction between
hull and deckhouse.

b) Deckhouse end and acting forces.

FIG. 2-8.   Detail of main deck and deckhouse in correspondence
with an opening.   (Ref. 3)

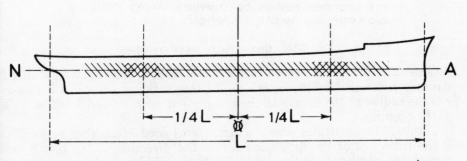

Notes 1). Hatching indicates areas where shear may be
significant.

2). Cross-hatching indicates areas where shear
may be more significant.

FIG. 2-9.   Hull areas where shear reaches higher values.

GEOMETRIC RATIOS IN OPENINGS

There are three ratios which are related to the geometry of openings in plates. The stress concentration factor K is generally a function of one or more of these ratios.

The ratio w/b between the width of the plate or structure, w, and the width of the opening, b, is sometimes called the *relative size* of the opening. Figure 2-10 illustrates both w and b in a plate with an opening. (It should be noted that where plates are welded to each other along their boundaries, w becomes the combined plate width of the multiple-plate coplanar structure.)

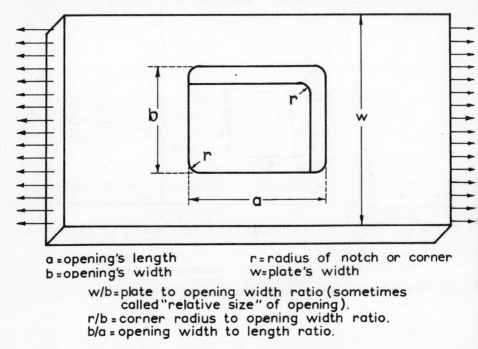

a = opening's length   r = radius of notch or corner
b = opening's width   w = plate's width

w/b = plate to opening width ratio (sometimes
    called "relative size" of opening).
r/b = corner radius to opening width ratio.
b/a = opening width to length ratio.

FIG. 2-10.   Geometric ratios of openings.

Generally, the stress concentration factor K in a rectangular opening is strongly influenced by the ratio r/b. In this ratio, as shown in Fig. 2-10, r is the radius at the corner of the rectangular opening and b is the width of the opening.

Figure 2-10 illustrates also the dimensions used in another ratio. This is the ratio b/a of the dimension across the direction of the tensile load (opening's width), b, to the dimension in the direction of the tensile load (opening's length), a.

STRESS CONCENTRATION FACTOR IN OPENINGS

All stress concentration information contained in this section is based upon elastic behavior of steel. This information is for guidance in contouring openings and reinforcing critical areas thereat. After reinforce-

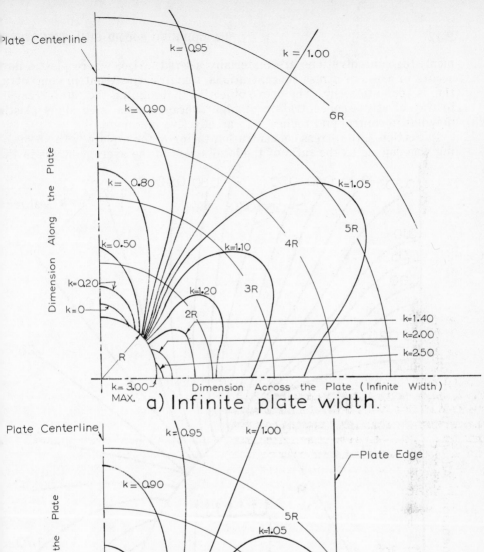

a) Infinite plate width.

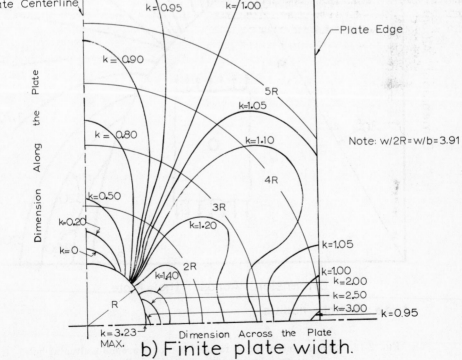

b) Finite plate width.

FIG. 2-11. Stress concentration factors around a circular hole in infinite and finite width plates. (Ref. 5)

ment, the concentrations are materially altered. Also, where plastic flow occurs in areas of stress concentrations, some readjustment in concentration is bound to occur. The prime objective in designing the reinforcement in way of stress concentration of high average stress is to allow plastic flow but to control and reduce it to an effective minimum.

In Section I, the stress concentration factor K for a plate with an opening was defined as the ratio of the local stress to the average stress in the

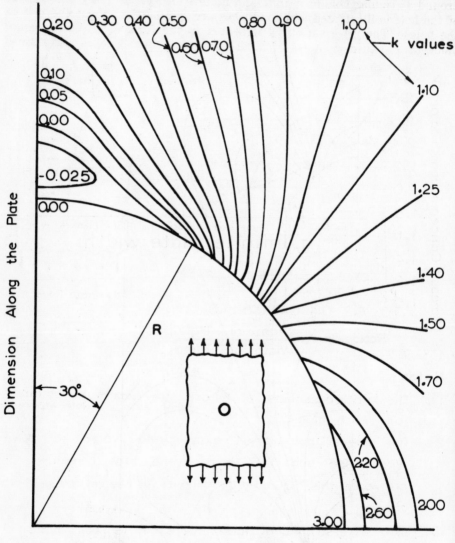

Fig. 2-12.   Stress concentration factor k contours around a circular hole in an infinite width plate. (Ref. 6)

minimum section. Also, the stress concentration factor, symbolized by k, was defined as the ratio of the local stress to the uniaxial stress applied at infinite distance from the opening. Furthermore, it was shown that the factor K was equal to k times the fraction $2a/A$, where $2a$ is the net cross-sectional area of the plate in way of the opening and A is the cross-sectional area of the intact plate (Fig. 1-25).

Figure 2-11 shows local values of the stress concentration factor k around a circular hole in infinite and finite width plates (only one-quarter of the hole is illustrated, but conditions are symmetrical about the rest of the hole). The information is presented in the form of curves of equal value of k, called *contours* of k. These values, which were determined

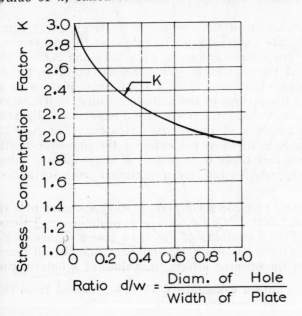
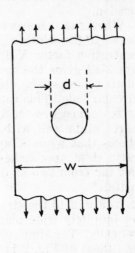

$$\text{Ratio } d/w = \frac{\text{Diam. of Hole}}{\text{Width of Plate}}$$

Notes :

1). The plotted values of K are the maximum obtained for each d/w.

2). The lowest and highest experimental values of d/w were 0.05 and 0.97 respectively. The K value curve in this figure was faired – in beyond these values.

3). The stress concentration factor K is the ratio of the local stress to the average stress in the minimum section.

FIG. 2-13. Curve of stress concentration factor K plotted against the ratio d/w for a narrow plate with a circular hole under stress. (Ref. 7)

theoretically, indicate that when the width of the plate is greater than about four times the diameter of the hole, the solution for a plate of infinite width gives satisfactory results. It can be seen also that in a plate of infinite width, the maximum value of the stress concentration factor k corresponding to a circular hole is three ($k = 3$).

Figure 2-12 shows at a larger scale the stress concentration factor k contours around a circular hole in an infinite width plate. This figure shows in more detail the variation of stress as a result of the discontinuity produced by the opening. There is a k contour in the figure for which a negative value is given. This indicates, as pointed out in Section I, that at that particular location the plate is stressed in compression rather than in tension.

When the transverse dimension of the opening is relatively large compared to the width of the plate under stress, the values of the stress concentration factor K differ from those shown in Figs. 2-11 and 2-12. Figure 2-13 gives the curve of the maximum stress concentration factor K plotted against the diameter-width ratio, d/w, for a narrow plate with a circular hole. This ratio is the inverse of the plate to opening width ratio, w/b, defined previously. The values of K were found experimentally and agree quite well with the findings of several investigators. Figure 2-13 shows that while K approaches three as the value of the diameter-width ratio, d/w, approaches zero (infinitely wide plate), K approaches a value not far from two as d/w approaches one (zero minimum cross section of plate).*

In Fig. 2-14 the stress concentration k contours around a square hole in an infinitely wide plate are plotted. These values were determined theoretically. The similarity of the k contours of Fig. 2-14 (for a square hole) and those of Fig. 2-11(a) (for a circular hole) indicates that for all practical purposes the shape of the opening affects the values of k only in the vicinity of the opening, i.e., not at a distance R (or $\frac{b}{2}$) removed from the edge of the opening.

Figure 2-15 shows the values of stress concentration factor k around the edges of a square hole with rounded corners in an infinitely wide plate under stress. These values were obtained using theoretical expressions. Because of symmetry, only a quadrant of the opening is shown. The two cases shown are for values of the corner radius to opening width ratio, r/b, of one-eighth and one-quarter. Values of k for other radius to width ratios are given in the same reference (8), but only the two ratios considered most interesting are included in Fig. 2-15.

The square opening illustrated in Fig. 2-16 has the particular characteristic of having the corners rounded by a parabolic curve rather than by the usual quadrant of a circle. The values of the stress concentration factor k were obtained by test and correspond to a plate of finite width where the ratio of the width of the plate to the width of the opening w/d, is equal to three.

---

* Note that K involves average stress on net section of opening. When this net section approaches zero, the average stress on the net section can be very high and the k concentration factor is applied to the high stress value.

It has been proven theoretically and confirmed experimentally that in a ectangular opening with rounded corners, the maximum stress concentraion factor is found at the tangency point of the rounded corner with the pening side parallel to the direction of uniaxial stress. Inset A of Fig. -17 and Figs. 2-14, 2-15 and 2-16 show the more critical areas around an pening in a plate under uniaxial stress. Inspection for defects and lack f smoothness in these areas should be very thorough. For instance, Fig. -17 shows dangerous defects in opening's corners resulting from poor ame cutting. Because of the normally high values of the stress concenration factor between points B and C, the defects shown in the sketches c) and (d) are particularly hazardous.

As mentioned previously, sharp or square corners associated with openngs in plates subject to tension stress are the source of very high stress oncentration factors plus structural notch effect and, therefore, should be efinitely avoided where stress levels are significant.

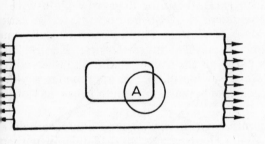

a) Plate with an opening, loaded uniaxially.

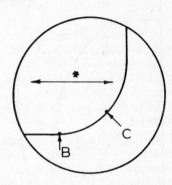

b) Inset A showing points B and C between which greatest values of k and K are found.

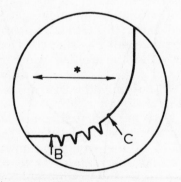

c) Inset A showing jagged corner cut.
* Stress direction.

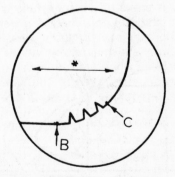

d) Inset A showing projections into the opening at the corner.

FIG. 2-17. Dangerous defects in opening's corners as a result of poor flame cutting.

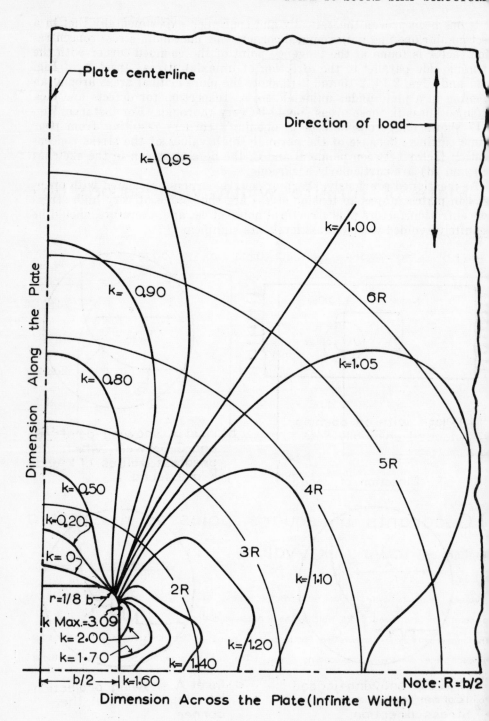

FIG. 2-14.   Stress concentration factor k contours around a square hole
in an infinite width plate.   (Ref. 5)

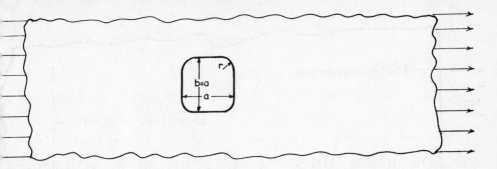

) Plate of infinite width with square hole

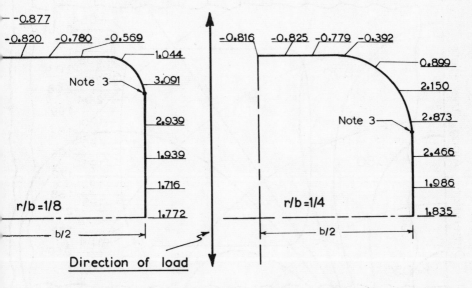

) Quadrants of square holes as illustrated (a) showing k values.

TES:

values in infinite plate is the ratio of the stress at the given point over the stress a point far removed from hole in the length direction.

The numerical values shown are for k at the point of intersection of the hole edge h each one of the corresponding lines. (The minus signs indicate that at those ts there is compression instead of tension.)

Points of tangency of corner radius.

FIG. 2-15. Stress concentration factor k values around a square hole in an infinitely wide plate. (Ref. 8)

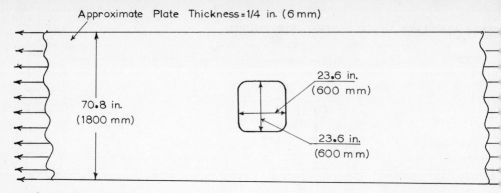

a) Specimen used to determine **k** values

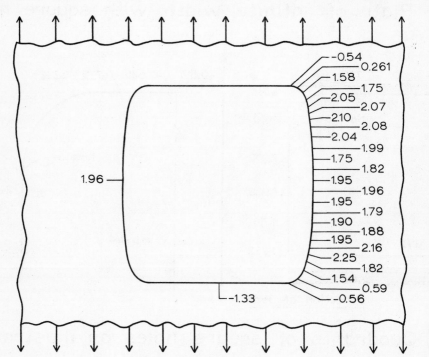

b) Square hole corresponding to specimen illustrated in (a) showing **k** values.

NOTES:

1) The numerical values shown are for k at the point of intersection of the hole edge each one of the corresponding lines. (The minus signs indicate that at those points there is compression instead of tension.)

2) The corners of the square are rounded by using a parabolic curve (as shown rather than the quadrant of a circle (approx. r/b =1/12).

3) The width of the plate to the width of the opening ratio, w/d, is equal to three.

FIG. 2-16. Stress concentration factor k values around a square hole in a plate of finite width. (Ref. 9)

Figure 2-18 illustrates the variation of the maximum stress concentration factor as a function of the corner radius to the opening width ratio r/b. A generous corner radius is fundamental to reduce stress concentration, and a value of r/b between one-fourth and one-eighth is desirable. Figure 2-19 illustrates a rectangle whose two upper and two lower corners have values of r/b of one-fourth and one-eighth, respectively.

The value of the plate to opening width ratio for the tests of Fig. 2-18 was w/b = 5.33, and for this value the relationship between the maximum stress concentration factors K' and k is illustrated. Figure 2-18 shows also a good agreement between the values of k obtained experimentally and theoretically. The corresponding numerical values are given in Table 2-1.

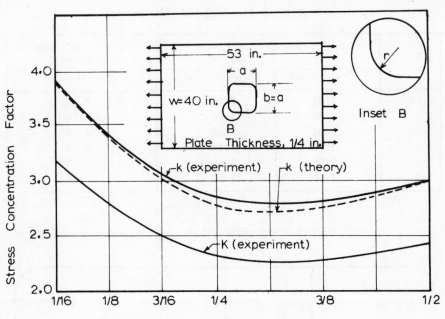

Notes:

1)   b= a = 7.5 in, Ratio w/b = 40/7.5 = 5.33 .

2)   The theory allows finding the value of k only.

3)   **For the experimental values of K the expression** $K = k \dfrac{2a}{A}$ **, introduced in Section I, was used.**

FIG. 2-18. Comparison of maximum stress concentration factors k and K. (Ref. 10)

Finally, in Fig. 2-18 for a ratio r/b = 1/2 (circular opening), the value of the stress concentration factor is $K = 2.44$. This value is for a ratio w/b = 5.33. For the corresponding value d/w = 1/5.33 = 0.1875, Fig. 2-13 indicates good agreement with a value of $K = 2.50$ approximately.

The b/a ratio (previously defined), of an opening in a stressed plate, has a definite influence on the value of the maximum stress concentration factor. In general, to keep the stress concentration factor low, we have to keep the long dimensions of openings parallel to the direction of the load. The opening sketches in Fig. 2-20 and their corresponding stress concentration curves indicate this. For an opening of constant width, the length has been varied from a value much less to a value greater than the width. With this variation, the stress concentration steadily reduces. This effect holds good when the ratio of w/b differs from the single value (essentially) indicated.

TABLE 2-1. Maximum stress concentration factors k and K (Fig. 2-18).

r/b	Stress Concentration Factor k		Stress Concentration Factor K
	Theoretical	Experimental	Experimental
1/16	3.87	3.90	3.17
1/8	3.38	3.40	2.76
3/16	3.00	3.08	2.50
1/4	2.80	2.88	2.34
3/8	2.75	2.80	2.28
1/2	3.00	3.00	2.44

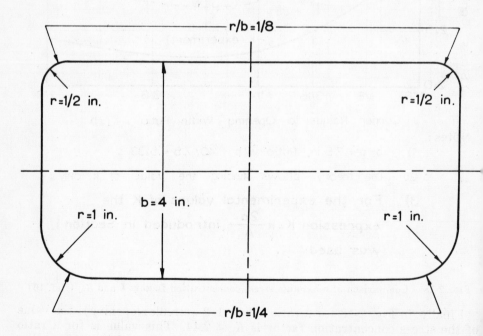

FIG. 2-19. Rectangle showing acceptable values of $\frac{r}{b}$ for an opening.

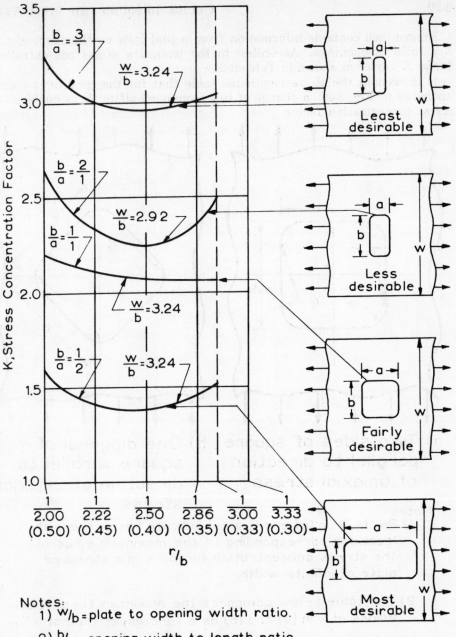

Notes:
1) w/b = plate to opening width ratio.

2) b/a = opening width to length ratio.

3) The stress concentration factor K is the ratio of the maximum to the average stress in the minimum section.

4) r = radius of the corner.

FIG. 2-20. Effect of the b/a ratio on the stress concentration factor. (Ref. 9)

2-21

Figure 2-20 contains information from actual tests on the effect of the b/a ratio in openings. According to the tests, the stress concentration factor K varied as shown in Table 2-2.

It is seen in the above mentioned table that for the conditions corresponding to Fig. 2-20, a change of b/a from one-half to three doubles the stress concentration factor.

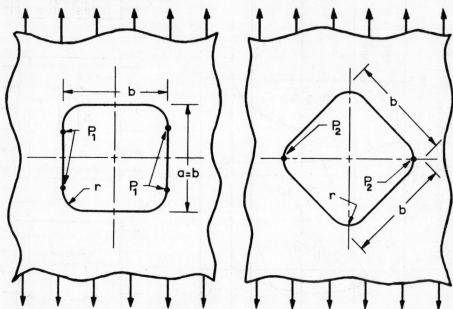

a) Two sides of square parallel to direction of uniaxial stress.

b) One diagonal of square parallel to direction of uniaxial stress.

Notes:
1) Points P_1 in (a) and P_2 in (b) indicate respectively the locations corresponding to the maximum value of the stress concentration factor k in a stressed plate of infinite width.

2) The table below compares the maximum theoretical values of k in (a) and (b) as a function of the ratio r/b:

$\dfrac{r}{b}$	$\dfrac{1}{32}$	$\dfrac{1}{16}$	$\dfrac{1}{8}$	$\dfrac{1}{4}$	$\dfrac{3}{8}$
$\dfrac{\text{k max in (b)}}{\text{k max in (a)}}$	2.19	1.98	1.69	1.46	1.22

FIG. 2-21. Effect of the orientation of a square opening in a stressed plate. (Ref. 8)

The orientation of a rectangular opening in a plate subject to a uniaxial stress has an important effect on the value of the stress concentration factor. Figure 2-21 shows this effect for a square opening in a plate of infinite width and also indicates its variation as a function of the ratio of the corner radius to the width of the square. Figure 2-21(a) illustrates a square opening with two sides parallel to the direction of the stress, while Fig. 2-21(b) shows the same opening, when one of its diagonals is parallel to the direction of the stress. The ratio of the maximum k of Fig. 2-21(b) to the maximum k of Fig. 2-21(a) indicates the additional factor resulting from change in orientation. This factor increases with decreasing values of r/b. For common shipbuilding r/b ratios (r/b = 1/4 to 1/8), k for a square opening with one diagonal parallel to the stress direction is approximately 50 per cent larger than the k corresponding to the same square with two sides parallel to the stress direction. Corresponding values for different orientations of a rectangular opening in a uniaxially stressed plate are not available, but a similar effect occurs. Therefore, rectangular openings always should be oriented with two sides parallel to the direction of the stress.

TABLE 2-2. Maximum stress concentration factor as a function of b/a.

b/a	K	b/a	K
1/2	1.38 - 1.59	2	2.24 - 2.70
1	2.08 - 2.21	3	2.98 - 3.11

REINFORCEMENT OF OPENINGS

Openings are reinforced to restore partially the effective cross-section area and reduce the stress concentration. Actually, in way of an opening, no amount of restored material (reinforcement), however disposed, can reduce the stress concentration to unity (i.e., eliminate the concentration) or restore the complete strength of the uncut plate.

In the past, the main intention in providing a reinforcement was to replace the amount of cross-section area removed by the opening and consider it effective. Today we are not only concerned with material replacement but with effective distribution for optimum strength and reduction of stress-raiser effect. It is commonly known that stress raisers increase the potential, both for ductile and for brittle fracture in way of notches.

Figure 2-22 shows the three types of reinforcement used almost exclusively in welded construction, namely: Fig. 2-22(d), single doubler reinforcement; Fig. 2-22(e), face bar reinforcement; Fig. 2-22(f), insert plate reinforcement. The percentage of reinforcement is defined by the following formula:

$$\text{Percentage of reinforcement} = \frac{2a}{A} \times 100$$

Where: A = Cross-section area of material removed.
    2a = Cross-section area of material added.

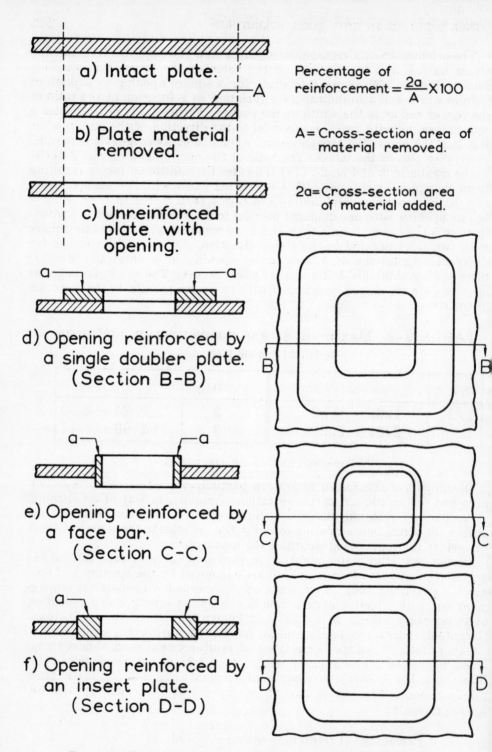

a) Intact plate.

b) Plate material removed.

c) Unreinforced plate with opening.

d) Opening reinforced by a single doubler plate. (Section B-B)

e) Opening reinforced by a face bar. (Section C-C)

f) Opening reinforced by an insert plate. (Section D-D)

Percentage of reinforcement $= \dfrac{2a}{A} \times 100$

A = Cross-section area of material removed.

2a = Cross-section area of material added.

FIG. 2-22. Types of reinforcements and percentage of reinforcements.

Using the formula on page 2-23, the percentage of reinforcement for a reinforced plate with a net cross-section area equal to the area of the intact plate would be 100 per cent. Unreinforced plates with openings would result with zero percentage of reinforcement.

Table 2-3, below, gives optimum percentages of reinforcement, as defined above, for each type of reinforcement. These values were obtained in tests with 21 specimens of steel plates 36 in. wide by 1/4 in. thick with openings. These values are only tentative because of the limited number of tests run.

TABLE 2-3. Optimum percentage of reinforcement.

Type of Reinforcement	Optimum Percentage of Reinforcement
Single doubler plate, Fig. 2-22(d)	90 to 100 per cent
Face bar, Fig. 2-22(e)	34 to 40 per cent
Insert plate, Fig. 2-22(f)	30 to 60 per cent

The tests mentioned above indicated also that when the percentage of reinforcement was smaller than the one prescribed in Table 2-3, for the particular type of reinforcement, the plates failed through the opening. When the percentage of reinforcement was greater than the optimum indicated in Table 2-3, the reinforcement acted as a rigid inclusion in the body plate, and failure occurred in the weld joining the outer edge of the reinforcement to the body plate.

The choice of type of opening reinforcement depends in varying degree on the following factors: a) type of construction (riveted or welded), b) workmanship required, c) fabrication and erection cost, d) weight, e) degree of interference with other structural members, f) required degree of smoothness in the reinforced plate (relative to obstruction created in deck plates and underwater shell plating), and g) appearance.

Table 2-3 indicates that when the single doubler plate type is used, to obtain its maximum efficiency, it is necessary to use 90 to 100 per cent reinforcement (the other two types of reinforcement realized their most efficient behavior at substantially lower percentages of reinforcement). The doubler is extensively used in merchant ship construction since fabrication and erection are generally faster and less expensive. This type is particularly well suited for riveted construction, as illustrated in Fig. 2-24(a) which shows the reinforcement at a side-port.

As indicated in Table 2-3, the face bar type requires the smallest percentage of reinforcement for its optimum performance. Supporting evidence is shown in Fig. 2-23 where maximum K values are given for reinforced square openings with rounded corners. Figure 2-23 suggests that for this type there is no advantage in going beyond 40 per cent reinforcement (however, unless area is added elsewhere, the moment of inertia of

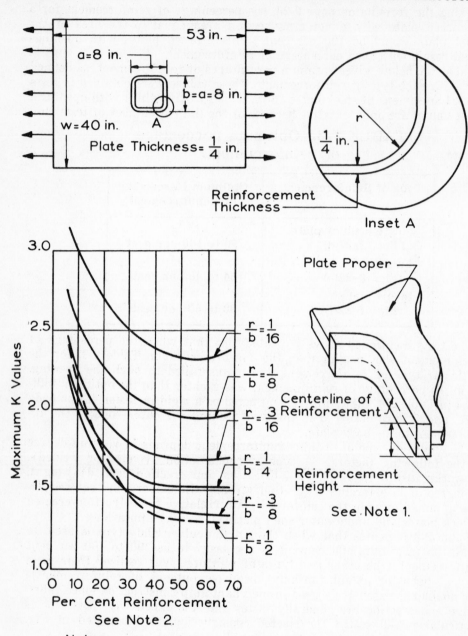

Notes:
1) Reinforcement is as defined in Fig. 2.22.
2) For plate thickness equal to 1/4 inch.

FIG. 2-23.   Maximum *K* values for face-bar reinforced square openings with rounded corners. (Ref. 10)

the hull girder is reduced in way of the opening). This explains why face bar reinforcement is favored in warship construction where weight saving is an important consideration. It is the natural choice when the face bar can serve, in addition, as the opening's coaming, as in the case of some hatchways. The butt joint in the face bar requires proper location (away from areas of high stress concentration). The complete face bar requires careful fitting to obtain a sound welded joint.

The insert plate type of reinforcement will provide smoother surfaces, better appearance, and sometimes will avoid structural interference, but requires proper fitting and a higher degree of workmanship. An example of its application to riveted construction is illustrated in Fig. 2-24(b), which shows the reinforcement at a side-port.

REINFORCEMENT OF OPENINGS IN THE STRENGTH ENVELOPE

When openings are cut in the strength envelope material, the opening must be compensated for by increasing the· thickness of the adjacent plating, or by providing local reinforcement, or by a combination of both. The compensation method selected should be based upon location of opening and local environment. This applies over the three-fifth length amidships. At the ends of the ship and where lower stress levels prevail, rounding of opening corners alone may be sufficient. The same compensation procedure also must be adopted in the case of openings in the ship's box girder components subject to significant stress levels, such as, effective longitudinal bulkheads, decks located at a substantial distance from the neutral axis, etc. Reinforcement must be carried well around the opening corners in all cases, irrespective of opening size.

The transverse sectional area of plating cut out, i.e., the thickness of plate times the transverse width of opening, should be compensated for by proper reinforcement. In spite of this, a cut plate with optimum reinforcement is never as strong as an uncut plate. Therefore, cutting and reinforcing should not be done indiscriminately.

If doublers are used as a means of reinforcement, usually the material should be distributed symmetrically on both sides of the opening. For openings in the side shell, it may be necessary to concentrate doubler material on one side only. For the symmetrical type, the transverse sectional area of the doubler should be approximately equal to the sectional area removed (*see* Table 2-3). Where space is limited, the thickness of the doublers may be increased reasonably and the width reduced, so long as the required sectional area is obtained, and the strength of the doubling can be developed by adequate riveting or welding. In general, however, the doubler should not be thicker than the base plate.

Figure 2-25 illustrates two typical, minor openings in a ship's deck and various means of reinforcement by using doublers.

Doublers for an opening in way of a riveted seam can be efficiently arranged as shown in Fig. 2-24(a).

When using face bar reinforcement, the opening should be reinforced by a continuous face bar without cuts or notches. Generally, the bar should be independent of other structural members, but it may be incorporated in

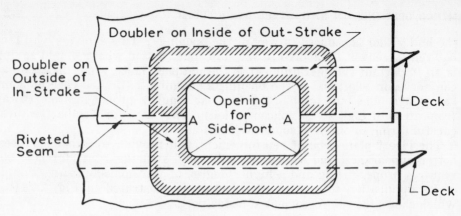

a) Single doubler plate at a side-port (all riveted).

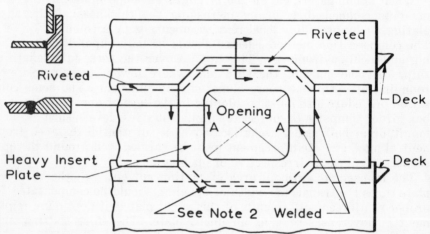

b) Insert plate at a side-port (partly welded)

Note:
1) The example given above shows the increased thickness carried the full length of the sides of the opening The extra material is not needed in the vicinity of points A from a strength point of view, as these areas are largely relieved of fore-and-aft stress by the presence of the opening. However, the advantages of a flush surface for fitting the side-port frame make it desirable to fit the doubler or insert plate right around the opening, as shown.
2) R min = 3 in.

FIG. 2-24. Opening reinforcement in riveted construction. (Ref. 21)

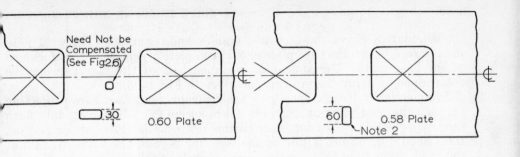

a) Sectional area cut out:
  30 × 0.60 = 18 sq. in.

b) Sectional area cut out:
  60 × 0.58 = 34.8 sq. in.

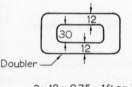

Doubler

2 × 15 × 0.60 = 18 sq. in.

If this dimension is too large for one plate use two plates thus.

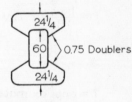

0.58 Doublers

2 × 30 × 0.58 = 34.8 sq. in.

Doubler

2 × 18 × 0.50 = 18 sq. in.

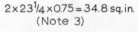

0.75 Doublers

2 × 23¼ × 0.75 = 34.8 sq. in.
(Note 3)

Doubler

2 × 12 × 0.75 = 18 sq. in.
(Note 3)

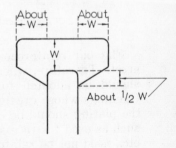

Notes:

1) All measurements in inches unless otherwise indicated.

2) Long dimension disposed transversely may be unavoidable but not recommended. However, schematic doubler details apply when 60 in.-opening has a much greater longitudinal dimension.

3) Whenever possible doublers thicker than the base plate should be avoided (see text).

FIG. 2-25. Typical doubler reinforcements of minor openings in a ship's deck.

the boundaries of sea chests, vents, trunks, and coamings. The weld joining the face bar to the base plate should completely penetrate the thickness
of the base plate. The approximate dimensions of the face bar may be
determined by using the information given in Fig. 2-26.

Symmetrically located face bars are desirable, and face bars projecting
through the base plate at least one T are acceptable. However, only flush
face bars should be used for inner bottom drain wells. For outside plating,
there should be no projection of the face bar beyond the outboard face of
the shell, other than that required for the welded joint.

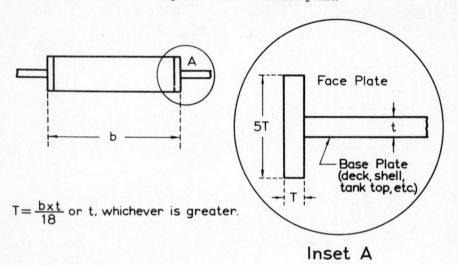

$$T = \frac{b \times t}{18} \text{ or } t, \text{ whichever is greater.}$$

Inset A

T = approximate thickness of face bar, inches.

b = opening's width or diameter, inches.

t = thickness of base plate, inches.

FIG. 2-26.   Typical face bar reinforcement of minor openings in a primary
component of the ship's box girder.

Flat bar reinforcement of round openings are easier to fabricate and
erect. Therefore, when using this type of reinforcement, round openings
should be adopted for ducts and similar openings whenever possible.
Openings whose greatest dimension is less than ten times the thickness of
the plating should be circular. Circular openings up to 5 in. in diameter,
such as used for recessed deck fittings for sounding tubes, operating gear,
etc., need not be reinforced.

Reinforcement not required ordinarily due to location of opening in
girder may be necessary for openings close to points of local stiffness, or
where deck fittings, such as fairleads, subject the plate to high local stress.

No exact requirements can be stated for the size and thickness of doubling plates fitted for reinforcement, although the same thickness as the
plates over which the doublers are fitted will usually be suitable. A sizable
area in association with reasonable doubler thickness is preferable to a
small, thick doubler.

REINFORCEMENT OF OPENINGS IN BEAMS, GIRDERS, LONGITUDINALS, AND STIFFENERS

In considering individual structural members formed by a web and a top and bottom flange, the location and size of the opening will determine the necessity for compensation. This structure may be under the same type of loading as those illustrated in Fig. 1-1, resulting in tension or compression, or they may be subject to bending and shear stresses also, as explained in Section I. More generally, a combination of these stresses will be present.

Figure 2-27 shows one of the structural members mentioned above. It consists of a flanged plate attached to a deck. In structures of this type, it is generally considered that a portion of the supported plating (the deck plating in Fig. 2-27) works together with the stiffener as an individual member (*see* hatched area in Fig. 2-27). Usually a breadth of thirty to sixty plating thicknesses is considered as effective. The position of the neutral axis shown in Fig. 2-27 results from such a consideration.

Openings and cuts in structural members, such as the one illustrated in Fig. 2-27, may be the source of much trouble when they are quite numerous, or when, for convenience in working, they are located without adequate control by those responsible for design.

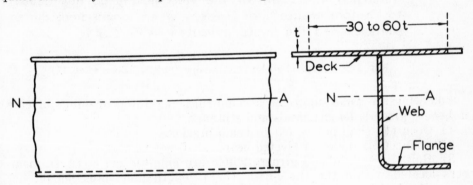

FIG. 2-27. Typical deck girder.

Small, round openings in the web near the neutral axis do not ordinarily require any reinforcement. In general, openings which cannot be located at the local girder neutral axis should be located closer to the supported plate than to the stiffener flange, as the neutral axis of the combined stiffener and plating is usually close to the plating, as shown in Figs. 2-27 and 2-28. This practice is recommended because the local girder bending stress in the web close to the supported plate is lower than the stress in the proximity of the stiffener flange (bending stresses being proportional to distance to N.A.).

Figure 2-28 illustrates openings at various locations in a girder and indicates, in general, what is considered "good practice." More specific guidance is given in the following illustrations.

In general, no cuts in the flanges of beams and stiffeners should be made without compensation; that is, any unavoidable cutting should be made up by equal or slightly greater additional sectional area, distributed well beyond the openings. Figure 2-30 illustrates two typical cases of structural members whose flanges were cut for the passage of piping and ventilation ducts. The same figure shows how the cuttings may be compensated for by the addition of reinforcements. In general, problems of this nature should be turned over to the Engineering Department for a more efficient solution.

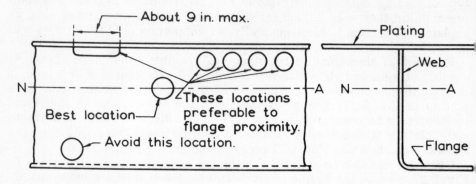

Note. Openings whose transverse dimensions are not over one-third (1/3) the depth of the web usually do not need to be compensated for (except when longitudinal dimensions exceed the limits indicated in Fig. 2.30).

FIG. 2-28.   Typical girder showing opening's location.   (Ref. 11)

Following are some suggested specific rules regarding openings or cuts in beams, girders, longitudinals and stiffeners:
1) Openings shall not be cut in beam brackets.
2) Connecting angles of riveted beams shall not be cut.
3) Holes in unlightened girders which are longitudinal strength members located within the three-fifth (3/5) length amidships should not exceed 15 per cent of the cross-sectional area of the member (plating not included), nor 40 per cent of the depth of the member. Holes exceeding either limit must be reinforced.
4) Except as indicated in Rule 3 above, unreinforced holes in webs of beams and stiffeners 13 inches or less in depth should not exceed the size indicated in Fig. 2-30, nor should they be spaced, with respect to their supports or between themselves, closer than indicated in Fig. 2-30. These requirements may be relaxed somewhat, upon approval of the Engineering Department, for a girder designed for a long span but which is continued over a short span.
5) Openings exceeding the depth given in Rule 4 will, in general, require a web doubler of the type shown in Fig. 2-31. Openings exceeding the length given in Rule 4 will, in general, require a face bar reinforcement. To insure effective reinforcement, openings should not exceed 50 per cent in depth or 150 per cent in length of the depth of the beam.
6) No cuts of flanges of beams and stiffeners will ordinarily be permitted. Any unavoidable penetration of flanges will require reinforcement.

7) When vents, ducts, cable banks, etc., penetrate girders and are of such dimensions as to require increased depths of girders, it is suggested that they be split into units of a size which can penetrate girders of normal depth. When this is not feasible, it may be preferable to run such leads under the girder rather than to increase the girder depth.

8) Holes for piping, etc., in transverse floors and in foundations are to be considered as special cases.

9) A single row of round holes in the webs of beams and stiffeners for a wiring run may be cut without notifying the Engineering Department, subject to the following restrictions:

a) The maximum size of the holes shall be as follows, except where limited by Rule 4:

Depth of Member in.	3	4	5	6	7	8	9	10	12	15	18	24
Hole Diameter in.	5/8	3/4	7/8	1	1-1/8	1-1/4	1-1/2	1-3/4	2	2-1/2	3	4

b) The holes are to be centered not over one-third of the depth of the beam from the supported plating.

c) In lightened beams, longitudinals, or stiffeners, one such hole may be placed midway between any two lightening holes.

d) In unlightened beams, longitudinals, or stiffeners, or in their unlightened portions, as at brackets, such holes are to be spaced at least five diameters center-to-center.

MISCELLANEOUS MINOR OPENINGS AND CUTS IN SHIP'S STRUCTURES

A large number of miscellaneous holes must be cut in the steel structure of a ship to provide for engineering systems, such as ventilation ducts, piping systems, and electric cables, and it is necessary to guard against the following faults:

a) Unduly weakening the structure by introduction of holes or by poor workmanship in cutting (and finishing) the holes.

b) Complicating the construction and maintenance by not allowing proper clearance between holes to allow satisfactory welding, ease of repair work, and effective inspection.

The following suggested rules apply to miscellaneous openings in decks and bulkheads (except non-tight partitions or non-structural bulkheads in which holes generally may be cut wherever necessary):

1) Pipes welded to plating, with or without sleeves, should have at least the clear edge distance between pipes or between pipe and adjacent deck or bulkhead plating, as indicated below:

Zero to 3 in. nominal pipe diameter, 4 in. clear.

Above 3 to 5 in. nominal pipe diameter, 5 in. clear.

Above 5 to 8 in. nominal pipe diameter, 6 in. clear.

These are welder's clearances. Tests have shown that such pipes do not weaken the plating as a diaphragm. If the aggregate diameter of such holes in any one line does not exceed 15 per cent of the total deck width, bulkhead height or width, reinforcement will not ordinarily be required. (The 15 per cent figure also corresponds approximately to the reduction of area in way of a row of rivets spaced seven diameters.)

2) Holes in non-tight structural decks or bulkheads, where pipes or sleeves are not welded to the deck or bulkheads, may be spaced as closely

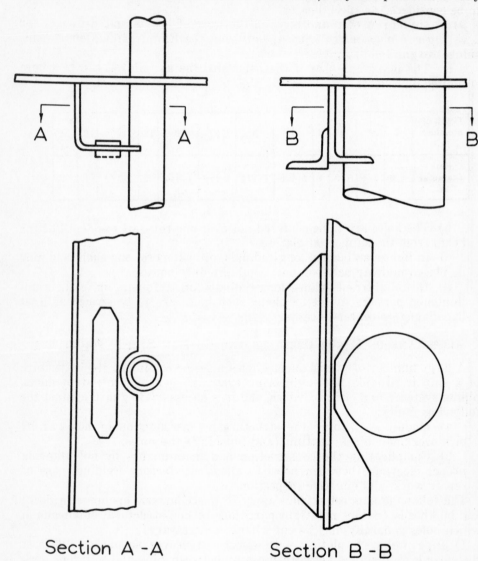

Section A-A

Section B-B

a) Flange partly cut. Area replaced by flat bar.

b) Flange cut off. Area of flange replaced by backing bar.

FIG. 2-29.   Compensation for openings in girder flange.

as working access permits. If the aggregate diameter of such holes in any one line does not exceed 10 per cent of the total deck width or height of bulkhead, reinforcement will not be required ordinarily. However, other cases will require special consideration.

3) An extended line of holes in any primary strength structure in a plane transverse to the direction of the longitudinal stress, such as a long transverse row of holes in a strength deck, particularly within the midship three-fifth length, will require special consideration.

4) Holes for ventilation, ammunition hoist, electric cables (where individual drillings are not made), and holes whose largest dimension is over

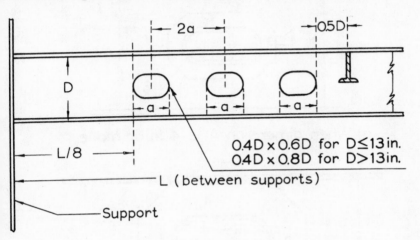

a) Openings in unbracketed beam.

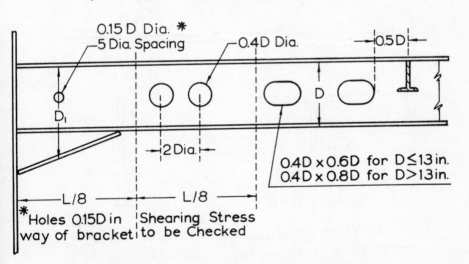

b) Openings in bracketed beam.

FIG. 2-30. Limiting sizes and spacing of unreinforced openings in beam.

5 inches should be given special consideration. Where sharp corners in openings appear unavoidable, due to passage of square trunks such as for hoists, the longitudinal dimension of the cut should be increased to provide for a corner radius, and a light cover plate should be used for the extension of the cut.

5) Holes should be kept at least 15 inches clear of intersecting bulkheads or decks. Where this is not possible, allowance should be made for deflection.

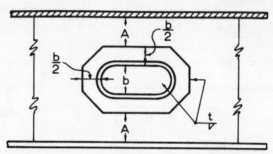

a) When dimension A is 4 in. or more.

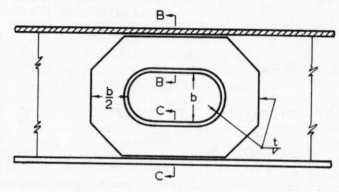

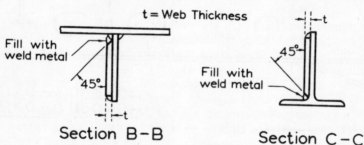

Section B–B   Section C–C

b) When dimension A, as shown in (a), is less than 4 in.

FIG. 2-31. Standard single doubler type of reinforcement for web of stiffeners and beams.

6) There should be no cuts of riveted straps, angles or seams.

7) Bolted bulkhead flanges are not to be considered as reinforcements.

SUMMARY

Openings must be cut in the steel structure of a ship for access, cargo handling, ventilation ducts, trunks, piping systems, electric cables, lightening of the structure, drainage and air escape, weld relief, etc.

The control of the number of openings, their location, workmanship, and proportions (including size, shape and rounding-of-the-corners), is dealt with in detail throughout this section. The relative importance of these factors is explained, and many practical rules to minimize their generally detrimental effects are suggested.

Regarding location of openings, the following general rules are suggested (these should not be violated without the approval of the Engineering Department):

1) Allow no openings in the stringer plate and sheer and bilge strakes within the three-fifths length amidship (rivet holes are not considered openings for the purpose of this rule).

2) When penetration of the strength envelope is unavoidable, place the opening as far from midship as possible and close to the centerline or mid-height (excepting the zone mentioned in Rule 4).

3) Openings in the principal longitudinal strength structure of the hull, such as upper strength deck, shell, inner-bottom or longitudinal bulkheads, should not be aligned in a transverse plane (i.e., local transverse belt). Where small openings of necessity fall in local groups, they should be combined to form a single opening of effective design.

4) Avoid openings close to or at the quarter points at about mid-height of the hull.

5) Avoid openings close to support points and wherever there is substantial load transfer from one structure to another (*see* Fig. 2-7).

6) Openings should be kept well removed from the ends of deckhouses and superstructures (i.e., where longitudinally rigid structure terminates, *see* Fig. 2-8) or from the end of any other discontinuous longitudinal structure.

7) The longitudinal stress in the deck material in certain areas within the line of hatches diminishes and becomes very low. Deck openings should, if possible, be located in these areas, well removed from the corners of the large openings (*see* Figs. 2-4 and 2-6).

Good *workmanship* and the avoidance of ragged edges, notches and similar defects (both in the hull plating and associated welding), are very important in and around openings. Figure 2-1 illustrates some of the most common geometrical stress raisers in the vicinity of an opening. Figure 2-17 shows the most dangerous portions of the edges of an opening (regions of high stress concentration), where inspection for defects and lack of smoothness must be more exacting.

The geometric characteristics of a rectangular opening in a plate may be expressed by means of the following three ratios (dimensions as illustrated in Fig. 2-10): a) w/b, width of the plate or structure over the width of the opening (width of plate is combined width of welded plates);

b) r/b, corner radius over width of the opening; c) b/a, width of the opening over length of the opening.

Value for the stress concentration factor, defined as the ratio of the local stress to the average stress in the minimum section, K, and also defined as the ratio of the local stress to the stress applied at an infinite distance from the opening, k, are given for different plate opening configurations in Figs. 2-11 through 2-16, 2-18 and 2-20. Figure 2-23 gives maximum K values for square, face bar reinforced openings with rounded corners.

The three above-mentioned geometric ratios are related to the maximum value of stress concentration factor and distribution of stress concentration in way of the opening.

In Fig. 2-13, the stress concentration factor K for a narrow plate under tension with a circular hole is given as a function of the ratio of the diameter of hole to plate width, d/w (this ratio is the inverse of the w/b ratio). The factor K varies from the well-known value of three for a very wide plate relative to the diameter of the hole, to a value slightly below two for a relatively narrow plate (although the K value may be lower, the maximum stress may be higher; *see* footnote on page 2-14).

The ratio r/b of an opening in a plate under tensile stress has an important effect on the maximum stress concentration factor which occurs at the opening corner. Figure 2-18 shows values of maximum k and K for unreinforced square openings in a plate as a function of r/b. Table 2-1 gives numerical values of k and K for various values of the ratio r/b. A generous corner radius is fundamental to reduction of stress concentration, and a value of r/b between one-fourth and one-eighth is desirable.

Figure 2-20 and Table 2-2 give information on the effect of variation in the ratio b/a (i.e., ratio of the dimension across the direction of the tensile load to the dimension in the direction of the tensile load) on the value of maximum K. It is shown for certain plate and opening configurations that a change of b/a from one-half to three doubles the maximum stress concentration factor. In general, to keep the stress concentration factor low, openings in the direction normal to the load must be kept as narrow as possible. Increase in opening widths results in increase in maximum stress concentration.

Figure 2-21 gives information on the effect of the orientation of a square opening relative to the direction of the uniaxial plate stress. This figure leads to the conclusion that a rectangular opening should be oriented always so two of its sides are parallel to the direction of the stress.

Openings are reinforced to restore (to the maximum extent practicable) the effective cross-section area of material removed and to reduce the stress concentration locally. Due to the time, expense and weight involved in fitting reinforcements, every effort should be made to avoid the necessity for such compensations whenever possible. Proper planning for locating openings in low stress areas and for combining numerous openings into single openings is necessary for this purpose.

Figure 2-22 shows the three basic types of reinforcement used almost exclusively in welded construction; namely, Fig. 2-22(d), single doubler reinforcement; Fig. 2-22(e), face bar reinforcements; Fig. 2-22(f), insert plate reinforcement. Figure 2-24 shows single doubler and insert plate

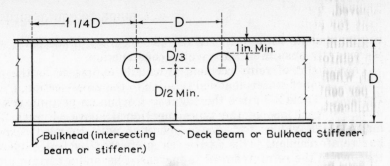

a) Non-reinforced opening. Type 1.

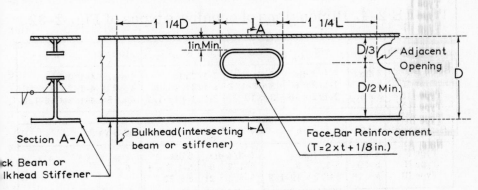

b) Face-bar reinforced opening. Type II. (See Table 2.4)

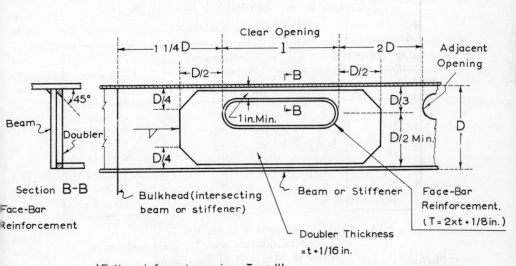

c) Fully reinforced opening. Type III.

Notes: T = face-bar thickness, in.   l = clear length of openings.
       t = web thickness, in.   L = length between supports.

FIG. 2-32. Non-reinforced openings, face bar reinforcement, and combination single doubler and face bar reinforcement of stiffeners and beams.

reinforcements as used in riveted construction. Face plate reinforcement is generally unsuitable for riveted construction.

The amount of reinforcement is usually expressed as the percentage of cross section of material added relative to the cross-section area of material removed. Table 2-3 gives the suggested optimum percentages of reinforcement for each one of the types mentioned above. Figure 2-23 indicates maximum K values for square openings with rounded corners and face bar reinforcement. This figure, as supported by test evidence, indicates that, when the reinforcement is increased beyond a certain amount (about 40 per cent of material removed), further reduction in maximum K is not significant.

TABLE 2-4. Dimensions of opening's types of Fig. 2-32.

Beam Depth	6	7	8	9	10	11
Type I	2 dia.	2-1/2 dia.	3 dia.	3-1/2 dia.	4 dia.	4-1/2 dia.
Type II	2 × 6	2-1/2 × 6	3 × 6-1/2	3-1/2 × 7	4 × 8	4-1/2 × 9
Type III	2 × 8	2-1/2 × 10	3 × 12	3-1/2 × 13-1/2	4 × 15	4-1/2 × 16-1/2

Beam Depth	12	13	14	15	Over 15
Type I	5 dia.	5-1/2 dia.	5-3/4 dia.	6 dia.	--
Type II	5 × 9	5-1/2 × 9	5-1/2 × 9	5-1/2 × 9	6 × 9
Type III	5 × 18	5-1/2 × 19-1/2	5-3/4 × 21	6 × 22	--

Note: All dimensions in inches.

TABLE 2-5. Standard openings for electrical cables.

Opening		Minimum Beam Depth	Face Bar
Type	Size		
A	1 × 3	3	3/16 × 1
B	1-1/2 × 4	5	3/16 × 1
C	1-1/2 × 5	5	3/16 × 1
D	2 × 4	6	1/4 × 1-1/2
E	2 × 5	6	1/4 × 1-1/2
F	3 × 8	8	5/16 × 2
G	4 × 8	10	5/16 × 2

Notes: 1) All dimensions in inches.
2) These standards may be used instead of Type II openings of Fig. 2-32.

Regarding the matter of reinforcement, openings have been grouped into three general categories, namely: reinforcement of openings in the strength envelope; reinforcement of openings in beams, girders, longitudinals and stiffeners; and miscellaneous minor openings and cuts in ship's structures. Rules and tables are presented in this section, and it is suggested that the reader consult them for specific information.

SECTION III

Major Openings
in Ship Steel Structures

INTRODUCTION

Section II, entitled *Minor Openings in Ship Steel Structures*, reviews the general problem of openings in ship structures under stress. Attention is called to the occurrence of structural notches in the vicinity of openings which may cause failures. The control of the number of openings, their location, workmanship, relative size, shape, proportions, and rounding-of-the-corners is dealt with in detail. The relative importance of these factors is discussed and many practical rules to minimize their generally detrimental effects are suggested.

While location and details of the major hull openings are established by the Engineering Department, it is considered advisable that others become aware of good and bad design features of such openings and how poor workmanship can adversely affect otherwise good design.

Major openings in strength decks necessary for cargo hatches, machinery casings, and stairway and elevator wells in large passenger vessels are potential sources of failure in both welded and riveted ships. This is especially true of many vessels where a high level tensile stress occurs in the deck.

In welded dry cargo ships, the structural integrity of the hull is most seriously threatened by discontinuities in the strength deck over the amidships region. A large percentage of the fractures experienced in this type of ship originated at the hatch corners located on the weather deck, within the three-fifths length amidship.

Large side openings, such as cargo ports, may be another potential source of failure, particularly when a part of the opening includes the sheer strake or when the opening is located close to or at the quarter points of the ship. When the side openings involving the sheer strake are in the same transverse belt as large deck openings, the failure potential is increased.

WELDED HATCH CORNER DESIGN

At one time, hatch corners were designed and fabricated with little concern for lessening local stress raisers (except for adding a corner doubler to the deck plating) or for eliminating structural notches.

Riveted ships are generally thought to be less liable to fracture than all-welded ones. This is based upon the inherent ability of the riveted structure to readjust itself somewhat in the presence of localized high stress peaks (by rivet slip, slight structural movement, etc.). In this manner, very high concentration of stress is diminished by redistribution of stress. However, in recent years riveted ships of advancing age also have experienced fractures at the hatch corners.

In all-welded ships, fractures at the strength deck hatch corners often have been the cause of major hull failures. Although designs have varied widely, depending on the designer or builder, presently, both the desirable and undesirable features of such corners have been recognized and are reasonably well understood. The intent of this section is to point out some of the undesirable features, and to suggest improvements in design and fabrication of welded hatch corners. Generally, the design recommendations which follow are applicable also to riveted construction.

UNSATISFACTORY WELDED HATCH CORNER DETAILS

Unsatisfactory welded hatch corner details may be due to improper design, poor welding or poor workmanship. Any of these features may be equally detrimental to the ship structure and can result in hull failure.

Figure 3-1 shows two hatch corner details to be avoided in welded construction. In both cases, the hatch opening has, in effect, square corners, as shown in Fig. 1-25(a). The square corners are the source of notches and involve very high stress concentration when the deck is stressed. To eliminate the notch and to decrease the stress concentration, the opening corners should have a fair and generous radius (for main hatches in typical cargo ships, a radius of one-twentieth the transverse dimension of the opening has proven to be satisfactory). Figure 3-1(a) is the most unsatisfactory of the two welded hatch corner details of Fig. 3-1. The detail of Fig. 3-1(b) shows the addition of a welded corner plate which somewhat improves the stress condition at the hatch corner of Fig. 3-1(a). However, the detail of Fig. 3-1(b) introduces an undesirable notch at each toe of the welded corner plate. These two notches can be eliminated in welded corner plates but not without complicating fabrication and erection.

The original "Liberty" ship hatch corner is shown in Fig. 3-2. This design proved to be one of the worst crack initiators experienced in welded ships, and it has been responsible for many major hull failures. This hatch corner is similar to that of Fig. 3-1(a), except for the addition of a relatively small, heavy-plate, square-cornered doubler under the deck plating. This small doubler proved quite inadequate as a corner reinforcement and was an additional source of failure. Today, the increased plate thickness at the corner is extended over a larger deck area and some prefer insert plate reinforcement to a doubler, as the latter increases the amount of welding necessary at the hatch corner. Perhaps the worst feature of the original "Liberty" ship hatch corner was the accumulation of several severe notches concentrated at the intersection of the deck, longitudinal girder and doubler, as shown in Fig. 3-2. Another undesirable feature of this hatch corner design was the welded joint around the coaming, especially at the corner, as shown in Section AA of Fig. 3-2. This welded joint was not designed for full penetration welding and allowed a notch void in highly stressed metal (lack of penetration in welded joints and its detrimental effects are discussed in Section IV).

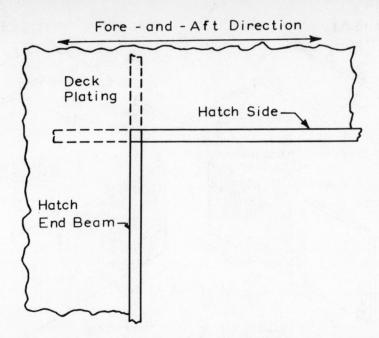

a) Very unsatisfactory welded hatch corner detail. Hatch opening with square cut corner.

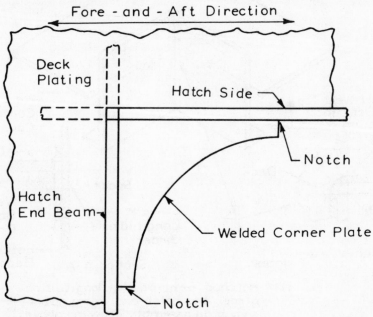

b) Unsatisfactory welded corner detail. Hatch
opening with square corner and welded
corner plate.

FIG. 3-1. Bad practice. Welded hatch corners having hatch
openings with square corners.

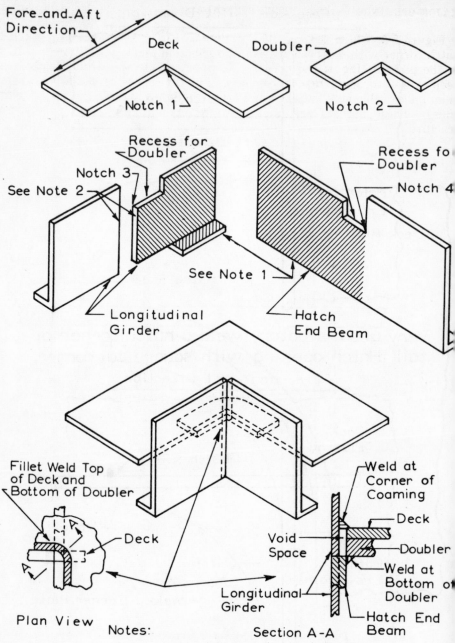

Fore-and-Aft Direction

Deck

Doubler

Notch 1

Notch 2

Recess for Doubler

Notch 3

See Note 2

Recess for Doubler

Notch 4

Longitudinal Girder

See Note 1

Hatch End Beam

Fillet Weld Top of Deck and Bottom of Doubler

Deck

Weld at Corner of Coaming

Deck

Void Space

Doubler

Weld at Bottom of Doubler

Plan View

Longitudinal Girder

Hatch End Beam

Section A-A

Notes:

1) Hatched portions of longitudinal girder and hatch end beam not shown on assembly drawing above.

2) Tee joints to hatch end beam, double fillet.

FIG. 3-2. "Liberty" ship original hatch corner assembly and exploded views. (Refs. 11 and 12)

Figure 3-3, which is somewhat similar to Fig. 3-1(b), shows a welded atch corner with a curved coaming intersection and a satisfactory radius the deck plating at the corner. However, where the deck plating has een slotted through the curved coaming at the corner of the hatch, there an undesirable notch at each end of the radiused plating (in way of slot ds). These notches are dangerous defects and may lead to plating acture.

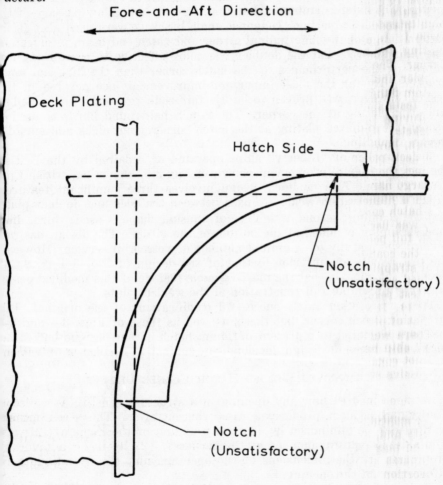

FIG. 3-3. Poor practice. Welded hatch corner with unsatisfactory notches in the deck plating.

MODIFICATIONS OF THE "LIBERTY" SHIP ORIGINAL HATCH CORNER DESIGN

The earlier failures of the original "Liberty" ship hatch corner of Fig. -2 led to the adoption of several modified designs which generally proved uccessful in service. In order to compare the relative merit of these modifications and to evaluate other new designs, an exploratory "welded-hatch corner" testing program was conducted at the University of California (Refs. 13 and 14.) Tests were made of ten full-scale welded hatch corners.

Figure 3-4 illustrates a successful modified "Liberty" hatch corner design introduced by the United States Coast Guard and known as U.S.C.G. Code 1. In this design, a relatively large doubler is placed on the deck plating, and both the doubler and deck plating have a radius of 12 in. at the corner. The hatch coaming is slotted at the corner to allow passage of the doubler and deck plating. Diagonal angle brackets were used also at the bottom flange of the longitudinal girder and hatch end beam intersection. The tests showed that the doubler was more effective in reinforcing and improving the performance of the hatch corner than the diagonal angle brackets. By far the most important improvement incorporated in the design, however, was proven to be the fair radii provided in the doubler and deck plating at the corner. The 2-inch half-round bar was used to protect the radiused plating at the hatch corner from nicks and cuts due to cargo handling.

On a number of "Liberty" ships operated or repaired by the British, the hatch corner reinforcement shown in Fig. 3-5, known as British Code 1A, was used. This modified design involves three significant features: first, full penetration welds are used between the deck and doubler plate and the coaming; second, a doubler of unusual shape is used; third, diagonal strapping is added at the bottom of the girder. The design has performed successfully on a limited number of vessels in service. However, the test results are inferior to that of the design of Fig. 3-4 (U.S.C.G. Code 1). It appears that the most valuable feature of this modified design is that of providing full penetration at the welded joints.

There were other fairly successful modifications of the original "Liberty" ship hatch corner, but these, as well as those of Figs. 3-4 and 3-5, are not considered to represent optimum hatch corner designs but rather successive stages of design development, subject to further improvement.

IMPROVED WELDED HATCH CORNER DETAILS

As mentioned earlier, any opening in a structure constitutes a discontinuity and, as such, produces a stress concentration. This stress concentration may be minimized by (1) the rounding of the corners (this also eliminates structural notches at the corners), (2) by using a favorable proportion for the dimensions of the opening, and, (3) by adequate reinforcement of the opening.

With corner notches eliminated, a reduction in the stress concentration factor generally lessens the danger of brittle fracture from other notch influences which may be inadvertently introduced in the high stress field.

Rounding or fairing out of structural notches promotes normal yielding (plastic flow) of the steel under high stress, i.e., avoids the local material constraint which leads to brittle fracture. This is a very important feature in hatch corners which are designed as rigid structures comparable to the rest of the hull. In addition, where elements of flexibility (lateral flexing) can be introduced to aid structural interaction of hatch-corner components, normal yielding behavior may be increased.

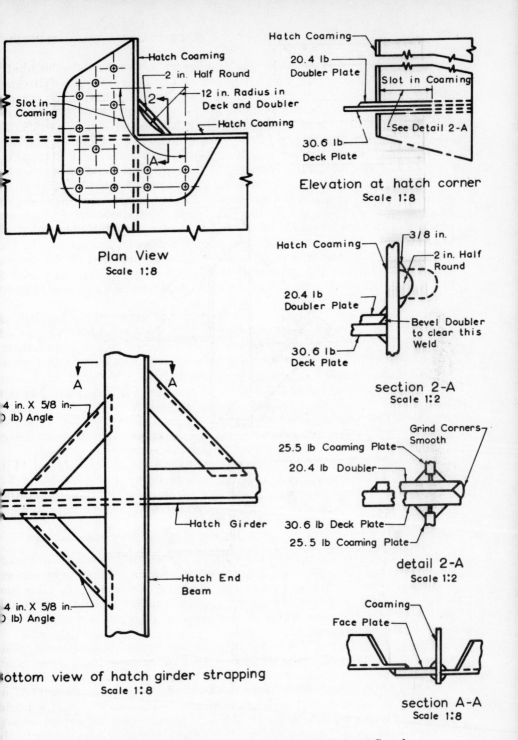

Hatch Coaming

2 in. Half Round

12 in. Radius in Deck and Doubler

Slot in Coaming

Hatch Coaming

2

A

Plan View
Scale 1:8

Hatch Coaming

20.4 lb Doubler Plate

Slot in Coaming

See Detail 2-A

30.6 lb Deck Plate

Elevation at hatch corner
Scale 1:8

3/8 in.

Hatch Coaming

2 in. Half Round

20.4 lb Doubler Plate

30.6 lb Deck Plate

Bevel Doubler to clear this Weld

section 2-A
Scale 1:2

4 in. X 5/8 in. lb) Angle

A   A

Hatch Girder

Hatch End Beam

4 in. X 5/8 in. lb) Angle

Grind Corners Smooth

25.5 lb Coaming Plate

20.4 lb Doubler

30.6 lb Deck Plate

25.5 lb Coaming Plate

detail 2-A
Scale 1:2

ottom view of hatch girder strapping
Scale 1:8

Coaming

Face Plate

section A-A
Scale 1:8

FIG. 3-4. Modified "Liberty" ship hatch corner. U.S. Coast Guard, Code 1. (Ref. 13)

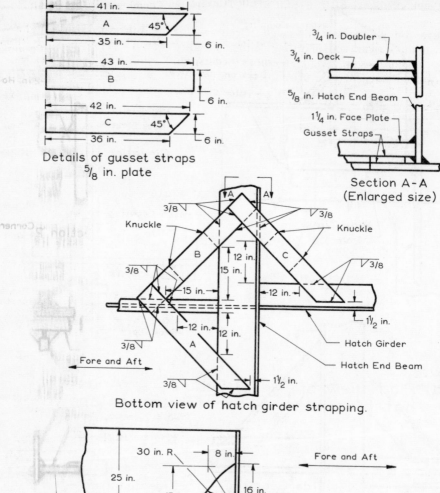

Details of gusset straps
$5/8$ in. plate

$3/4$ in. Doubler
$3/4$ in. Deck
$5/8$ in. Hatch End Beam
$1\frac{1}{4}$ in. Face Plate
Gusset Straps

Section A-A
(Enlarged size)

Bottom view of hatch girder strapping.

Plan view

FIG. 3-5. Modified "Liberty" ship hatch corner. British Code 1A. (Ref. 13)

3-8

Figure 3-6 shows an improved hatch corner of the rigid type. The improvements over the original "Liberty" ship hatch corner consist of asing the notches in tensile members (deck and longitudinal girder below), and concurrently improving the stress distribution in this area. A

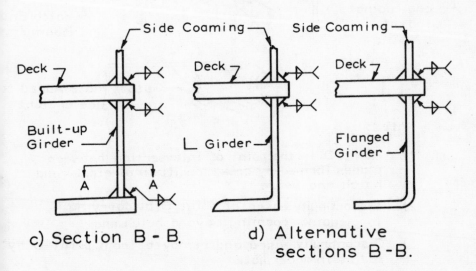

a) Plan view of hatch corner.

b) Section A-A at the hatch corner (drawn at a scale smaller than that of Fig. 3-6a.)

c) Section B-B.

d) Alternative sections B-B.

FIG. 3-6. Improved welded hatch corner with squared coaming. (Ref. 15)

3-10

A GUIDE TO SOUND SHIP STRUCTURE

relatively thick gusset plate is provided to tie in the beam and girder below deck. The corners in both the gusset plate and deck are rounded with a generous radius. The coaming is squared at the corners for ease of construction.

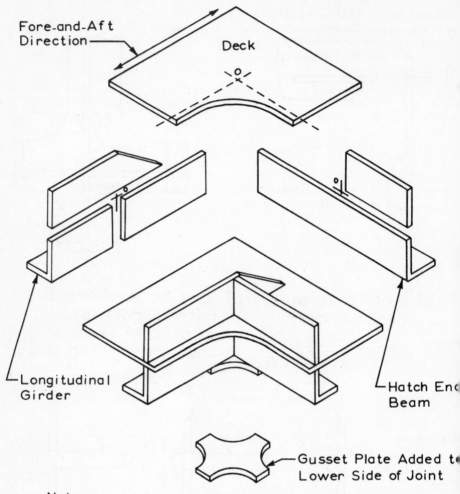

Fore-and-Aft Direction

Deck

Longitudinal Girder

Hatch End Beam

Gusset Plate Added to Lower Side of Joint

Notes:

1) Point O is the point of intersection between planes formed by deck, longitudinal girder and hatch end beam.

2) Discontinuity eased at point O by carrying longitudinal coaming beyond hatch end.

3) Discontinuity eased and removed from point O by radius in deck plate.

FIG. 3-7. "Victory" ship hatch corner assembly and exploded views. (Refs. 11 and 14)

The "Victory" ship hatch corner of Fig. 3-7 is essentially the same as that of Fig. 3-6. The fore-and-aft members of the hatch coamings have tapered endings beyond the hatch, rather than abruptly ending at the hatch corner. The removal of this ending from the immediate hatch corner area prevents superposition of the two attendant concentrations in a single localized area. In the tests conducted at the University of California (refs. 13 and 14), an original "Liberty" ship hatch corner specimen had the hatch side extended for a frame space beyond the corner intersection, and this modification alone improved test results considerably. Figure 3-7 also shows the adoption of the gusset plate intersection for lower flanges of girder and end beam in the "Victory" ship hatch corner. It has never been proven that this gusset plate is an effective factor in fracture prevention. However, it does give a clean intersection of the lower flanges of the girder and hatch-end beam, and minimizes the possibility of defective details. The detail of Fig. 3-6(c) illustrates a practical and desirable way of incorporating the gusset plate in the structure. Figure 3-6(d) illustrates alternative arrangements which require the superposition of the gusset plate on the lower flanges of the underdeck members, unless these are recessed. The detail of Fig. 3-6(c) illustrates that the gusset plate can be included in the structure more easily, while the details of Fig. 3-6(d) call for recesses in the underdeck members. The merits of the "Victory" ship design have been proven by service experience as shown in Table 3-1.

TABLE 3-1. Service experience of original "Liberty" and "Victory" ship hatch corner. (Ref. 12)

Ship type	Liberty (Original Square Corner)	Victory
Ship years in service	Over 2000*	Over 2000*
Fractures reported at hatch corners	224	1

*This figure is the sum of years of service of all the ships of the type considered in the survey up to 1953.

Another hatch corner arrangement similar to that of Fig. 3-6 is that proposed by the American Bureau of Shipping, as illustrated in Fig. 3-8. The test program already mentioned indicated that the hatch corner of Fig. 3-8, known as the A.B.S. design, is very satisfactory. The A.B.S. design is similar to the one used on the "Victory" ship, but specimen scantlings are lighter than in the latter. The main features of the A.B.S. hatch corner are the following: (1) an 18 in. radius in the deck plate to reduce stress concentration at the corners, (2) tapered extension of the longitudinal coaming beyond the corner for about 2 ft to avoid abrupt ending and also to avoid superposition of discontinuities in members under tension stress, (3) a substantial one-piece flange, containing generous radii, at the bottom of the main girder intersection to increase overall area rigidity, (4) end-beam snipes to avoid a concentration of welding at the

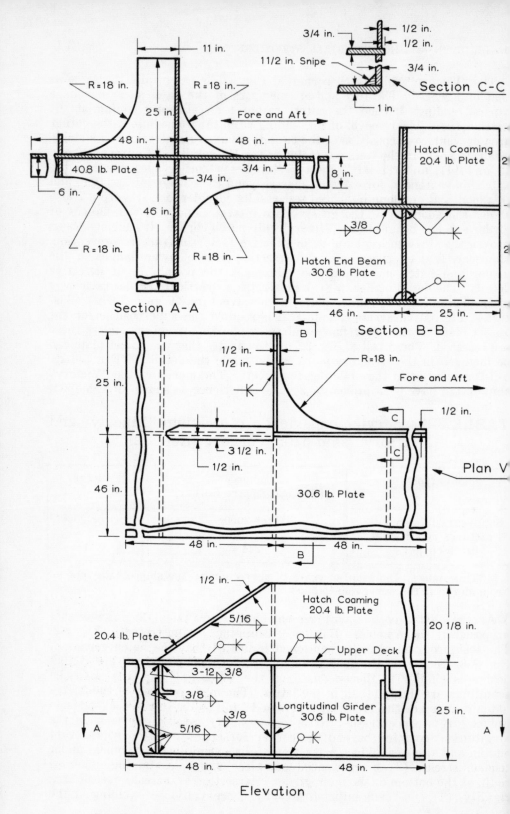

FIG. 3-8.   American Bureau of Shipping hatch corner design.   (Ref. 13)

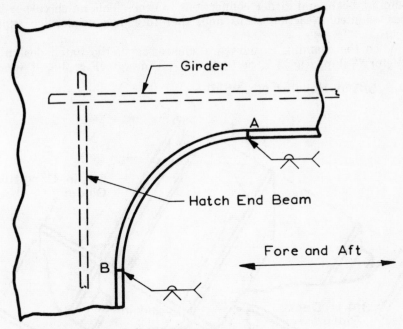

a) Plan view of hatch corner.

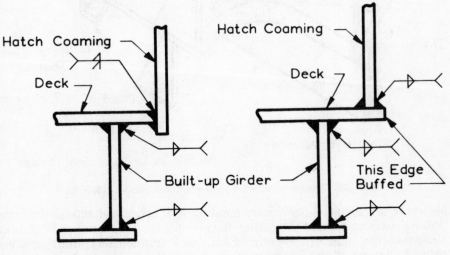

b) Typical section.   c) Alternate typical section.

FIG. 3-9.   Improved welded hatch corner with rounded coaming.   (Ref. 15)

intersection of three plates, and (5) full penetration welds for principa
coaming, beam and girder connections to deck. This hatch corner has no
been adopted in actual ships and, therefore, has no service experienc
record.

When the coaming corners are square, as in the hatch design of th
"Victory" ship, Fig. 3-7, or in the A.B.S. design, Fig. 3-8, it was foun

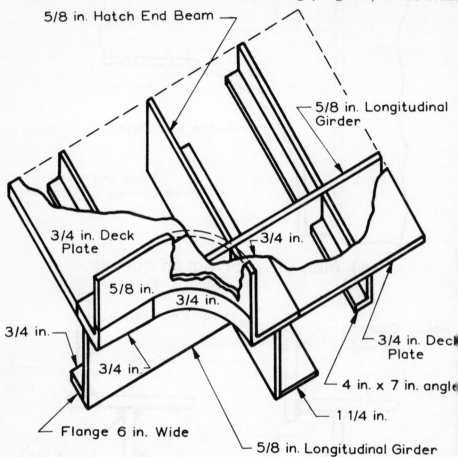

5/8 in. Hatch End Beam

5/8 in. Longitudinal
Girder

3/4 in. Deck
Plate

3/4 in.

5/8 in.

3/4 in.

3/4 in.

3/4 in. Deck
Plate

3/4 in.

4 in. x 7 in. angle

1 1/4 in.

Flange 6 in. Wide

5/8 in. Longitudinal Girder

FIG. 3-10.   Isometric view of Kennedy hatch corner.   (Ref. 13)

desirable for purposes previously mentioned to taper and extend the longi
tudinal coaming beyond the corner for about 2 ft. This hatch-side coaming
extension may interfere sometimes with deck arrangement, limiting acces
around the end of the hatch and restricting the location of winches and
fittings in that area. Figure 3-9 shows a welded hatch with round coaming
corners, designed to eliminate the square corner at the coaming intersec
tion. This feature is intended to transfer the load carried by the longi
tudinal coaming to the deck plating and longitudinal girder gradually.

In Fig. 3-9(a), the coaming rounded corner piece extends from point
A to B, and it is butt welded to the rest of the coaming. The butt welded
joint at point A is a particularly important one because of the deck an

coaming stress concentration in the immediate area (*see* Figs. 2-15 and 2-16). This butt welded joint could be eliminated by combining the coaming and the girder at the edge of the opening, then splitting the combined side coaming-girder plate at the point of tangency, A. After this split the girder portion would be carried through and the side coaming wrapped around the deck edge to join the end coaming at, say, B. Either the deck or the coaming would need to be beveled in way of the rounded corner to ensure an efficient connection. In any event, it would be best to place the butt welded joint A in a less critical location.

Some believe that the hatch corner design of Fig. 3-9, or the variation mentioned above, is more rational than those having square coaming intersection. However, their relative merits have not been established either by test or service. Coamings with square corners are somewhat easier to fabricate and lend themselves more easily to the use of the cheaper, rectangular hatch covers.

The hatch corner shown in Fig. 3-10 behaved considerably better than the rest of the ten specimens of refs. 13 and 14. This design introduces lateral (vertical) flexibility at the corner due to the tendency of the side coaming to establish longitudinal continuity with the deck, not at corner tangency but distributed *around* the corner of the opening. This continuity tendency occurs in the radius roll joining horizontal deck plating with vertical deck plating. The main feature of the Kennedy type, as this hatch corner is called, is the use of a hot-formed section at the corner. The rounded coaming corner and the (radius roll) transition pieces between the deck and coaming can be formed cold. These forming operations make this type of hatch corner more expensive and more difficult to repair and renew than other types.

OTHER LARGE OPENINGS

Besides cargo hatches, there are other large openings in ships which require special consideration. These may be located also in areas where tension stresses are significant and, therefore, extreme care is required to avoid structural notches which encourage brittle fracture. Such openings are: machinery casings, stairway and elevator wells in large passenger vessels, and cargo side openings.

In general, in the design and fabrication of structural details of large openings, other than cargo hatches, the same general rules applicable to the latter should be followed for cases of structural similarity.

Figure 3-11 illustrates a typical opening corresponding to the machinery casing of a tanker. The figure shows a satisfactory radius in the deck plating to reduce stress concentration at the corners. In addition, a heavier insert plate is used in the fore-and-aft portion of the casing sill where this abuts against the transverse bulkhead.

It should be mentioned here that openings in way of the machinery casing of tankers are not as critical as cargo hatch openings located in the midship half-length with regard to brittle fracture because of the following reasons: 1) Their fore and aft location corresponds to regions of low bending moment; hence, low deck tensile stress. 2) Due to high local ambient temperature, there is somewhat improved steel structural performance.

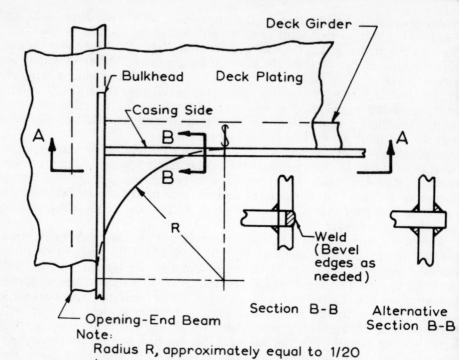

Note:
Radius R, approximately equal to 1/20
transverse dimension of opening.

a) Plan view of corner detail.

b) Elevation of corner detail. Section A-A.

FIG. 3-11.   Corner detail of the machinery casing of a tanker.

SUMMARY

The effectiveness, i.e., structural soundness, of a large opening's corner depends largely on the design and fabrication of structural details. The important basic points applying to a cargo hatch corner are clearly listed in the following quotation taken from ref. 14:

"a) General Principles

1) Ease notches in all members and especially those carrying main longitudinal stresses.

2) Avoid coincidences of notches.

3) Avoid the intersection of welded joints as far as possible, especially at points of stress concentration.

4) Minimize welding defects by proper design for welding.

"b) Specific Suggestions

Selection of specific suggestions listed below must depend upon the ship design. Effective hatch corner reinforcement need not incorporate all of the features listed below. The judgment of the designer must prevail.

1) At the corner provide a heavier deck plate with a generous radius (for main hatches in typical cargo ships, such as the "Liberty," a radius = 1/20 of the transverse dimension of the opening was satisfactory).

2) Taper hatch side coaming beyond hatch end.

3) Ease longitudinal girder to hatch end beam connection at flange level as by radiused gusset.

4) Specify full penetration welds for joining deck to coaming in way of the hatch corner and for such joints as are subject to direct loading, in order to avoid cavities or piping in such welds, especially those perpendicular to the principal tensile stresses."

Welding Joint Details

Introduction

Welding is used now almost universally as the means of joining ship's steel structural members. The substitution of welding for riveting in ship construction and repair resulted from the following advantages: 1) increased deadweight of vessel; 2) improved oil and water tightness of structure; 3) building speed; 4) ease of training operators; 5) reduced hull upkeep, and, 6) usually a smoother hull surface.

Welded joints, as used today, are accepted as generally reliable and practical. However, great care is required in the design, preparation and execution of welded joints to avoid defects leading to serious vessel fracture.

Welding processes used in shipbuilding are numerous, but this section will refer mainly to manual metal arc welding. No attempt to cover all aspects of metal arc welding as applied to shipbuilding will be made, as such coverage would be beyond the purpose and scope of this work. Moreover, a goodly number of handbooks and similar publications deal exhaustively with the subject in a most effective manner.

In this section, the reader will find information on welding joint preparation with all fabrication and erection details. Only those joints most commonly used in shipbuilding will be considered.

Techniques and procedures in making welded joints are considered beyond the scope of this publication. The reader will find valuable information on this subject in refs. 16, 17, and 18.

Defects in welded joints as they affect ship structural integrity are considered in detail herein, and corrective measures related to design, fabrication and erection are suggested.

To facilitate presentation of the subject material, this is preceded by an explanation of standard welding symbols.

Standard Welding Symbols

Welding requires great care in the design and construction of details. To avoid defects, a means is required to transmit precise information from the designer to the workman.

Standard welding symbols have been adopted almost universally to place complete welding information on drawings.

Figure 4-1 shows the standard location of elements on a welding symbol. The assembled welding symbol consists of the following elements:

Reference line	Supplementary symbols
Arrow	Finish symbols
Basic weld symbols	Tail
Dimensions and other data	Specification, process, or other reference

Of the eight elements listed above, only a few will be necessary in most cases.

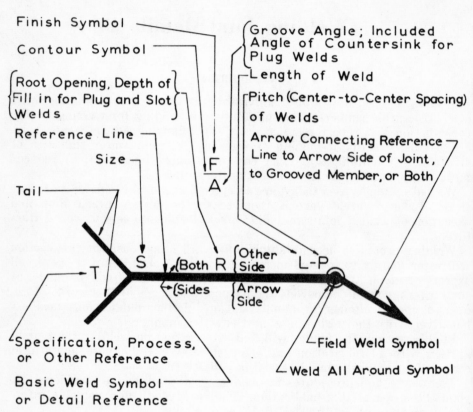

FIG. 4-1.   Standard location of elements on a welding symbol.   (Ref. 16)

It is very important to point out whether one or both sides of a joint are to be welded. When only one side of a joint is to be welded, this side has to be clearly indicated. Figure 4-2 illustrates the identification of the sides of a welding joint with respect to the arrow of the welding symbol. While we are concerned generally with identifying the near-side and the far-side of a joint between two structural members, there are cases when we need to distinguish between the arrow-side and other-side member of a joint, as illustrated in Fig. 4-3.

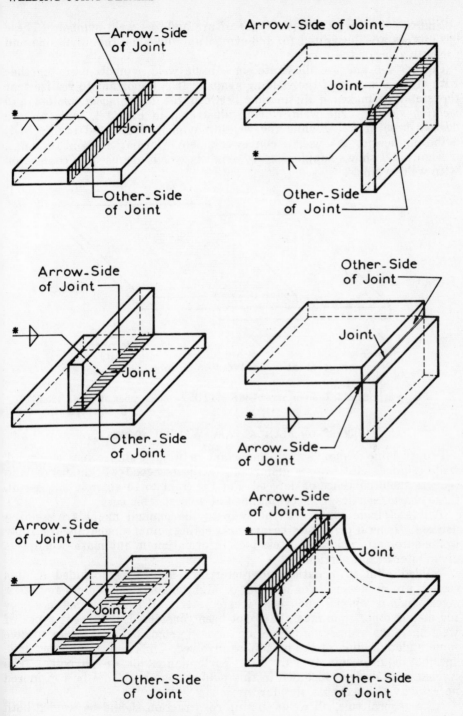

*Arrow of welding symbol.

FIG. 4-2.   Identification of arrow-side and other-side of joint. (Ref. 16)

Figure 4-4 shows the basic types of arc and gas weld symbols. These basic types are illustrated for the symbol's arrow-side, the other-side and for both sides of the joint.

Figures 4-5 and 4-6 illustrate some basic weld symbols used together with other elements of the welding symbol. It is important to realize that the standard makes a distinction between the terms *weld symbol* and *welding symbol*. The weld symbol, illustrated in Fig. 4-4, indicates the desired type of weld, while the welding symbol, illustrated in Fig. 4-1, is the engineering tool used to convey complete information about the joint.

Figure 4-7 shows supplementary symbols which are used in connection with weld symbols.

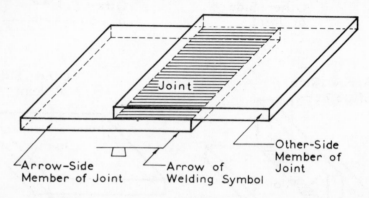

FIG. 4-3.   Identification of arrow-side and other-side member of joint. (Ref. 16)

TYPES OF MANUAL ARC WELDED JOINTS

Proper joint design is very important in welded ship construction. A well-designed joint lessens distortion, facilitates good workmanship, and reduces the occurrence of defects. For the joint to be entirely successful, these characteristics must be obtained at a reasonable cost.

This section is concerned chiefly with the manual metal arc welding process. General principles regarding welding joints almost always apply to the automatic welding process too. Information on automatic welding is given later in this section.

Welded joint information, characteristics and types included in this section are, in general, for medium or high tensile steel. Joints for other steels, such as special alloy heat treated steels (S.T.S., for instance), or for metals other than steel, have not been considered. Different types of welding joints are presented and discussed in some detail in order to give some understanding of the principles involved. Different authorities have specific requirements to suit their particular needs or purposes. The welded joint designs included in this publication should not be considered necessarily the accepted standard.

As a general rule, all welds in ship construction should be welded both sides, unless a backing strap or structure is used on one side. Some welding joints welded from one side only are included in this section, but they should never be used in primary hull girder components. Elsewhere, when

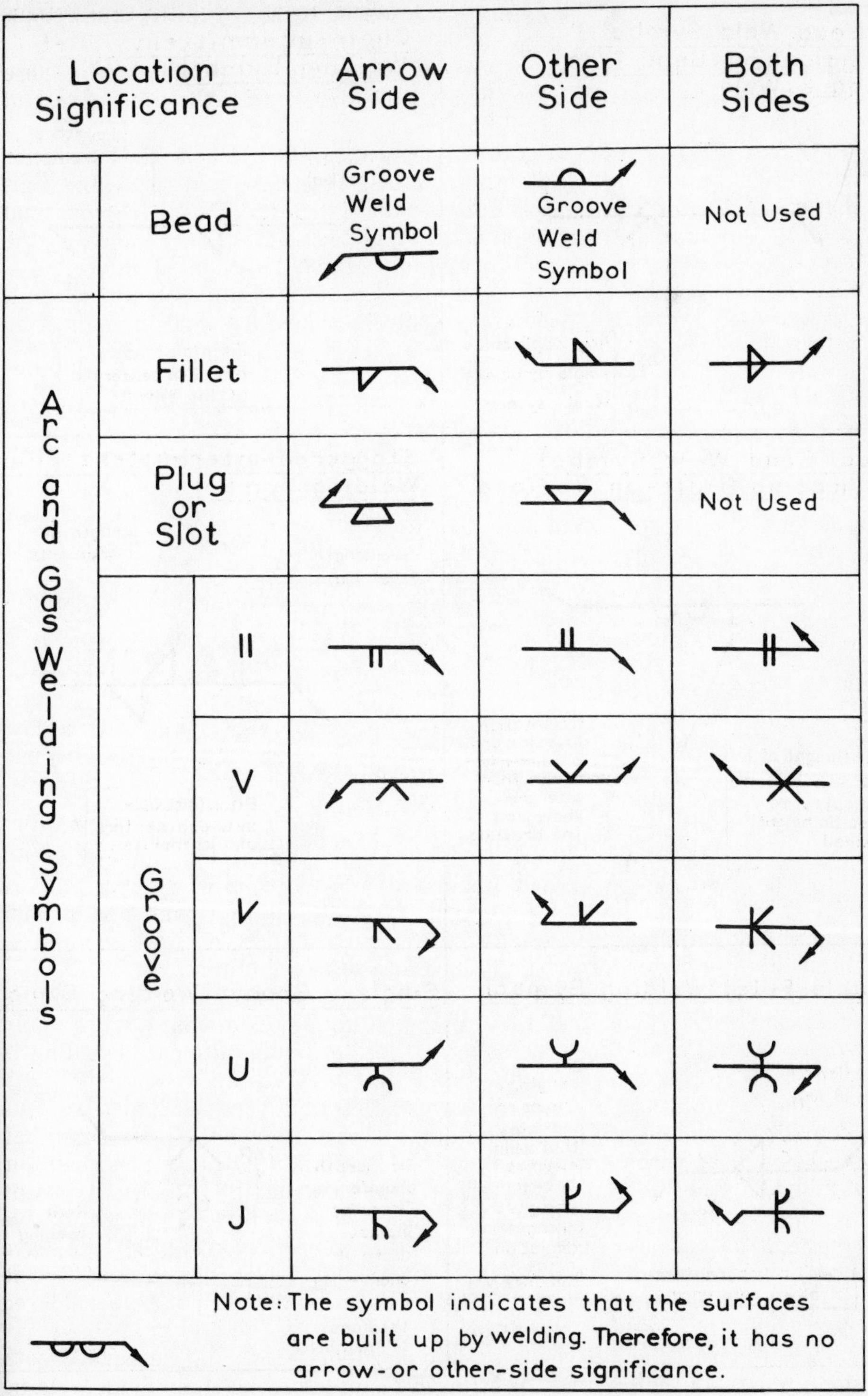

Location Significance		Arrow Side	Other Side	Both Sides
	Bead	Groove Weld Symbol	Groove Weld Symbol	Not Used
Arc and Gas Welding Symbols	Fillet			
	Plug or Slot			Not Used
	Groove — ‖			
	Groove — V			
	Groove — V (bevel)			
	Groove — U			
	Groove — J			

Note: The symbol indicates that the surfaces are built up by welding. Therefore, it has no arrow- or other-side significance.

FIG. 4-4. Basic arc and gas weld symbols. (Ref. 16)

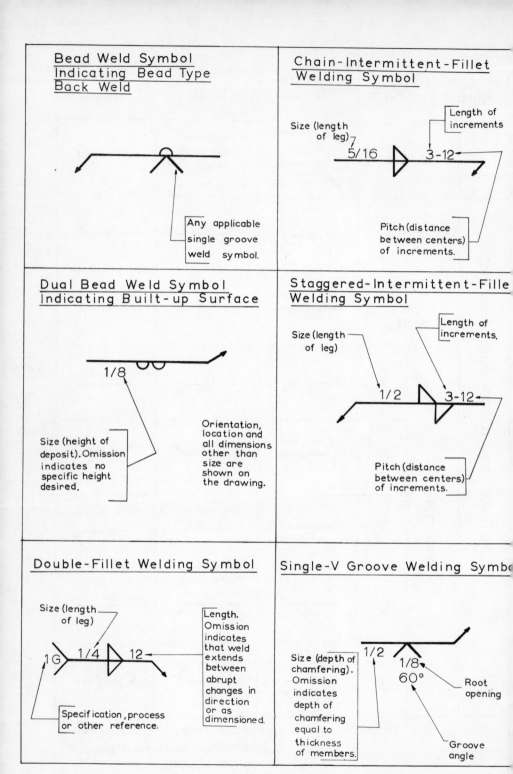

FIG. 4-5.   Typical welding symbols.   (Ref. 16)

4-6

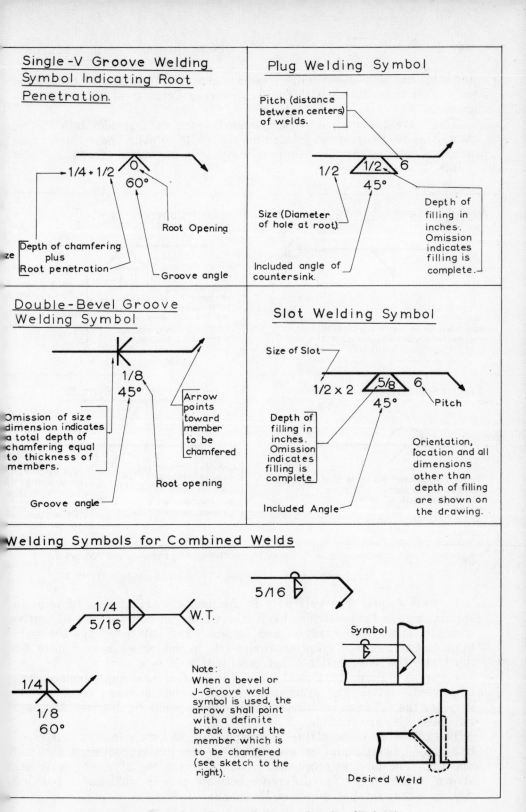

Single-V Groove Welding Symbol Indicating Root Penetration.

1/4 + 1/2 0 60°

Root Opening

Depth of chamfering plus Root penetration

Groove angle

Plug Welding Symbol

Pitch (distance between centers) of welds.

1/2 1/2 6 45°

Size (Diameter of hole at root)

Included angle of countersink.

Depth of filling in inches. Omission indicates filling is complete.

Double-Bevel Groove Welding Symbol

1/8 45°

Arrow points toward member to be chamfered

Omission of size dimension indicates a total depth of chamfering equal to thickness of members.

Groove angle

Root opening

Slot Welding Symbol

Size of Slot

1/2 x 2 5/8 6 45° Pitch

Depth of filling in inches. Omission indicates filling is complete

Included Angle

Orientation, location and all dimensions other than depth of filling are shown on the drawing.

Welding Symbols for Combined Welds

1/4
5/16 W.T.

5/16

1/4
1/8
60°

Note:
When a bevel or J-Groove weld symbol is used, the arrow shall point with a definite break toward the member which is to be chamfered (see sketch to the right).

Symbol

Desired Weld

Fɪɢ. 4-6. Typical welding symbols (continued). (Ref. 16)

4-7

the joint has poor accessibility from one side, their use may be considered only after consultation with the Engineering Department or welding engineer.

There are three types of arc welded joints of foremost importance, namely: butt joints, fillet joints and composite joints. These three types are considered separately below, followed by a discussion of plug and slot joints.

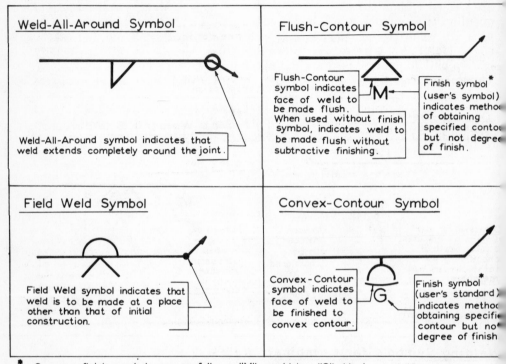

Weld-All-Around Symbol

Weld-All-Around symbol indicates that weld extends completely around the joint.

Flush-Contour Symbol

Flush-Contour symbol indicates face of weld to be made flush. When used without finish symbol, indicates weld to be made flush without subtractive finishing.

Finish symbol* (user's symbol) indicates method of obtaining specified contour but not degree of finish.

Field Weld Symbol

Field Weld symbol indicates that weld is to be made at a place other than that of initial construction.

Convex-Contour Symbol

Convex-Contour symbol indicates face of weld to be finished to convex contour.

Finish symbol* (user's standard) indicates method obtaining specific contour but not degree of finish.

* Common finish symbols are as follows: "M"= machining, "C"= chipping, and "G"= grinding.

FIG. 4-7.   Supplementary symbols used with welding symbols. (Ref. 16)

1) *Butt Joints.* The butt weld is the most important type of joint in shipbuilding and is preferable to all others from the point of view of tensile strength, stress concentration and fatigue. The butt joint has the weld between two members lying approximately in the same plane. Figure 4-8 illustrates the cross section of a typical butt weld in a joint.

Figure 4-9 shows butt welds in four different positions, namely, flat, horizontal, vertical and overhead. Welding conditions and requirements vary for the different positions. Intermediate positions, between the ones indicated, also are possible.

The following nomenclature corresponding to butt joints is illustrated in Fig. 4-10, bevel angle: groove angle, face and radius; root edge, face and opening. The face, reinforcement, root, size and toe of a butt weld are shown in Fig. 4-11. The difference between a back weld and a backing weld in a butt joint is shown in Fig. 4-12.

Figures 4-13 through 4-17 give detailed information for manual butt welded joints most commonly used in shipbuilding.

The simplest and least expensive butt weld is obtained when two square-edged plates are butted together and weld beads deposited with or without separation (Figs. 4-13 and 4-14). A manual arc does not penetrate more than 1/16 in. to 1/8 in. Consequently, a square-edged butt joint with no root opening is limited to a maximum plate thickness of 1/16 in. for a single weld bead, and to 1/8 in. maximum plate thickness when both sides are welded (joints B-1 and B-2, Fig. 4-13). When providing adequate root opening, 1/16 in. to 1/8 in., square-edged plates of 1/4 in. maximum thickness are welded, since the plate separation facilitates the melting of the edges (joint B-3, Fig. 4-14). When structure backing is present, square groove butt joints are used up to a maximum plating thickness of 3/16 in. (joint B-4, Fig. 4-14). In this latter joint, the root opening generally is made equal to the plate thickness.

To ensure complete penetration in butt welds, it is very desirable to bevel the plate edges to form a groove. This groove is shaped to provide sufficient clearance to allow the arc to strike the bottom, rather than short-

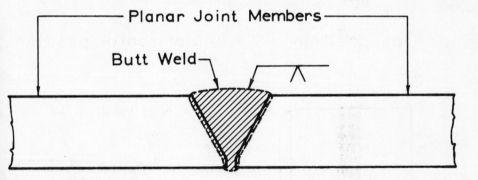

FIG. 4-8. Typical cross section of a butt weld (V-groove single bevel).

circuit itself to the side walls, and to allow angling of the electrode. For thicknesses larger than 1/4 in., a V-shaped groove is a definite necessity in manual arc welding. For plates of moderate thickness, less than 3/4 in. (30.6 lb), a single groove generally is used (joint B-5, Fig. 4-15). For the heavier plates, 3/4 in. (30.6 lb) and above, a double groove usually is required (joint B-6, Fig. 4-15). For plate thicknesses of 5/8 in. (25.5 lb) and above, for the same root angle and opening, the higher cost of preparing a double groove as compared to the single one may be offset by the reduction in weld material deposited. This reduction in deposited metal and the inherent symmetry of the double-grooved joint results in less distortion tendency on cooling. A double-V grooved butt joint, however, has the following disadvantages: a) it makes back gouging to clean metal more difficult, and b) it complicates minor adjustments that may require the removal of some material at the root edges. For this type of joint, the grooves may be symmetrical, as illustrated in B-6, Fig. 4-15, or the plates

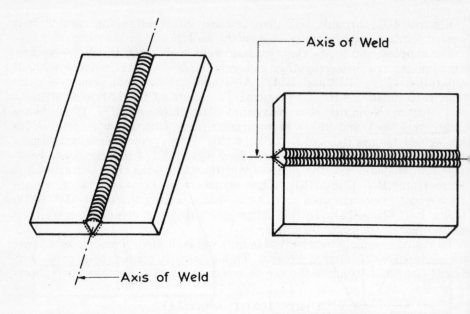

a) Flat position.   b) Horizontal position.

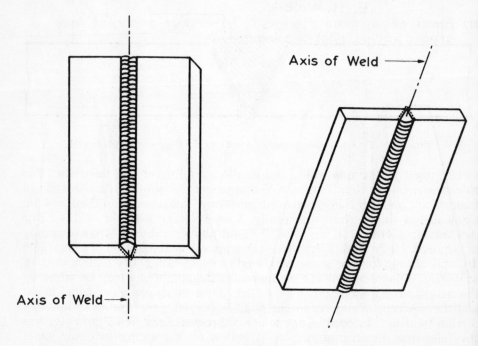

c) Vertical position.   d) Overhead position.

FIG. 4-9.   Four positions of welding for butt welds.

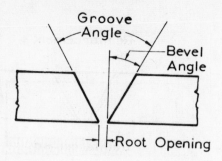

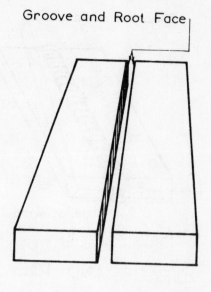

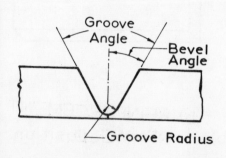

a) Bevel angle, groove angle, groove radius, root opening.

b) Groove and root face.

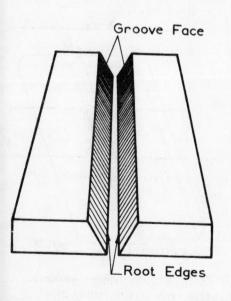

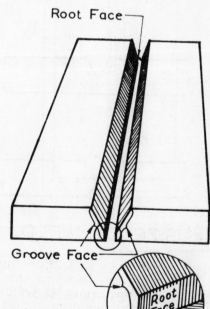

c) Groove face, root face, and root edge.

FIG. 4-10.   Butt joint nomenclature.

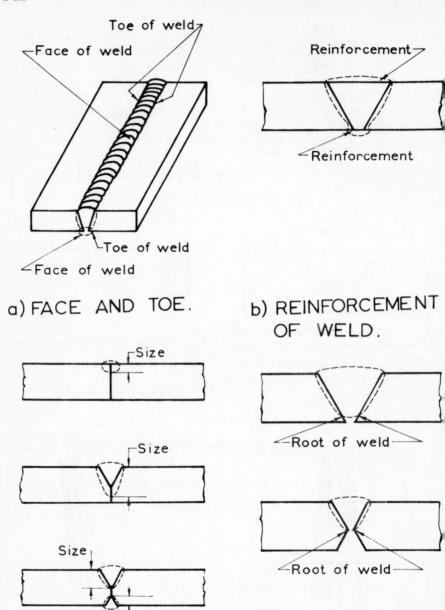

a) FACE AND TOE.

b) REINFORCEMENT OF WELD.

c) SIZE OF WELD.

d) ROOT OF WELD.

Note:
Sketches (c) & (d) are used to illustrate weld nomenclature. To keep the illustrations clear, only part of the required welding is shown (they are uncompleted welding joints).

FIG. 4-11.   Butt weld nomenclature.   (Rêf. 16)

may be beveled so that the depth of one groove is 1/3 and the other 2/3 of the plate thickness. In this case, the side of the deeper groove usually is welded first to facilitate back gouging.

When using backing with a single groove, the root opening may be increased to facilitate a good bond between the backing and the root edges. Joint B-7, Fig. 4-16, shows the recommended details for a butt weld with backing for plate thickness under 3/4 in. (30.6 lb), and it may be seen that there is an allowed reduction in the bevel angle corresponding to the increase in root opening. Joint B-8 of Fig. 4-16 is recommended for plate

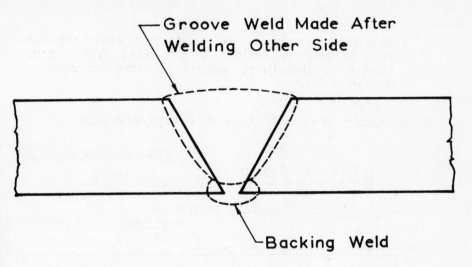

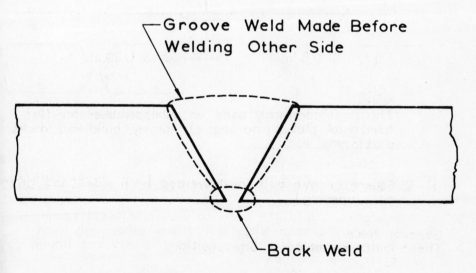

FIG. 4-12.   Back and backing welds in a butt joint.

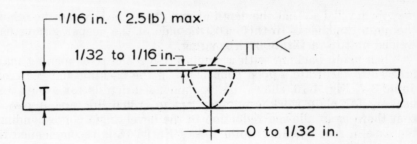

Note:
This joint should not be used on a structure subject to bending, fatigue or gun blast. Where practicable, in structures subject to these stresses
use joint B-2.

B-1. Square groove butt joint welded one side.

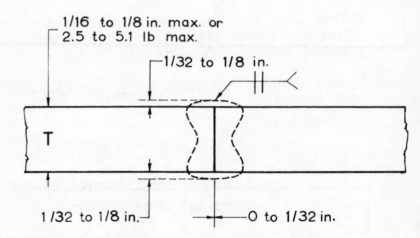

Note:
This joint commonly used on subassemblies for flat
horizontal plates (no shape), namely, bulkheads, decks,
platforms, etc.

B-2. Square groove butt joint welded both sides(negligible
root opening).

General Note:
These joints suitable for any position.

FIG. 4-13.   Square groove butt joints (negligible root opening).

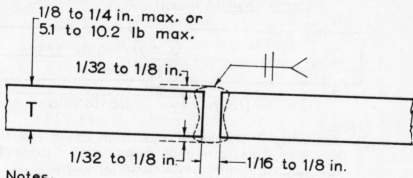

1/8 to 1/4 in. max. or
5.1 to 10.2 lb max.

1/32 to 1/8 in.

T

1/32 to 1/8 in.   1/16 to 1/8 in.

Notes:
1). Back gouge root of weld to sound metal before welding other side.

2). This joint not to be used for welding butt joints in the webs or flanges of T's, I's, Z's, angles or other rolled shapes (see B-5).

3). This joint commonly used on subassemblies for flat horizontal plates (no shape), namely, bulkheads, decks, platforms, etc.

B – 3. Square groove butt joint welded both sides (with root opening).

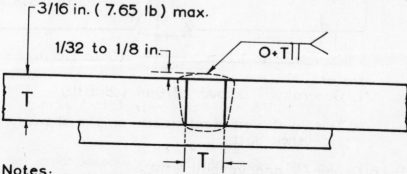

3/16 in. (7.65 lb) max.

1/32 to 1/8 in.   O+T

T

T

Notes:
1). This joint commonly used on subassemblies or on the shipway for accommodation decks, platforms, etc.

2) For backing data see Fig. 4-17.

B – 4 Square groove butt joint welded on backing.
General Note:
These joints suitable for any position.

FIG. 4-14.   Square groove butt joints (with root opening).

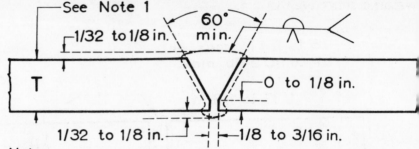

Notes

1). Generally T should be less than 3/4 in. (30.6 lb). However, this joint has been used successfully for substantially greater thicknesses.

2). This joint commonly used on the shipway for bottom shell, deck and tank top.

B- 5. Single - V butt groove joint welded both sides.

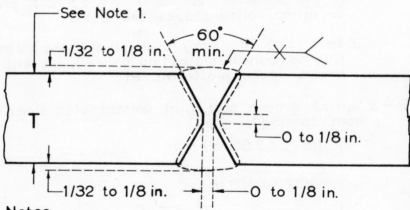

Notes:

1). Generally T is over 5/8 in. (25.5 lb).

2). This joint commonly used on the shipway for side shell butts.

B - 6 Double - V groove butt joint.

General Notes:
a). These joints suitable for any position.
b). The following misalignments, though undesirable, have been accepted for these joints: 0 to 1/8 in. for flat surfaces, and 0 to 3/16 in. for curved surfaces.
c). Back gouge root of weld to sound metal before welding other side.

FIG. 4-15. V-grooved butt joints welded both sides.

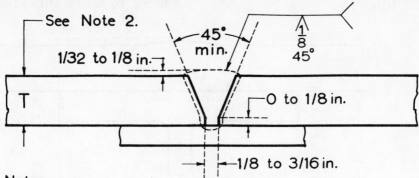

Notes:

1). This joint suitable for any position.

2). Generally to be used for T smaller than 3/4 in. (30.6 lb). However, this joint may be used for greater thicknesses in cases where backing structure is encountered in the vertical, horizontal and overhead positions.

B-7. Single - V groove butt joint for plate under 30.6 lb welded on backing.

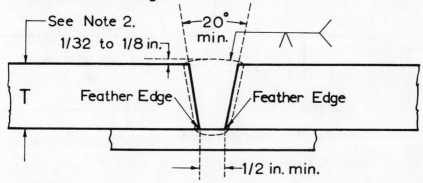

Notes:

1). This joint generally used in the flat position only (for other positions see B.7).

2). Generally T should be 3/4 in. (30.6 lb) or over.

3) This joint should not be used in the horizontal position.

B-8. Single - V groove butt joint for plate over 30.6 lb welded on backing.

General note:
For backing data see Fig. 4.17.

FIG. 4-16.   Single-V groove butt joints welded on backing.

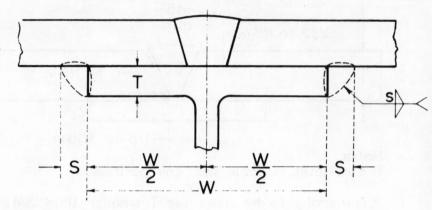

Note: S as required.

a). Permanent backing structure.

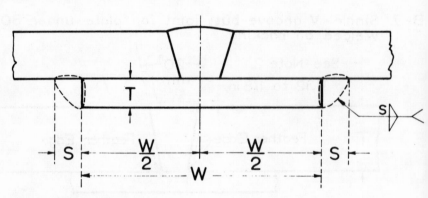

Note: S as required.

b). Permanent backing strip

Backing Data		
Plate Thickness	Backing Dimensions	
	T min.	W min.
1/8 in.	1/8 in.	1 in.
3/16 through 5/16 in.	3/16 in.	1 in.
3/8 in. and over	1/4 in.	2 in.

FIG. 4-17.   Date for use of backing structures or strap with single groove butt joint

hicknesses of 3/4 in. (30.6 lb) and over. This latter joint indicates a further increase of the root opening and a corresponding decrease of the bevel angle. For any reduction of the bevel angle, the corresponding increase of the root opening should be such as to ensure proper electrode positioning during welding. The reduced bevel angle avoids increasing the amount of weld material deposited, and, therefore, it holds down the welding cost and distortion. Data for use of backing structure or strap with single groove butt joints are given in Fig. 4-17. This type of joint is seldom used in merchant shipbuilding.

When the plates to be butt welded differ in thickness by more than 1/8 in., a special detail is required for the groove preparation. The groove should be arranged so that sudden changes of thickness are avoided and the amount of weld material deposited is reduced to an adequate minimum. Joint B-9 of Fig. 4-18 illustrates a suggested practice for the joining of plates of dissimilar thickness for bulkheads and where the difference in thickness is on the underside of decks and inside of shell plating. For butts and seams where the difference in thickness is on the top of deck and outside of shell, a different practice is recommended, as shown in joint B-10, Fig. 4-18. Sometimes the reduction of the thicker member in way of the weld, as indicated by the 30° chamfer of joint B-10, is required only for joints located normal to the main line of stress (deck and shell butts on ships). An additional plating requirement regarding the maximum difference in thickness in the longitudinal direction between adjacent plates may be established at times to minimize discontinuity.

Figures 4-13 to 4-18 illustrate the manual butt joints more commonly used in shipbuilding. Figure 4-19 shows some types of butt joints which are used in special cases. In general they require more elaborate preparation or closer supervision, and for the most part should not be used in the vertical or overhead positions.

2) *Fillet Joints.* The cross section of a fillet weld closely resembles a triangle and is used to join two members approximately at right angles to each other. Figure 4-20 illustrates several typical fillet joints, e.g., (a) double fillet T-joint, (b) double fillet lap joint, (c) single fillet corner joint, and (d) intermittent fillet joints.

The fillet joint does not require any special type of plate preparation. The plate edges, however, should be fair enough to allow a reasonably good tight fit at the joint. Any grease, dirt, paint and excessive scale at the plate edges or surfaces in way of the joint should be removed prior to welding.

Figure 4-21 shows fillet welds in four different positions, e.g., flat, horizontal, vertical and overhead. Welding condition requirements vary for the different positions.

The size and shape of fillet welds is illustrated in Fig. 4-22, where convex, concave and ideal shapes are indicated. The size is equal to the throat over seven hundred and seven thousandths ($S = $ Throat$/0.707$). The strength of the fillet joint is directly proportional to the throat dimension. This requires that edges and fitting allow full root penetration. A concave fillet, Fig. 4-22(b), produces a smooth change of cross section at the joint. However, as compared with a convex fillet, Fig. 4-22(a), it has more tendency to crack as a result of welding shrinkage, and requires larger legs

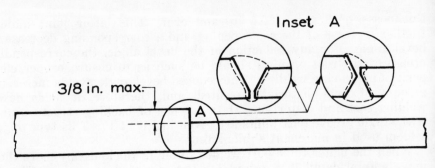

Inset A

3/8 in. max.

Note:
For bulkheads, and where difference in thickness is on underside of decks and inside of shell plating.

B-9. Butt joint without tapering of the thicker plate.

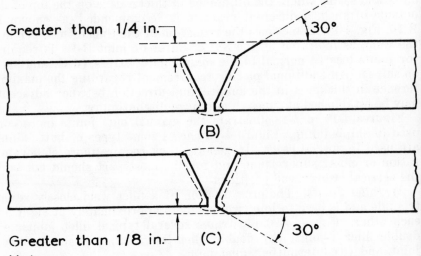

Greater than 1/4 in.   30°

(B)

Greater than 1/8 in.   (C)   30°

Notes:
1). These joints used where difference in thickness is on top of decks and outside of shell.

2). Bevel plates as shown in (B) and (C) when difference in plate thickness exceeds 1/8 in. on root side or 1/4 in. on groove or face side.

B-10. Butt joint with tapered thicker plate.

General Notes:
a). Back gouge root of weld to sound metal before welding other side.
b). For joint details see butt joints for plates of similar thickness.

Fig. 4-18.   Butt joints between plates of different thickness.

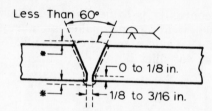

B-11. Single - V butt groove joint with reduced bevel angle, welded both sides.

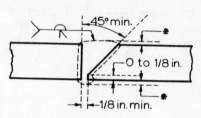

B-12. Single - beveled butt joint, welded both sides.

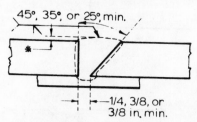

B-13. Single - beveled butt joint, welded on backing.

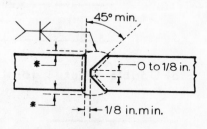

B-14. Double - beveled butt joint, welded both sides.

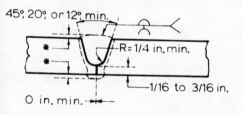

B-15. Single - U butt joint, welded both sides.

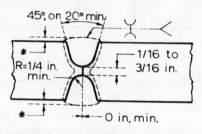

B-16. Double - U butt joint.

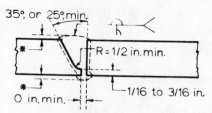

B-17. Single - J butt joint, welded both sides.

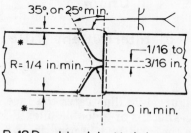

B-18. Double - J butt joint.

Notes:

* Reinforcement of groove welds 1/32 - 1/8 in.

a) Back gouge root of weld to sound metal before welding other side except for joint B-13.

FIG. 4-19.   Special types of butt joints.

for the same strength. Excessive fillet convexity is to be avoided because
it requires more weld metal, slows down welding and makes an abrupt
change in the joint section. The ideal shape is shown in Fig. 4-22(c)
which approaches a flat or slightly convex 45° fillet.

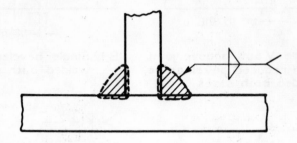

a) Double fillet T joint.

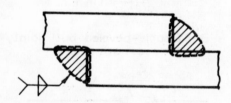

b) Double fillet lap joint.

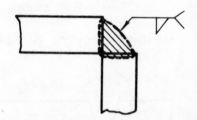

c) Single fillet corner joint

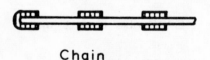

Chain

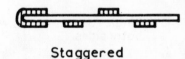

Staggered

d) Intermittent fillet joints.

FIG. 4-20.   Typical fillet joints.

Figure 4-23 illustrates the face, toe and root of fillet welds.
The details of a double fillet T-joint are shown in Fig. 4-24. This is perhaps the most widely used joint employing fillet welds. The fitting of this
joint is very simple. The gap A between the edge of the abutting and the
passing member should be carefully controlled, if a satisfactory joint is to
result. The T-fillet joint is used for the attachment of stiffeners and to
connect intersecting members.
Lap fillet joints are of limited use in structural members subject to direct
stresses. These joints are only acceptable for small structures involving

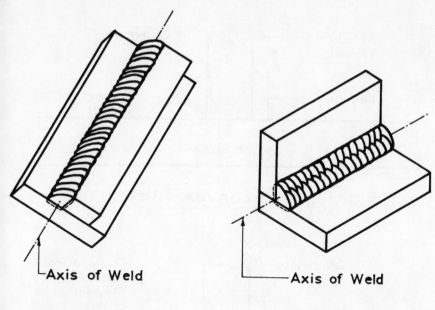

Axis of Weld

a) Flat position.

Axis of Weld

b) Horizontal position.

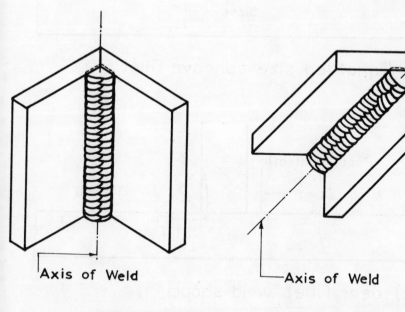

Axis of Weld

c) Vertical position.

Axis of Weld

d) Overhead position.

FIG. 4-21.   Four positions of welding for fillet welds.

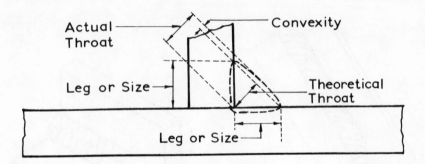

a) Equal leg size convex fillet

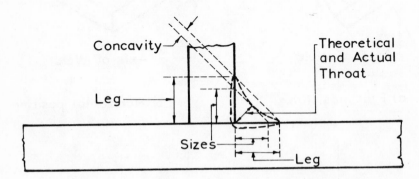

b) Equal leg size concave fillet

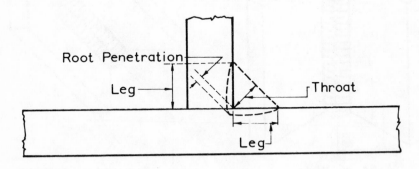

c) Ideal fillet weld shape

General Note:
The size of an equal leg fillet weld is, $S = \dfrac{\text{Throat}}{0.707}$

FIG. 4-22.   Size and shape of fillet welds.

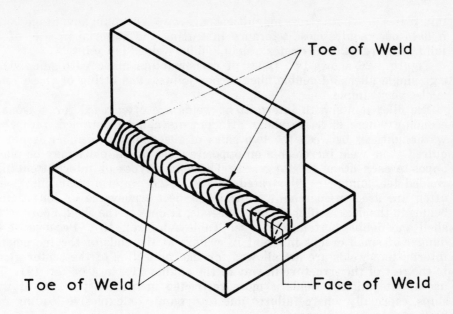

Toe of Weld

Toe of Weld

Face of Weld

a) Face and toe of weld.

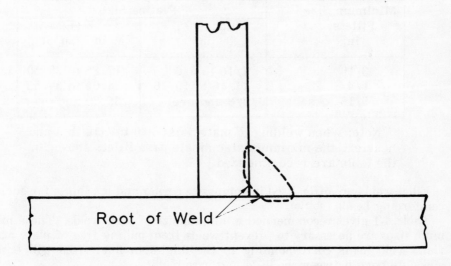

Root of Weld

b) Root of weld (illustrative only).

FIG. 4-23.   Fillet weld face, toe and root.

thin plates or where stress magnitudes are low. The main advantage is that it does not require close tolerance in cutting the material in way of the joint. Figure 4-25 illustrates a double fillet welded lap joint.

Figure 4-26 shows two types of corner joints made with fillet welds e.g., single fillet and double fillet corner joints. The fitting of these joints is also very simple.

Tee fillet joints with intermittent welds are often used for reasons of economy where effective shear attachments can be obtained and where watertightness between the two sides of the abutting member is not required. The weld increments on opposite sides of the plate may be placed opposite each other or staggered. These two types of intermittent fillet welded tee joints are illustrated in Fig. 4-27. Intermittent fillet welds often are used in merchant ships to connect transverse or longitudinal beams to the deck, stiffeners to bulkheads, frames to the shell, floors to the shell and double bottom, etc. (*see* Table A of ref. 19). Because of the danger of small cracks inherent in craters at the ends of the increments, intermittent welds are not allowed for the connection of the center girder to the rest of the structure in way of the engine (Table A of ref. 19). The use of intermittent welds is more restricted in the construction of war ships, especially where failures due to dynamic or explosive loading may have serious consequences.

TABLE 4-1. Minimum size of fillet welds.

Minimum Size Fillets, in.	Plating Size	
	Thickness, T, in.	Weight lb / sq ft
3/16	7/16 to 5/8	17.85 to 25.50
1/4	11/16 to 13/16	28.05 to 34.53
5/16	7/8 and over	35.70 and over

Note: When welding to materials 7/16 in. (18 lb) and heavier, the minimum size single pass fillets shown in the table are recommended.

Fillet welds are often used in composite corner and tee joints for surface reinforcing beads.

Table 4-1 gives recommended minimum size of fillet welds. These minimum sizes are necessary to prevent welds from pulling free of plate material. Weld heats corresponding to the minimum fillet sizes will ensure adequate bond between the weld and base metal.

Where weld beads for miscellaneous identification purposes are deposited on primary hull structure, the above table may be used for guidance purposes. This is necessary to prevent weld quench with attendant microscopic cracking which can lead to extensive fracture of the hull girder.

3) *Full Penetration Tee or Corner Joints.* If the stem of the tee joint of Fig. 4-28(a) is beveled where it abuts against the other member, as shown in Figs. 4-28(b) and 4-28(c), complete fusion is obtainable at the

root of the weld. These full penetration joints are preferable in tee joints of certain major longitudinal strength members where the stem of the tee is in line with the high level longitudinal stress or where the joint may be subject to local fatigue action.

If full penetration is desired where accessibility to the joint is adequate only from one side of the stem of the tee, or when a simpler joint preparation is desired (and permitted), a single bevel may be used, as shown in Fig. 4-28(b). This, in general, may require "pre-setting" of the stem of the joint to avoid undue distortion (*see* Fig. 4-56).

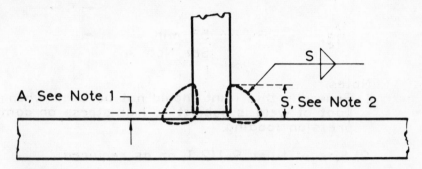

Notes:

1). A = 0 to 3/16 in. is acceptable.

2). Size of fillet, S, as required. Where A is greater than 1/16 in., S = the size governed by design requirements plus A.

3). This joint generally used where the required continuous weld size is less than 1/2 in.

4). This joint suitable for any position.

T-1. Double-fillet-welded tee joint.

FIG. 4-24.   Double fillet T joint.

Figure 4-28.(c) shows a typical full penetration welded symmetrical tee joint. The double bevel preparation is more expensive but lessens undesirable distortion due to welding.

Full penetration corner joints are compared with the fillet corner joint in Fig. 4-29. In general, the full penetration corner joint will give the same strength using less weld material than in a fillet corner joint. A smaller amount of deposited material produces less distortion in the joint, Figs. 4-29(b) and (c). When it is desired to reduce distortion to a minimum, the double bevel corner joint is recommended, Fig. 4-29(d).

The full penetration welded T-joints are used only in special cases. They are more expensive than the simpler fillet joints, sometimes require special positioning and, in general, a closer supervision of the welding procedure is necessary.

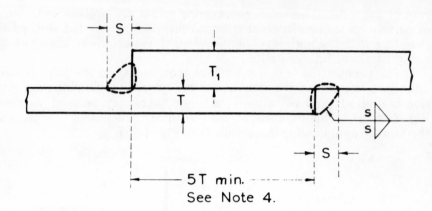

Notes:

1). Generally this joint should not be used when root of weld is subject to high stress or compression loading.

2). Size of fillet S=1/2 T, or as required.

3). Thickness of two plates welded may be different.

4). Sometimes minimum lap made equal to 4T or 2T+1in.

L-1. Double fillet welded lap joint.

FIG. 4-25.   Welded lap joint.

TABLE 4-2. Slot welds standard dimensions.

Plating Size, lb /sq ft	Length of Slot, in.	Width of Slot, in.
Over 6 to 12.5 lbs incl.	2	1/2
Over 12.5 to 19 " "	2-1/2	3/4
Over 19 to 29 " "	2-1/2	1-1/8
Over 29 to 39 " "	3-1/2	1-1/2
Over 39 to 49 " "	3-1/2	1-7/8

4) *Plug and Slot Joints.* Plug or slot welds should only be used where quilting is necessary to keep plate faying surfaces in tied-down contac with each other, and where boundary fillet welds connecting such plates are inadequate. Unless preheat is used or radial emanating sequence is fol lowed, plug welds should be avoided due to their tendency to crack free after welding. In some minor lap joints where access to the work is from one side only, it may be convenient to use plug or slot welds. These, how

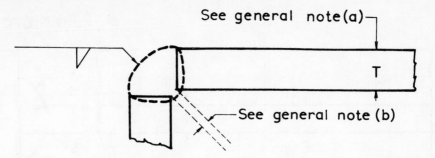

Notes:
1). This joint not to be used on a structure subject
   to bending, fatigue or blast.

2). This joint not to be used where both sides are
   accessible for welding.

C-1. Single fillet corner joint.

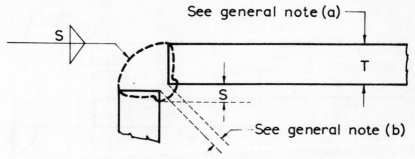

Notes:
1). Back gouge root of weld to sound metal before
   welding other side when T is over 1/8 in. (5.10 lb).

2). Size of fillet S=1/2 T but in no case greater than
   3/8 in.

C-2. Double fillet corner joint.

General Notes:
a). For T under 3/4 in. (30.6 lb).

b). Generally this dimension equal to 1/8 in. Sometimes
   the plate corners are arranged with an overlap from
   0 to 1/8 in., provided that full penetration is obtained
   and that proper back gouging is used.

FIG. 4-26.   Fillet weld corner joints.

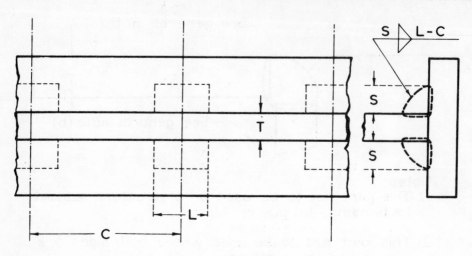

T-2. Chain intermittent welded tee joint.

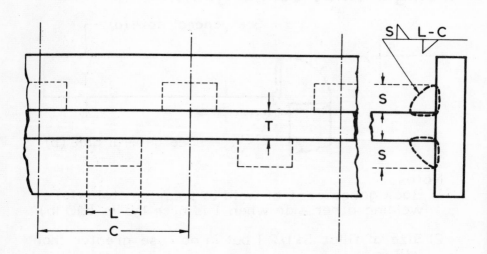

T-3. Staggered intermittent welded tee joint.

General Notes:
a). Size of fillet S = T/2 or as required.
b) Length of increment L min. = 8S, but in no case less than
   1 1/2 in.
c). L max. = 6 in. ⎫ {Also see Table A of reference 16.
d). C max. = 12 in. ⎭
e). This joint suitable for any position.

FIG. 4-27.   Intermittent fillet welded tee joints.

ever, should be avoided whenever possible (due to inadequate strength and unreliability) and should never be used where shock or fatigue is present. If plug or slot welds cannot be avoided, the slot weld should be given preference. Where the slot permits a completely fused bead to be applied

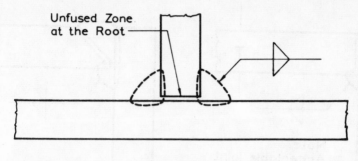

a) Double fillet T joint.

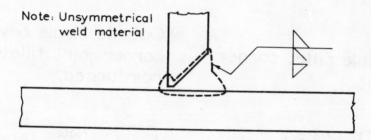

b) Single bevel T joint.

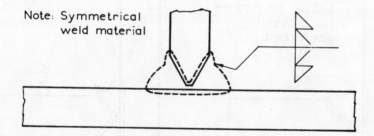

c) Double bevel T joint.

Fig. 4-28. Comparison of fillet and composite T joints.

all around the bottom edge of the slot, there is little likelihood of cracking free. If a space can remain open between the fillets, a separation of the members will show on inspection. The most commonly used plug and slot joints are shown in Figs. 4-30 and 4-31.

Table 4-2 gives recommended standard dimensions for slot welds.

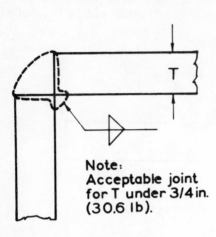

Note:
Acceptable joint
for T under 3/4 in.
(30.6 lb).

a) Double fillet corner
joint.

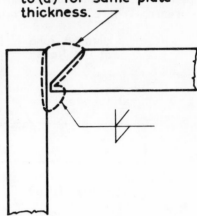

Reduced amount of weld
material as compared
to (a) for same plate
thickness.

b) Outside single bevel
corner joint fillet
reinforced.

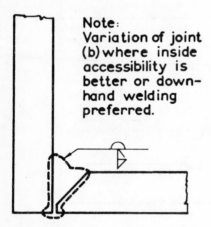

Note:
Variation of joint
(b) where inside
accessibility is
better or down-
hand welding
preferred.

c) Inside single bevel
corner joint, welded
both sides, fillet
reinforced.

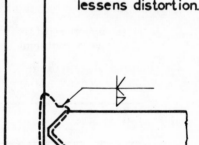

Note:
Symmetrical joint
preparation
lessens distortion.

d) Double bevel corner
joint fillet rein-
forced.

FIG. 4-29. Comparison of fillet and composite corner welds.

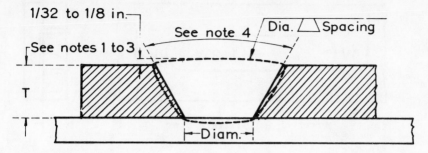

Notes:

1). When T is 1/8 in. or less, diameter=1/4 in. min.

2). When T is 1/8 to 1/2 in., diameter = 2T min.

3). When T is over 1/2 in., diameter= 1T + 1/2 in.

4). Bevel angle = 0 deg under T = 1/2 in. and 45 deg min. over 1/2 in.

L-1. Plug welded lap joint.

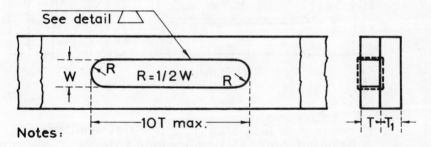

Notes:

1). When T is less than 1/4 in., W=1 1/2T min. When T is 1/4 in. or over, W= T min.

2). When T is more than 1/2 in., slot shall be beveled to a 45 deg included angle.

3). When T_1 is less than T, use joint L-4.

4). Length, width, spacing, etc., must be shown by a detail in the drawing.

L-2. Slot welded lap joint.

General Note:
a). Also see A.B.S. Rules, Section 26. I (4) (e).

FIG. 4-30.   Plug and slot joints.

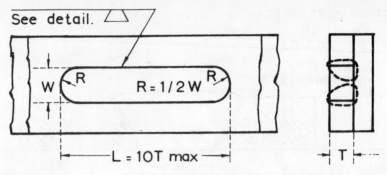

Notes:

1). When T is less than 1/2 in., use L-2.

2). W=1 1/2 T or 1/2 in., Whichever is greater.

L-3. Slot lap joint, fillet welded.

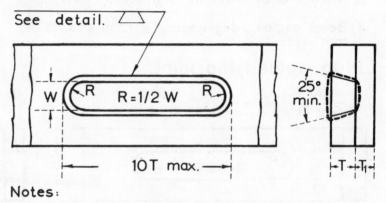

Notes:

1). When T is less than 1/2 in., slot shall be beveled to a 45 deg included angle.

2). When T_1 is equal to or greater than T, use L-2.

3). W = T.

L-4. Beveled slot welded lap joint.

General Notes:
a). Length, width, spacing, etc., must be shown by a detail drawing.

b). Also see A.B.S. Rules, Section 26, I (4) (e).

FIG. 4-31. Slot welds.

AUTOMATIC WELDING

The submerged-arc process is the most widely used automatic welding method in shipbuilding. It is very well adapted for the fast welding of plated structures, especially in subassemblies.

The submerged-arc process is characterized by the use of high welding current, which often reaches five or six times the value used in shielded metal-arc welding. This high current produces deep penetration of the base metal and fast deposition of the electrode wire. A much larger amount of base metal is melted with the submerged-arc process than in the manual-arc method. A typical proportion is that of two volumes of base metal to one of filler metal. In general, only one pass is necessary for each welding side.

Higher welding speeds (2 to 10 times that of the manual-arc method) reduce the cost of welding with submerged-arc machines. In addition, these high but rigidly controlled welding speeds, together with a more uniform heat application, reduce the amount of distortion in the work. Since the arc penetration is high, plate edge preparation may be simplified and in some cases eliminated. Plate edge design, i.e., beveling, need only provide for free run-in of weld metal for regions of the plate thickness which the arc fails to penetrate.

There are some special necessary precautions when using the submerged-arc process. The base material in way of the joint should be thoroughly cleaned and the surfaces and grooves should be clean dry steel. Generally, the welding requires more accurate edge preparation and fitting at the joint, as weld metal has low consistency and will run through a small opening. In making subassemblies which have little extra stock, tabs or run-off plates should be welded to the plates at both ends of the automatic weld, one for starting the weld and one for finishing the weld. These run-off plates should be of the same thickness as the plates being welded, so that the weld can be started before reaching the designed plate edge weld, continue past the designed length and be cut off clear of the weld crater. See Fig. 4-32(a) and (b). The use of run-off tabs beyond the ends of the weld is necessary to avoid submerged cracks near the ends. The only exception to this is where special gouging techniques and modified edge preparation for manual welding is provided at the end of the weld.

For the successful application of the automatic process for each type, position and size of joint, the machine voltage, current and speed should be properly adjusted. Proper selection of these variables will provide optimum finished weld cross-section contour without recourse to further finishing.

Generally, submerged-arc welding must be done in a flat position. For this reason, the process is used mainly on subassemblies in shops or on fabricating platens. There are, however, many automatic welding operations which may be carried out on the shipway, but these require approval of the classification societies or other regulatory bodies.

Figures 4-33 to 4-35 show some typical butt joints for submerged-arc automatic welding.

Because of the deep penetration obtained with automatic machines, it is possible to make satisfactory square-groove butt joints with much thicker plates than the manual-arc process. Joint B-19 of Fig. 4-33 indi-

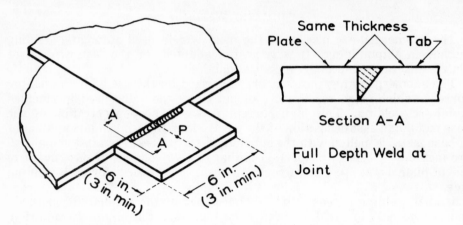

Same Thickness
Plate   Tab

Section A-A

Full Depth Weld at
Joint

Notes:
1). Automatic weld to start or finish at P.
2). Tab to have same edge preparation as plate.

a). Detail of run-off tab.

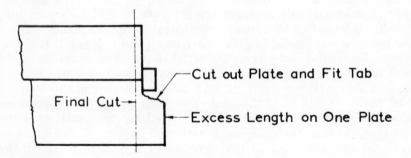

Cut out Plate and Fit Tab

Final Cut

Excess Length on One Plate

b). Plates of different lengths.

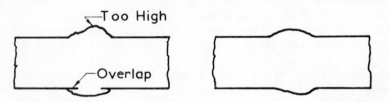

Too High

Overlap

Incorrect reinforcement.
(Not harmful)

Satisfactory reinforcement.

c). Weld reinforcement.

FIG. 4-32.   Detail for automatic welding.

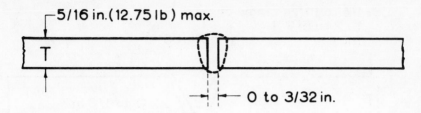

Note:
Joint welded on backing material.

B-19. Square groove butt joint welded one side.

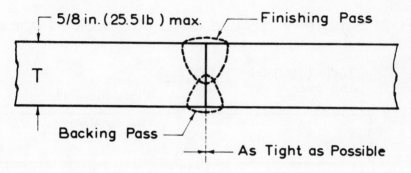

Note:
Sometimes maximum T is 3/4 in. (30.6 lb).

B-20. Square groove butt joint welded both sides.

General Notes:
a). These joints for medium-carbon steel.

b). These joints used on subassemblies for flat horizontal plates only.

FIG. 4-33.   Square groove automatic welding butt joints.

ates a maximum plate thickness of 5/16 in. (12.75 lb) when welding on ne side. When the square-groove butt joint is welded on both sides, plate hicknesses of 5/8 in. (25.5 lb) may be welded, as illustrated in B-20 of 'ig. 4-33.

Since the penetration obtained with automatic machines is very large, he grooves in joints for automatic welding are shallower and smaller than hose for manual welding. The angular opening of the groove also may be maller for automatic welding since, 1) the weld metal is run-in, 2) the aelted plate metal forms a large part of the finished weld, and 3) angular lectrode positioning is not necessary. The size of the groove and the

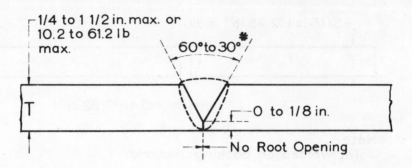

Note:
Joint welded on backing material.

B-21. Single-V groove butt joint welded one side

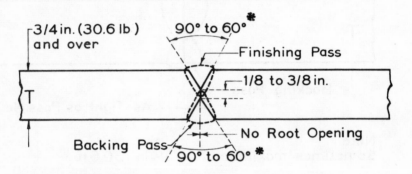

Note:
The depth of the V groove for the backing pass
may be equal to the depth of the V groove for
the finishing pass, or may be reduced down to
one-third the depth of the latter.

B-22. Double-V groove butt joint.

General Notes:
* The larger groove angles used for the thinner plates and
vice versa.

a).These joints for medium-carbon steel.

b).These joints used on subassemblies for flat horizontal
plates only.

FIG. 4-34.   V-grooved automatic welding butt joints.

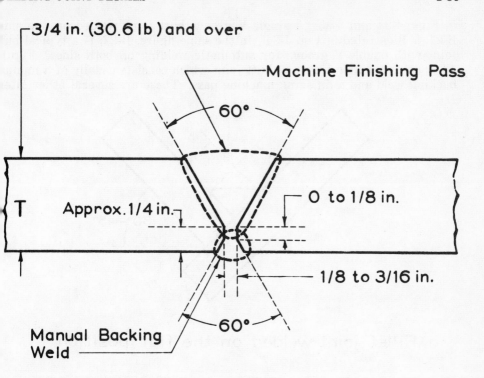

Notes:

1). This joint for medium-carbon steel.

2). This joint used on subassemblies or on the shipway for keel, bottom shell, tank top, decks, etc., and on subassemblies only for side shell.

3). The manual backing weld is generally done overhead.

4). Manual backing of machine weld passes is objected to by some because it may result in slag inclusions.

FIG. 4-35.   Combination machine and manual butt joint.

mount of filler metal deposited by the higher current used to obtain deep penetration must be balanced if excessive reinforcement is to be avoided. A fairly large angular opening is used in grooved joints for relatively thin steel plates. The resulting wider opening is usually necessary to avoid excessive weld reinforcement, i.e., by distributing relatively free flowing surface weld metal.

Three typical grooved butt joints for submerged-arc welding are shown in Figs. 4-34 and 4-35. A single-V groove butt joint welded on one side, B-21, is illustrated in Fig. 4-34. In the same figure, B-22, is a typical butt joint with double-V groove for automatic welding on both sides. Figure 4-35 shows a double-V groove butt joint which consists usually of a manual backing weld and a finishing machine pass. There are several other alter-

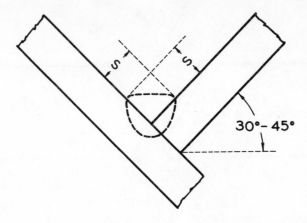

a). Fillet joint welded on the flat position.

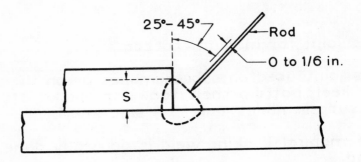

b). Fillet joint welded on the horizontal position.

FIG. 4-36.   Automatic welding on fillet joints.

native grooved butt joints for submerged-arc welding which are used successfully in shipbuilding.

When using automatic welding in butt joints which are welded on both sides, it is not necessary to back gouge the root before the automatic welding on the second side. Due to the arc penetration, the root remelts and fluxing is adequate to remove root impurities and float them off into surface slag. However, there is a practical limit to the assumed depth of penetration of an automatic weld, as perfect arc condition and perfect centering over the joint cannot be assured.

Manual backing of machine weld passes is sometimes objected to because slag inclusion may result (Fig. 4-35).

Figure 4-36(a) shows a typical fillet joint welded automatically on the flat position. Figure 4-36(b) shows a typical fillet joint where the automatic weld is done on the horizontal position. In this case, the head of the welding machine is tilted 25° to 45° to direct the wire into the apex of the joint.

Recent experience has indicated that where two plates are joined by automatic welding, one of these plates must have relatively complete freedom from restraint to prevent weld cracking.

DEFECTS IN WELDED JOINTS

To understand most of the difficulties experienced with steel arc welding, a detailed knowledge of welding metallurgy is required. The reader will find ref. 17 very helpful in this regard. However, certain significant practical aspects may be grasped without reference to such detail. Among these is an understanding of difficulties and defects occurring while heating, making the weld, or upon cooling.

In this section, we will consider defects which affect the dimensions or shape of the welded joint (dimensional defects) and notably those which involve structural discontinuities and result in cracking (soundness defects). In connection with dimensional defects, means of lessening distortion will be analyzed and illustrated.

DIMENSIONAL DEFECTS

Two difficulties are often present in welding processes, namely, *metal contraction and upsetting*. Generally, they are responsible for a defect called *distortion*.

The welding operation involves the application of heat and the fusion of metal in localized sections in the welded structure. When metal is heated, it *expands* and as it cools, it *contracts* in all directions; the amount of expansion and contraction depends upon the initial and final temperature. When molten steel cools and solidifies, it contracts approximately 2 per cent. As the bond is established between the weld metal and the plate material, the weld, on solidifying and contracting, pulls the plate with it. This contracting pull can result in a certain amount of structural deflection and distortion as we shall see later. Also, while the weld pulls the plate with it in contracting, the restraining action of the plate prevents the weld metal from fully contracting upon cooling.

Upsetting results when a metal is heated to a high temperature while it is restricted from moving in at least one direction and is subsequently cooled. Figure 4-37 illustrates the effect of successive heating and cooling on a restrained bar. The bar of Fig. 4-37(a) when heated tends to expand in all directions, but since it is held between two rigid supports, it can only expand in two directions. Figure 4-37(b) shows what happens upon heating (solid lines). When the bar is cooled, it contracts in all directions, and the solid lines of Fig. 4-37(c) show its final dimensions. The bar is now shorter in length and larger in cross section than it was originally. This change in dimensions, called upsetting, has resulted from heating the

metal bar against restraint. Figure 4-37 illustrates the case of a piece of
metal prevented from expanding in only one direction while heated to a
high temperature. We can imagine the same piece of metal with expansion
restricted in two directions while the temperature is raised sufficiently.
On cooling, we would find that the final dimensions in the two directions
of restraint would be smaller than they were originally. This indicates
that the piece of metal has been upset in those two directions. Upon
cooling, it would be found also that the dimension in the direction of free
expansion had grown correspondingly.

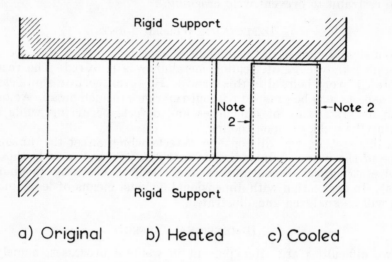

a) Original   b) Heated   c) Cooled

Notes:

　1) Dotted lines show original size.

　2) Final dimensions.

FIG. 4-37.   Heating and cooling effect on restrained bar.

   An effect contrary to that of upsetting may be attained with the metal
bar of Fig. 4-37. Suppose that first we heat it to a high temperature while
unrestricted in all three directions. The immediate result will be that of
an increase in dimensions in all directions. Next, while at this temperature, we clamp firmly two of its free ends in a single chosen direction and
start cooling. By so doing, we will restrict the bar from contracting in
the direction of clamping. Upon complete cooling, we will find that the
dimension of the bar is larger than it was originally in the direction of
clamping. Correspondingly, it will be found that the dimensions of the bar
in the other two directions have decreased. The net result has been a
stretching of the bar in the direction of clamping.
   We can imagine the same piece of metal clamped, while still at a high
temperature, in such a manner that, upon cooling, contraction in two
directions is prevented. In the cooled condition, the dimensions of the
clamped bar in the two directions of restricted contraction will be larger
than they were before heating. Correspondingly, it will be found that the

limension of the bar in the third direction has decreased. The resulting ffect has been a stretching of the bar in the two directions of restriction.

The preceding discussion on upsetting and stretching has been concerned vith relatively simple conditions of restriction. These effects will be present in structures subjected to heating and subsequent cooling, gen-rally under more complex conditions. However, the foregoing examples erve to give an understanding of these effects in welding and cutting perations.

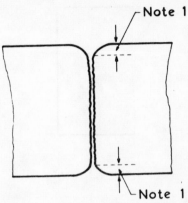

Note 1:
Upsetting effect due to flame cutting

a) Original metal plate.

b) Flame-cut metal plate after cooling.

FIG. 4-38.   Upsetting effect due to flame cutting.

During welding and burning, upsetting results because a relatively mall area of heated metal with a tendency to expand is restrained from loing so by the rest of the plate which stays cool. This results in short-ning of the hot metal in the immediate vicinity of the molten weld or cut n the direction in which the process is carried out. In addition, the hot netal, on cooling, contracts and produces shrinkage of the adjacent cooler netal in the same direction. Shrinkage of the molten metal as it cools produces additional shrinkage. At the same time, the solidifying metal is tretched since boundary restraint prevents normal shrinkage.

These effects are exaggerated for more effective illustration in Figs. 1-38 and 4-39. The upsetting effect due to flame cutting can become very roublesome if the burned edge must be flanged, as it may cause the plate o bow after flanging.

Planar distortion may be defined as the combined or separate result of shrinkage, upsetting, and stretching. It also may be defined as the by-product of plate metal expansion and contraction under certain conditions of temperature variation and boundary restraint. Later, several of the nost important types of distortion will be explained and illustrated.

In addition to the distortion along the weld, transverse distortion of shrinkage occurs across a welded butt-joint, as illustrated in Fig. 4-40 The amount of transverse shrinkage depends primarily upon the cross section of the weld. The larger the cross section, the greater is the shrinkage. It may be considered as approximately equal to 1/4 in. per square inch of weld cross section.

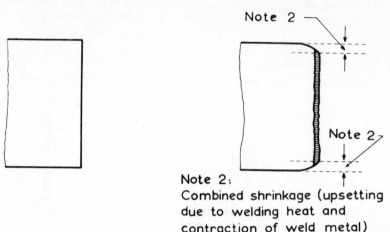

Note 2:
Combined shrinkage (upsetting due to welding heat and contraction of weld metal)

a) Original metal plate.

b) Same plate as (a) but with weld bead deposited on one edge, after cooling.

FIG. 4-39.   Upsetting effect due to welding.

Figures 4-41 and 4-42 show some typical results of a recent theoretical investigation of the transverse shrinkage on butt-welded joints. The investigators studied the transverse shrinkage on plates of different thicknesses for various welding conditions and procedures. The theoretical results have been compared with actual observed shrinkage values in butt welds of shell and deck plating and the agreement has been quite satisfactory. In Fig. 4-41 the total transverse shrinkage on butt-welded joint for each plate thickness is represented by a band comprising the range of values corresponding to the welding conditions indicated in the figure Figure 4-42 is based on the data of Fig. 4-41, but the transverse shrinkage is plotted in inches per square inch of cross-sectional area of weld groove For practical purposes, the shrinkage allowances given in Table 4-3 may be used.

Distortion or shrinkage along a welded butt-joint is illustrated in Fig 4-43. This figure shows that shrinkage along a butt weld results in reduction of the width of the plate at the weld. The amount of shrinkage varies proportionally to the length of the weld. Typical values of the shrinkage allowance are given in Table 4-3. To facilitate visual interpretation, the effect of shrinkage has been exaggerated in Fig. 4-43, and this procedure will be adopted in illustrating other distortions to follow.

Angular distortion, i.e., change in angularity of original planes of joined members, occurs usually in single-V butt and certain fillet welded joints.

If, by the use of external restraint such as shown in Fig. 4-44, angular displacement of the plates is avoided in a single-V groove butt joint, distortion attained is similar to the one illustrated in Fig. 4-40 for a double-V groove butt joint.

When the plates in a single-V groove butt joint are free to move, in addition to the planar distortions or shrinkages across and along the weld, an angular distortion results, as shown in Fig. 4-45.

Figure 4-46 illustrates the angular distortion attained in single and double fillet joints.

TABLE 4-3. Average shrinkage allowances. (Ref. 21)

Butt Welds.

Transverse: 1/16 to 3/32 in. for all thicknesses.
Longitudinal:

Over 1/2 in. thick................	1/32 in. in 10 ft
3/8 to 1/2 in. thick..............	1/32 to 1/16 in. in 10 ft
1/4 to 3/8 in. thick..............	1/32 to 3/92 in. in 10 ft
Up to 1/4 in. thick	1/16 to 1/8 in. in 10 ft

Fillet Welds. (Use same as tucking allowance below.)

Tucking or Corrugating. (See Fig. 4-48.)

Over 1/2 in. thick.............	No allowance
3/8 to 1/2 in. thick	1/64 in. each stiffener
1/4 to 3/8 in. thick	1/32 in. each stiffener
Up to 1/4 in. thick	1/16 in. each stiffener

Note: Developed for use on flat plates with continuously welded stiffeners. Intermittent welding will result in about one-half the tucking tabulated above, when the weld lengths and spacings conform to the American Bureau of Shipping requirements.

Figure 4-47 indicates the type of misaligning distortion which might occur in a fillet welded T-joint as a result of depositing a single fillet weld on one side of the T.

A common type of distortion in welded ships is that called corrugating or tucking. This is illustrated in Fig. 4-48.

Distortion in corner joints, beveled tee joints and other types of welded attachments has not been mentioned or illustrated. Following the reasoning of the preceding discussion, the reader will be able to evaluate the effect of shrinkage in these types of joint as well.

Another type of dimensional defect is called *incorrect weld profile*. The three most common cases of incorrect weld profile, namely, overlap, undercutting and size reduction, are shown and explained in Fig. 4-49. Requirements concerning defects of this nature in finished welds are usually

included in the specifications and drawings involved (similar to Fig.
4-13 through 4-19). Dimensional defects of the type shown in Fig. 4-40
can be minimized or avoided by using adequate welding procedures. These
include the selection of proper welding current, voltage, speed, etc., and
are given in most welding handbooks and similar publications.

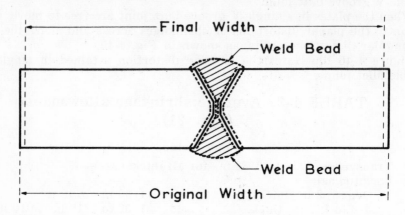

Notes:

1) The solid lines indicate the position of the plates
   before depositing weld metal. The dash lines
   indicate the position and contour of plate and
   weld bead fully deposited, after cooling.

2) In a single–V groove butt joint in addition to the
   effect illustrated in this figure there is an
   angular distortion (see Fig. 4.45)

FIG. 4-40.   Distortion or shrinkage across a double-V groove butt joint.

LESSENING DISTORTION

The most desirable way to lessen distortion is to design and fabricate
welded structures in such a manner that on cooling the tendency to shrink
will be at a minimum.

In many cases, distortion can be kept very small by providing adequate
restraint during welding and subsequent cooling. However, in general, the
greater the applied restraint, the greater will be the built-up or "residual"
stresses due to welding. Since excessive built-up stresses can increase the
tendency to cracking, this method of minimizing distortion should be used
with extreme care and only when other methods are ineffective.

No strict rules can be established for the purpose of lessening dimensional defects in welded ship construction. Following are some general
recommendations, however, based on the typical behavior of welded structures.

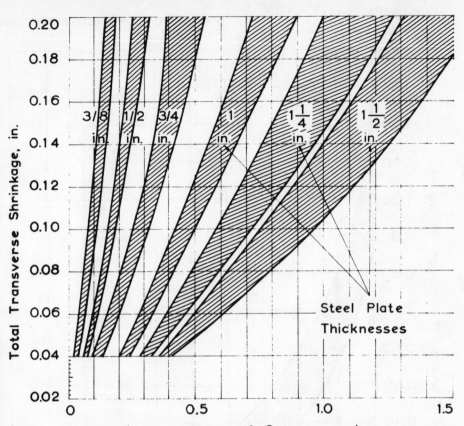

Notes:

1) Approximate electrode diameters and corresponding
   welding currents during tests were as follows: 5/32
   in., 150 amp.; 3/16 in., 210 amp.; and 1/4 in., 260 amp.

2) Welding speed during tests, 7 in./min.

3) Cross-sectional area of back gouging groove
   0.0875 sq in.

4) The hatched bands in the figure indicate a
   range of possible values rather than a single value
   for each set of conditions. Thus, the total transverse
   shrinkage in a 1 1/2 in. thick plate corresponding
   to a cross-sectional area of groove of 1.1 sq in. may
   vary between 0.12 to 0.16 in. approximately.

FIG. 4-41.   Total transverse shrinkage on butt welded joints.   (Ref. 20)

4-47

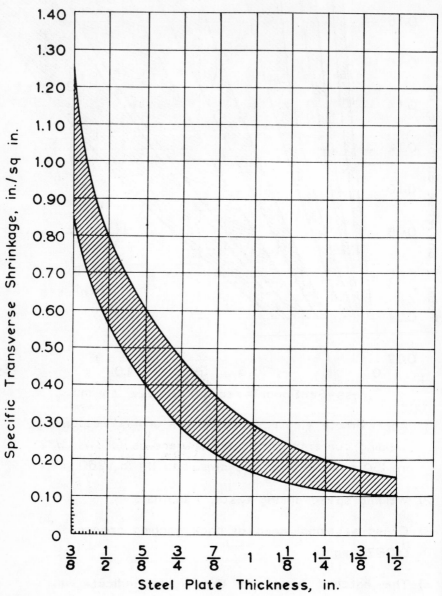

Notes:

1. Welding procedure and conditions equal to those of Fig. 4.41.

2. The specific transverse shrinkage is given in in. per sq in. of cross-sectional area of groove.

FIG. 4-42.   Specific transverse shrinkage on butt welded joints. (Ref. 20)

Detrimental factors regarding distortion are illustrated in Figs. 4-50, 51 and 4-52, and means to minimize their effect are presented.

Tables 4-4 and 4-5 give typical recommended welding conditions for ngle-V and double-V butt joints and fillet welded T-joints. For each plate uickness, the tables give the number of passes, size of electrode, and elding current, voltage and speed.

Figures 4-53 through 4-57 illustrate means to decrease distortion in elded joints.

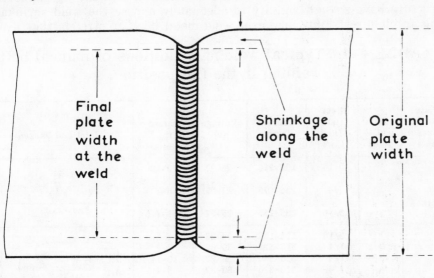

Final plate width at the weld

Shrinkage along the weld

Original plate width

Note:

The shrinkage across the weld is not shown in this figure. This is illustrated in Fig. 4-40.

FIG. 4-43.   Distortion or shrinkage along a welded butt joint.

Sometimes, to avoid or to lessen angular distortion in double fillet velded T-joints, the passing plate is pre-sprung before welding in the pposite direction, as shown in Fig. 4-57(a). This elastic pre-springing s a very effective method of controlling angular distortion and, when roperly used, may reduce distortion entirely when the restraint is re-noved. The amount of pre-springing necessary in this method has been letermined experimentally for various plate thicknesses and fillet weld izes. (Ref. 22.) Figure 4-57(b) gives recommended amounts of pre-pringing for double fillet welded T-joints. These values are based on a pan, or distance, between double fillet welded T-joints comparable to that ommonly used between stiffeners in plated structures.

Table 4-3 gives suggested average shrinkage allowances for butt and illet welds.

Peening is sometimes used to lessen distortion. This operation, generally ipplied to the hot deposited weld metal, stretches it, counteracting its endency to contract and shrink as it cools. For best results, in a multipass

weld all beads should be peened except the first and last ones. Peenin
should be done with great care by an experienced operator, otherwise t
weld metal may be damaged.

As previously mentioned, an effective way to minimize distortion is
use restraint, such as clamps, jigs and fixtures, to hold the work in a rig
position during welding. In this method, the shrinkage forces of the we
are balanced with counter forces and moments to minimize distortion.
the desired effect is to be produced, it is essential that the jig supporti
structure have enough rigidity to adequately oppose the weld shrinkag
This forcible restraint causes the weld metal itself to stretch, thus avoi

TABLE 4-4. Typical welding conditions of manual butt
welding in the flat position.

Plate Thickness (in.)	No. of Pass	Electrode Dia. (in.)	Current (amp)	Voltage (v)	Speed (in.) min.	Joint and Passes
5/16	1	3/16	190-210	25-27	9-10	
	2	1/4	255-275	25-27	6-7	
	3	3/16	235-255	25-27	6.5-7.5	
5/8	1	3/16	175-195	24-26	5.5-6.0	
	2	1/4	315-335	30-32	7-8	
	3	1/4	320-340	30-32	10-11	
	4	1/4	310-330	30-32	6-7	
	5	5/32	180-200	27-29	14-15	
	6	1/4	285-305	27-29	8-9	
1	1	3/16	200-220	27-29	6-7	
	2	3/16	260-280	27-29	8-9	
	3	1/4	300-330	30-32	7.5-8.5	
	4	1/4	310-330	30-32	7.5-8.5	
	5	1/4	300-320	30-32	5-6	
	6	3/16	210-230	27-29	5-6	
	7	3/16	250-270	27-29	9-10	
	8	1/4	310-330	30-32	11-12	
1-1/8	1	3/16	200-220	27-29	6.5-7.5	
	2	3/16	220-240	27-29	7-8	
	3	1/4	310-330	30-32	7.5-8.5	
	4	1/4	300-320	30-32	8-9	
	5	1/4	300-320	30-32	7-8	
	6	1/4	300-320	30-32	12-13	
	7	1/4	300-320	30-32	12-13	
	8	1/4	300-320	30-32	7.5-8.5	
	9	3/16	220-240	27-29	9.5-10.5	
	10	1/4	330-350	30-32	12-13	
	11	1/4	330-350	30-32	11-12	
	12	1/4	310-330	30-32	8-9	

Note: Size of electrode, welding current, voltage and speed change somewhat
on different joint designs when using conventional and iron powder low hydrogen
electrodes.

ng most of the distortion. It is important to note that generally, by estricting distortion, undesirable shrinkage stresses are produced which ecome greater as the degree of restraint is increased, as mentioned pre-iously. In many cases, this method cannot be applied to reduce distortion ecause of the size or geometry of the structure, or because the necessary igs or fixtures would be economically impractical. Typical and common ypes of restraint to avoid angular distortion, called temporary supports r strongbacks, are shown in Fig. 4-58.

TABLE 4-5. Typical welding conditions of positioned (flat) fillet welded T joints.

Plate Thickness (in.)	No. of Pass	Electrode Dia. (in.)	Current (amp)	Voltage (v)	Speed (in./min.)	Joint and Passes
1/4	1	3/16	270-290	30-32	9.5-10.5	
11/32	1	3/16	300-320	30-32	8.0-9.0	
3/8	1	3/16	225-245	29-31	11.0-12.0	
	2	1/4	320-340	30-32	9.0-10.0	
7/16	1	3/16	235-255	29-31	9.5-10.5	
	2	1/4	330-350	30-32	7.0-8.0	
1/2	1	3/16	235-255	29-31	8.5-9.5	
	2	1/4	325-355	30-32	6.0-7.0	

Note: Same as that of Table 4-4.

SOUNDNESS DEFECTS

For lack of a better way to classify defects in welds, we include, under he general heading of soundness defects, all those that cannot be identi-ed as dimensional defects. Soundness defects often involve structural otches (with their attendant stress concentration) which lead to struc-ural cracking. The more serious defects, in general, are unacceptable veld voids and plate undercutting caused by poor welding procedure, poor esign for welding, carelessness, illegal slugging, wrong type of electrode, nd poor workmanship or materials. Some of the most important sound-ess defects are further explained and illustrated subsequently.

Because of its overriding seriousness, cracking in welded joints is dealt vith separately.

Penetration, when referring to welds, may have more than one meanin▮
Figure 4-59 illustrates two meanings which are important in weldin▮
One of the most serious defects in welding is that of *incomplete penetr*
tion, or insufficient heat of the weld and inadequate deposition of the we▮

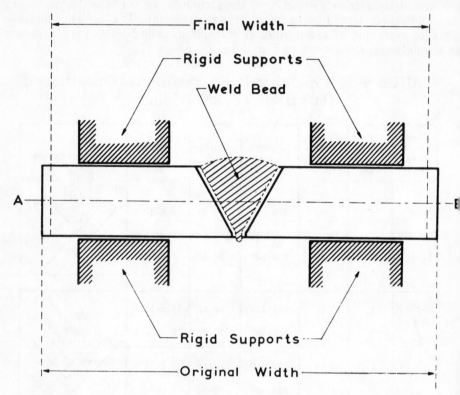

Notes:

1) The rigid supports allow movement of the plates
   in the direction of line AB only.

2) The solid lines indicate the position of the plates
   before depositing weld metal. The dash lines indicate
   the position and contour of plates and weld bead
   fully deposited, after cooling.

3) The shrinkage effect is similar to that of Fig. 4.40
   for a double-V groove butt joint, because of the
   restraint of the rigid supports.

FIG. 4-44.   Distortion or shrinkage of a single-V groove butt joint with
restraint perpendicular to the plane of the plate.

metal to complete the metallic bond for the full depth of the designed weld, as per Fig. 4-59(a). Figure 4-60 illustrates several additional examples of incomplete penetration which form serious weld notches. These are dangerous where the weld is subject to tensile stress. It is quite common to find incipient cracks at the root of the cooled weld when there is incomplete penetration. These cracks may progress until they extend for the full weld thickness, even before being subjected to structural loading. When subject to structural loading as in deck and bottom shell plating, welds involving incomplete penetration can cause plate cracking extensive enough to fracture a vessel in two.

Lack of fusion (not to be confused with *incomplete penetration*) is the failure of weld metal to fuse with the parent metal or with previous layers of weld metal. This defect may be caused by injurious foreign material which is not removed upon cleaning prior to welding, or by improper

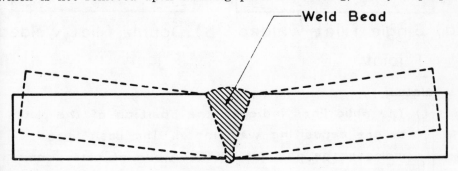

Weld Bead

Notes:

1) The solid lines indicate the position of the plates before depositing weld metal. The dash lines indicate the position and contour of plates and weld bead fully deposited, after cooling.

2) Because the weld metal is deposited fully expanded, the entire width across the joint decreases somewhat upon cooling (same amount as in Fig. 4-44.)

3) The angular distortion, indicated by the dash lines, is caused by the greater total contraction of the weld metal at the face than at the root of the weld. Ways to minimize this angular distortion are listed in this section.

FIG. 4-45.   Angular distortion of a single-V groove butt joint.

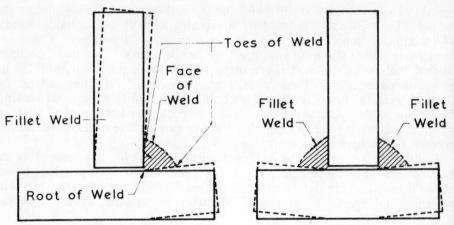

a) Single fillet welded T joint.

b) Double fillet welded T joint.

Notes:

1) The solid lines indicate the position of the plates before depositing weld metal. The dash lines indicate the position and contour of plates and weld fillets fully deposited, after cooling.

2) In fillet welds the maximum total shrinkage occurs at the face of the weld. As a result, in single fillet welded T joints, see (a), the upright plate is pulled out of the vertical and there is a tendency for the flat plate to bend upwards. The greater the thickness, the smaller the distortion of the flat plate.

3) The upright piece can be pulled close to the vertical by depositing another weld fillet on the other side of the joint, as shown in (b). However, this will produce a bending of the other side of the flat plate, as indicated in the figure.

4) Means to minimize distortion in fillet weld joints are listed in this section.

FIG. 4-46.   Angular distortion of single and double fillet welded T joints.

elding procedure, welding heat, or workmanship. As illustrated in Fig.
-61, the result of lack of fusion is the creation of notches. The notches
nown in Figs. 4-60 (a) and 4-60 (c) are just as serious as those mentioned
bove under *incomplete penetration*. Solid foreign matter left in a weld
generally a *slag inclusion* resulting from the welding process. Except for
ailure to properly back-gouge or to clean a previous pass, this foreign

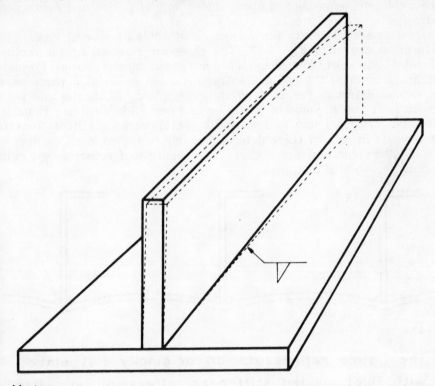

Notes:

1) **The solid lines indicate the position of the plates before depositing weld metal. The dash lines indicate the position of the plates after a single fillet has been fully deposited and cooled.**

2) **This type of distortion is due to the accumulative effect of upsetting and shrinkage combination.**

3) **Means to minimize this type of distortion are listed in this section.**

FIG. 4-47. Misaligning distortion of fillet welded T-joints.

matter is usually slag which has not had time to come to the surface befor
the freezing of the weld. To avoid dripping, overhead welds are made t
freeze quickly, and therefore, unless care is exercised, we may expect mor
slag inclusions in them. The most serious form of slag inclusion is tha
which forms a notch in the structural continuity. Figure 4-62 illustrate
different types of slag inclusion. These slag inclusions can be as seriou
as the weld defects mentioned above under *lack of fusion* and *incomplet*
penetration.

Gas entrapment leads to the formation of voids of several types, siz
and form, as shown in Fig. 4-63. The gases are released by the coolin
weld metal because of reduced solubility as the temperature drops. *Porosit*
is the most common type of gas entrapment and in isolated particles i
not a serious defect as far as strength is concerned. *Blowholes* and *pipe*
are somewhat larger voids of a similar nature. Blowholes are rounde
while pipes are elongated and worm-like in appearance. Stress concer
tration exists in way of these defects, but due to the rounded corners o
the voids, the structural notch effect with regard to fracture is not quit
so serious for isolated instances.

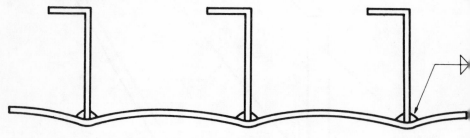

Notes:

1) The figure represents an originally flat plate
   with fillet welded stiffeners, after cooling. This
   type of distortion, called <u>corrugating or tucking</u>
   (in Japan it is called "hungry horse"), is often
   found in welded ships.

2) This distortion is the result of accumulated
   angular distortions of the type illustrated in
   Fig. 4.46.

3) Means to minimize distortions of this type are
   presented in this section.

FIG. 4-48.   Plate corrugating or tucking distortion.

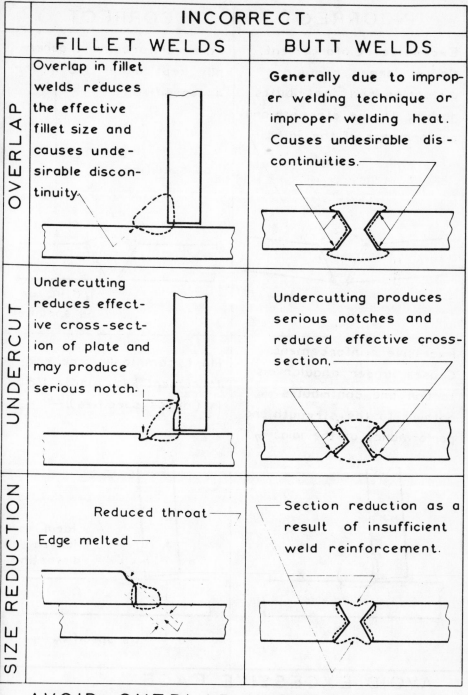

	INCORRECT	
	FILLET WELDS	BUTT WELDS
OVERLAP	Overlap in fillet welds reduces the effective fillet size and causes unde- sirable discon- tinuity.	Generally due to improp- er welding technique or improper welding heat. Causes undesirable dis- continuities.
UNDERCUT	Undercutting reduces effect- ive cross-sect- ion of plate and may produce serious notch.	Undercutting produces serious notches and reduced effective cross- section.
SIZE REDUCTION	Reduced throat Edge melted	Section reduction as a result of insufficient weld reinforcement.

AVOID OVERLAP, UNDERCUT AND SIZE REDUCTION

FIG. 4-49. Effect of overlap, undercut and size reduction on welded joints.

INCORRECT	CORRECT
Excessive reinforcement. Causes larger angular distortion and contributes nothing to the strength and performance of the joint. 	Face reinforcement generally kept under 1/8 in. (or as specified). as specified. 1/8 in., or as specified 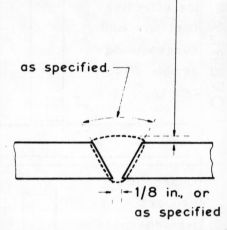
Excessive reinforcement. Causes larger angular distortion and contributes nothing to the strength and performance of the joint. 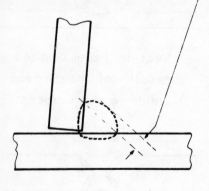	Most commonly, face reinforcement kept under 1/8 in. (or as specified). Ideal to lessen distortion. as specified 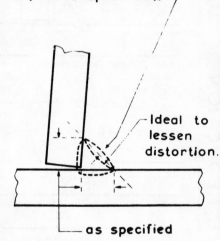

AVOID EXCESSIVE FACE REINFORCEMENT

FIG. 4-50. Effect of excessive weld face reinforcement.

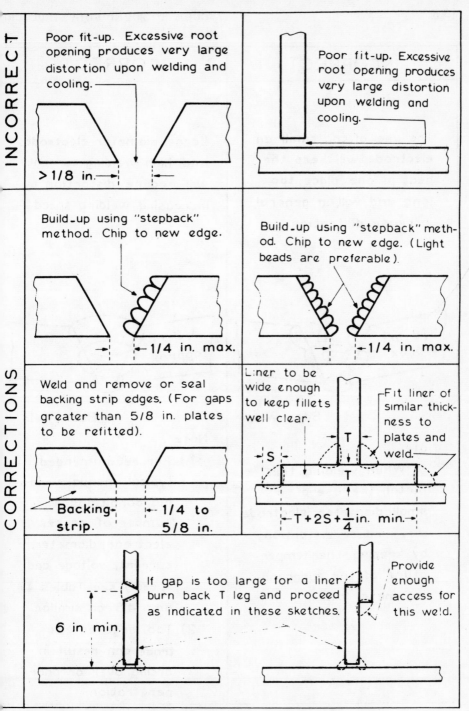

Poor fit-up. Excessive root opening produces very large distortion upon welding and cooling.

> 1/8 in.

Poor fit-up. Excessive root opening produces very large distortion upon welding and cooling.

Build-up using "stepback" method. Chip to new edge.

1/4 in. max.

Build-up using "stepback" method. Chip to new edge. (Light beads are preferable).

1/4 in. max.

Weld and remove or seal backing strip edges. (For gaps greater than 5/8 in. plates to be refitted).

Backing-strip.

1/4 to 5/8 in.

Liner to be wide enough to keep fillets well clear.

Fit liner of similar thickness to plates and weld.

S

T

T

$T + 2S + \frac{1}{4}$ in. min.

If gap is too large for a liner burn back T leg and proceed as indicated in these sketches.

Provide enough access for this weld.

6 in. min.

POOR FIT-UP WHICH LEADS TO EXCESSIVE DISTORTION

FIG. 4-51. Effect of poor fit-up on distortion of welded joints.

4-59

INCORRECT	CORRECT
The use of too small an electrode will keep the heat in one place too long and will, in general, increase distortion. 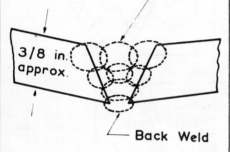 Back Weld Note: When welding thin metal, the use of a small diameter electrode may reduce distortion by keeping the temperature of the surrounding metal low.	Large diameter electrodes and high welding current will reduce distortion by increasing welding speed. 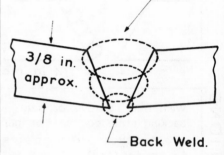 Back Weld. Note: 1) For recommended typical manual welding conditions (number of passes, electrode diameter, current, voltage and speed) see Tables 4.4 and 4.5 or similar. 2) Too large an electrode can result in arcing over or poor penetration.

AVOID EXCESSIVE NUMBER OF PASSES

FIG. 4-52.   Effect of excessive number of passes on a welded joint.

INCORRECT	CORRECT
Too much weld metal deposited on one side of a joint without welding the other side causes excessive distortion. ⁊	Balance passes on both sides as structural arrangement permits within reasonable fabricating cost. ⟶

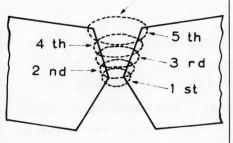

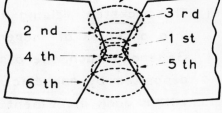

Note:	**Note:**
The weld on the underside will not eliminate joint angular distortion completely.	Completing weld on the underside before completing topside will result in practically zero joint angular distortion.

KEEP PASSES BALANCED ON BOTH SIDES OF THE JOINT

FIG. 4-53.   Effect of unbalanced passes on a welded joint.

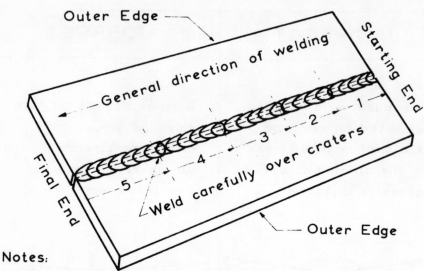

Notes:

1) The <u>backstep</u> welding method breaks a long weld into a series of increments (1, 2, 3, 4, 5, etc.). Generally each one of these increments is deposited by one electrode. The welding direction within each increment is opposite to the general direction of welding, as shown in the above sketch.

2) As each increment is deposited, the heat from the weld along the edges of the groove causes expansion there and this separates the plates at the "final end." However, as the heat moves out across the plate towards the "starting end", the expansion along the outer edges of the plates brings the plates back together at the groove. This results in minimized distortion.

3) The action indicated in (2) is most effective in the first weld pass. The same tendency will be present in laying successive passes, but the action is less pronounced because of the locking effect of previous beads.

FIG. 4-54.   Backstep method of welding to reduce welded joint distortion.

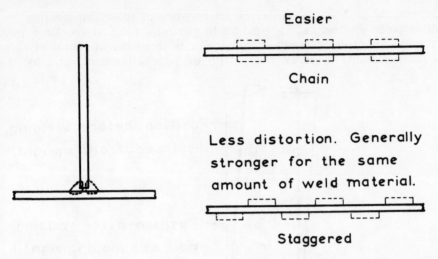

Easier

Chain

Less distortion. Generally stronger for the same amount of weld material.

Staggered

Notes:

1) Intermittent fillet welds illustrated in the sketch above may be used to connect some ship structural members. Where acceptable, they may reduce the amount of deposited metal to about two-thirds the material required for a continuous weld of equivalent strength.

2) The use of intermittent fillet welds distributes the heat more uniformly throughout the structure. Since, in addition, the amount of deposited metal is smaller than that required for a continuous weld, the resulting distortion is smaller.

3) In spite of the minimized distortion corresponding to intermittent fillet welds, they have some inherent disadvantages, mentioned elsewhere, which preclude their extensive use. In general, they may be used when the required weld area is less than that of a continuous fillet weld of the minimum permissible size.

FIG. 4-55.   Effect of intermittent fillet welds on joint distortion.

Slugging is an intentional defect. It consists of inserting welding rod or other piece of steel before welding to partially fill a groove or a poor fit-up gap. Slugging is resorted to, with or without the approval of shipyard management, to cover poor fit-up or poor alignment, and by the

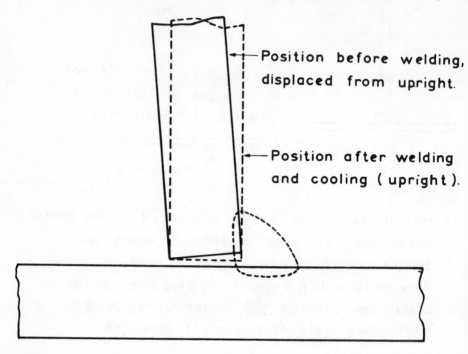

Position before welding, displaced from upright.

Position after welding and cooling (upright).

Notes:

1) To minimize the effect of angular distortion in a single fillet welded T joint one may intentionally displace the upright plate, as shown by the solid lines of the above sketch, before welding. On cooling, shrinkage of the fillet weld will pull this plate to the upright position (dash lines).

2) The single fillet welded T joint is not usually permitted in shipbuilding. However, the purpose of the above sketch is mainly to illustrate the principle which can be applied to other situations.

FIG. 4-56. Effect of preventive misalignment to minimize distortion in welded joints.

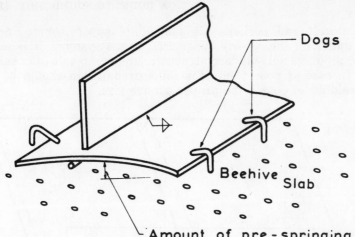

Note:
The procedure illustrated in the above sketch
may be used to minimize the angular distortion
in double fillet welded T joints. The shrinkage of
the weld fillets will pull the plates into the desired
alignment if the dogs are released before the weld cools.

a) Pre-springing procedure.

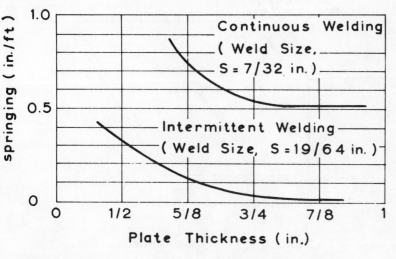

b) Amount of pre-springing for
different plate thicknesses.

FIG. 4-57.   Use of pre-springing to lessen angular distortion in
double fillet welded T-joints.

4-65

welder himself and perhaps his immediate supervisor to increase his footage under an improperly supervised bonus system. It is contrary to all codes, produces substandard structure, and can result in criminal prosecution. In case of poor fit-up, the joint preparation should be corrected before welding to obtain the proper groove size.

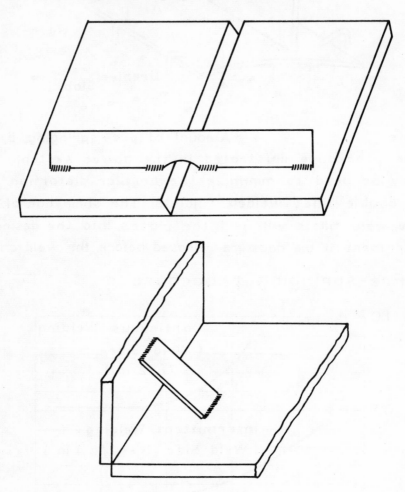

Fig. 4-58.   Temporary supports or strongbacks to reduce angular distortion.

CRACKING IN WELDED JOINTS

As the joint cools cracks may develop. In cracking, the steel behaves in a brittle fashion with negligible deformation or ductility exhibited at the fractures. Cracks in welded joints may occur at almost any temperature up to the fusion point of steel depending upon its chemical composition, including alloying elements and traces of impurities within the limits tolerated in the specifications. Cracks are generally classified in two groups, namely *hot cracks* and *cold cracks*, on the basis of the temperature

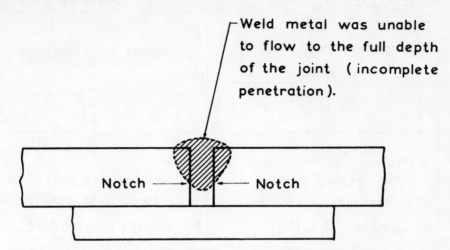

Weld metal was unable
to flow to the full depth
of the joint (incomplete
penetration).

Notch ——————— Notch

a) Meaning of "penetration" with reference to the
   ability of the deposited metal and base metal
   to fuse integrally at the root of the weld.

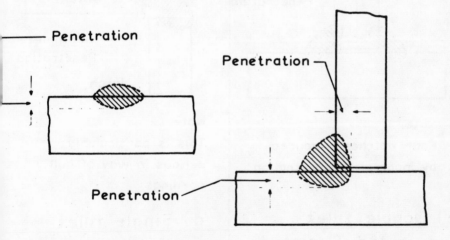

Penetration

Penetration

Penetration

b) Meaning of "penetration" with reference to the
   depth to which the fused zone extends below
   the surface (depth of fusion).

FIG. 4-59.   Illustration of two meanings of penetration with reference to welds.

EXAMPLES OF INCOMPLETE PENETRATION

Incomplete Penetration ⌐

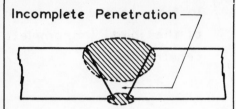

Incomplete Penetration ⌐

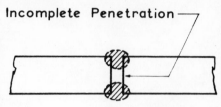

Note:
Four notches produced
by incomplete penetration.

a) Single - V butt groove joint.

Note:
Four notches produced
by incomplete penetration.

b) Square groove butt joint welded both sides.

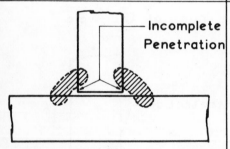

Incomplete Penetration

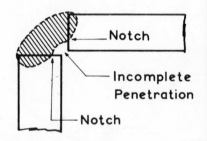

Notch

Incomplete Penetration

Notch

Note:
Four notches produced
by incomplete penetration.

c) Double fillet welded T joint.

Note:
This is particularly
serious in way of hull
openings.

d) Single fillet corner joint.

Note:
Proper joint preparation and correct electrode size
to prevent arcing to sides before reaching root
needed.

FIG. 4-60.   Incomplete penetration in four different welded joints.

EXAMPLES OF LACK OF FUSION

Lack of fusion between weld, parent metal and backing.

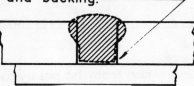

Note:
Two notches produced by lack of fusion.

a) Square groove butt joint welded on backing.

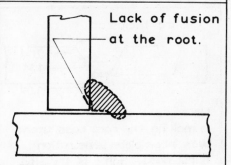

Lack of fusion at the root.

Note:
Two notches produced by lack of fusion.

b) Single fillet welded T joint.

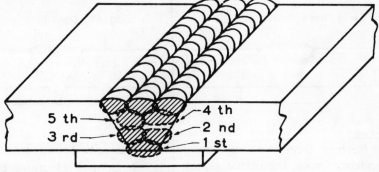

5 th
3 rd
4 th
2 nd
1 st

Notes:
1) The fourth pass has failed to fuse with the second pass.

2) The fifth pass has failed to fuse with the parent metal.

3) Looking at the sketch above, it will be found that the lack of fusion has created several notches between the weld and parent metal.

c) Multipass single - V groove butt joint welded on backing.

FIG. 4-61.   Lack of fusion in three different welded joints.

EXAMPLES OF SLAG INCLUSIONS

Slag Inclusion

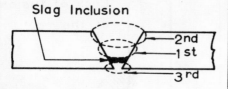

Note:

In making the root pass there was incomplete penetration (first pass). Some of the slag rolled down and filled the gap at the root. Before depositing the backing bead (3rd pass) the root was not properly back gouged.
a) Slag inclusion at the root of the weld.

Slag Inclusion

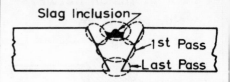

Note:

Some slag from 1st pass was not removed. The heat from subsequent passes was not enough to melt and raise slag to the surface.
c) Slag inclusion between successive passes

Slag Inclusion

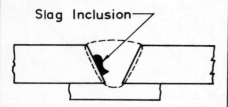

Notes:
1) Rather than showing each separate pass, the above sketch shows the weld metal as a whole.
2) The slag in the fusion zone (groove sides) may be left on cleaning between passes or as the result of under-cutting at the groove sides. In most cases, the slag will be melted and rise to the sur-face. Failure to do this will result in slag inclusions.
b) Slag inclusion at the fusion zone.

Slag Inclusions

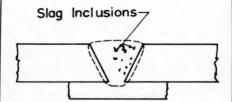

Notes:
1) See note (1) in (b).
2) Improper cleaning may leave some pieces of slag from previous passes. These pieces will interfere with the arc and prevent fusion of the weld metal and complete remelting of the slag. This will result in scattered slag inclusions within the weld metal.
d) Scattered slag inclusions.

FIG. 4-62. Different types of slag inclusion.

anges in which they occur. "Hot cracks" occur at temperatures of 1000° F and above. Between 600° F and 1000° F no cracking of significance occurs in steel. Below 600° F, so-called "cold cracking" occurs. For a thorough explanation of cracking in steel, the reader is referred to ref. 17.

In all cases, the causes of cracking must be investigated and conditions leading to them corrected. Also, it is vital that cracked portions of welds be found, traced out and completely removed for proper rewelding.

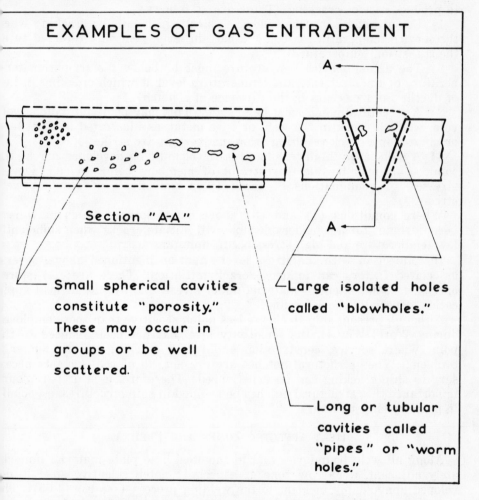

EXAMPLES OF GAS ENTRAPMENT

Section "A-A"

Small spherical cavities constitute "porosity." These may occur in groups or be well scattered.

Large isolated holes called "blowholes."

Long or tubular cavities called "pipes" or "worm holes."

Fig. 4-63. Different types of weld defects due to gas entrapment.

Hot weld cracking and its avoidance requires a thorough knowledge of metallurgical behavior for proper specifications and selection of materials. The Engineering Department is responsible for adequacy in this respect. Even when using adequate materials, hot cracks may develop in welded joints if the root bead is too small and the members being joined are too strongly restrained across the joint to permit adequate contraction of the weld metal. Such a condition should be avoided.

The essential problem in ship construction, repair, and service is the avoidance of "cold cracking" when proper materials are employed. In service, such cracking is associated with materials (i.e., steels) cold to the touch. In construction and repair, the temperatures may be somewhat higher but are associated with weld cooling processes. With such cooling, the conditions under which cracking takes place in construction and repair do not differ significantly from those necessary for service cracking.

Four simultaneously occurring basic features are generally necessary to produce service cracking. These are as follows:

1) Use of notch sensitive steel (i.e., steel which fails by cracking when the service temperature is below a certain level, generally referred to as the transition temperature).

2) The actual service temperature must be below the transition temperature of the steel (i.e., the temperature level at which cracking in lieu of ductile failure occurs in the presence of a notch).

3) A structural notch must be present. This may be design notch, weld void, welding crack in the weld or base metal, as illustrated in Fig. 4-64, or microscopic crack resulting from inadvertent arc strike.

4) A sufficiently high tensile stress level must be developed across the joint. This may be due to restraint of members being welded, service stresses, or combinations of these (plus the effects of residual weld stresses).

Where conditions (1) and (3) above exist, notches which may have been dormant for a considerable time will initiate cracks when sufficiently low temperature and high stress occur simultaneously.

In connection with the stress level situation mentioned above, several associated factors can influence crack initiation. These are: a) stored energy, i.e., the extent of material under stress, and b) rate of load application, especially shock loading.

Although present ship steels are less notch sensitive than those employed during World War II, the sensitivity level has not been reduced to the point where service, construction and repair cracking are no longer a problem. When structural notches are present, all of the elements necessary to ship cracking can be experienced. Therefore, it is of paramount importance that structural notches be avoided in ship structures, especially in primary ship structure.

HEAT-AFFECTED ZONES AND PREHEAT

Along all weld boundaries and in the steel base plate material immediately adjacent, a narrow zone of especially notch sensitive steel is developed unavoidably incident to the welding process (see Fig. 4-65). The sensitivity of this zone, which is roughly subject to full weld heat during welding, is due to metallurgical effects associated with steel chemical content and with quench effect (i.e., the cooling of such zone by the cold plate material adjacent thereto). When weld undercutting occurs, it is unavoidably in such zone and creates an unacceptable notch. When such a notch occurs in way of structural discontinuities, a severe cracking liability is created.

CRACKS IN WELD METAL	CRACKS IN BASE METAL

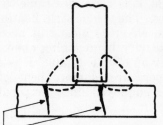

Transverse surface weld crack may or may not extend into base metal.

Longitudinal shrinkage crack, straight, continuous and generally quite visible.

Crater

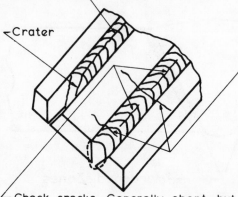

Check cracks. Generally short, but may be long and continuous. Very fine and sometimes hard to detect.

Plate crack started at weld root.

Plate crack started at one of the weld toes.

d) Typical longi-tudinal cracks in base metal.

a) Longitudinal and Transverse cracks in weld metal.

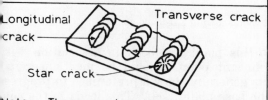

Longitudinal crack

Transverse crack

Star crack

Note: These cracks generally visible to the naked eye.

b) Crater cracks.

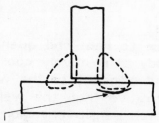

Under-bead crack. Seldom found, except in highly hardenable steels.

Note:
Cracking of the base metal is generally longitudinal. It is not as common as weld metal cracking and more usually happens in hardenable steels.

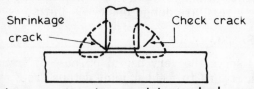

Shrinkage crack

Check crack

c) Cracks in weld metal.

e) Under-bead type of cracking.

FIG. 4-64. Cracks in weld metal and base metal.

Where welding under restraint, in way of structural discontinuities or where severe weld quench is liable to occur as in depositing surface weld beads, it is often desirable to reduce the notch sensitivity of heat-affected zones. The use of strip heating (i.e., preheat) adjacent to weld boundaries is an effective means of accomplishing this. The preheat reduces notch sensitivity by reducing quench effect at weld boundaries. Preheat of the order of 150° F to 400° F is effective to varying extent. While the higher temperature is more beneficial, a compromise of 200° F to 250° F is often employed since temperature distortion effects are less of a problem.

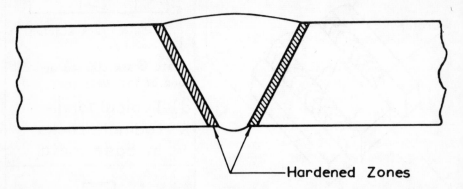

Hardened Zones

Note:
Due to heat and quench, i.e., rapid cooling, by the adjacent body of relatively cool base metal, the hatched area at and adjacent to the weld edge becomes more notch sensitive than the weld or original base metal. This notch sensitive region is termed the "heat affected zone"

FIG. 4-65. Butt weld showing hardened zones.

Cracking as mentioned up to this point has been in association with welding. However, several significant points should be mentioned: a) cracks originating in weld defects generally show a preference to progress in the heat-affected zone or in the base plate itself. This leads to the conclusion that sound welds offer more resistance to crack propagation than the other areas, and b) welding itself, or a heat-affected zone, are not essential to crack initiation. Sharp notch cuts or square-cornered cuts such as might occur at a deck penetration, in a sheer strake coaming, or similar location subject to tensile stress, are dangerous crack initiators.

SUMMARY

The standard welding symbols serve the very useful purpose of transmitting precise information with regard to welded joint details from the designer to the workman. Also, they constitute a practical means of recording technical information on plans and drawings. The first part of this section deals with this subject, using pictorial presentation as much as possible.

The matter of choosing an adequate type of joint is very important in welded ship construction. In general, this is the function of the structural designer. The information included in this publication aims at illustrating the importance of this choice.

The butt weld is the most important type of joint in shipbuilding, from the viewpoint of strength and overall structural continuity. Detailed information for most common butt welded joint types is given in Figs. 4-13 through 4-18 (manual), and in Figs. 4-33 through 4-35 (automatic).

Fillet welded joints are illustrated with details in Figs. 4-24 through 4-27 (manual), and Fig. 4-36 (automatic).

Table 4-1 gives minimum size of fillet welds, while information on fillet, lug and slot-welded joints is presented in Figs. 4-30 and 4-31. Table 4-2 lists the standard dimensions for slot welds.

The aforementioned material gives the essential information concerning the detailed preparation of joints before welding. Departures from proven good practice result in a high percentage of defective welded joints.

Defects in welded joints can be caused by improper joint preparation, but other factors also may be partly or wholly responsible for them. Among these factors, we find improper welding procedures, poor welding workmanship, and improper equipment and materials.

Defects which affect the dimensions or shape of welded joints are called *dimensional defects*. In Figs. 4-37 through 4-49, some of these defects, the underlying reasons for their occurrence, and their effects on the ship structure, are analyzed and illustrated. Table 4-3 gives shrinkage allowances which may be used for practical purposes. Factors that aggravate distortion are shown in Figs. 4-50, 4-51 and 4-52, and ways to minimize them are suggested. Tables 4-4 and 4-5 give typical welding conditions for manual arc-welded butt and T-fillet joints. They are presented as an illustrative sample. The reader is referred to welding handbooks for more extensive and detailed information on this subject. Figures 4-53 through 4-57 illustrate means to decrease distortion in welded joints.

Defects, notably lack of fusion, incomplete penetration, weld undercutting, etc., which result in crack-initiating structural discontinuities, i.e., structural notches, are grouped separately under the heading of soundness defects. Figures 4-59 through 4-63 illustrate these defects and show their effect in producing structural notches.

Because of its overriding seriousness, cracking in welding joints is dealt with separately. Explanations of the conditions which tend to favor the development of structural steel cracks are given. Remedies for some of these conditions are indicated.

SECTION V

Welding Sequence

INTRODUCTION

The order of progression in the making of related welds is called welding sequence.

Distortion in welded joints, because of shrinkage due to welding, is largely influenced by welding sequence.

The main reasons for using specific sequences in making welded joints is to control shrinkage. By controlling shrinkage, distortion and dimensional changes may be minimized. Frequently, the reduction in distortion results in increased residual stresses, so the problem becomes that of arriving at a safe and acceptable compromise between distortion and stress.

When welding a plated structure, the purpose of an adequate welding sequence is to reduce distortion while at the same time lessening the possibility of cracking.

For a welding sequence to be successful, it should be both simple and practical. If it is simple, it will be easily understood and therefore more likely to be followed by everybody concerned. Also, it should be practical, so that it does not interfere with production requirements or with the placement of a sufficiently large number of men on the job.

Most ship structures consist of plating and attached reinforcing members. The welding sequence of these attachments must be coordinated with that for the plating.

When inserting new material between existing structures, as in repair work, and in welding in the vicinity of riveting, special attention must be given to sequence and to the design and fabrication of details.

Straightening precautions or operations to reduce unfairness of structures due to welding are related to overall welding sequence. Fairing tolerances are difficult to formulate and sometimes are established arbitrarily. If weight margin permits, an increase in plating thickness substantially reduces fairing and shrinking operations.

SEQUENCE IN WELDED JOINTS

Welding sequence is an important factor in the shrinkage of welded joints. The results of shrinkage in welded joints are illustrated in Figs. 4-29, 4-39 through 4-48, 4-50 and 4-52 through 4-58.

5-1

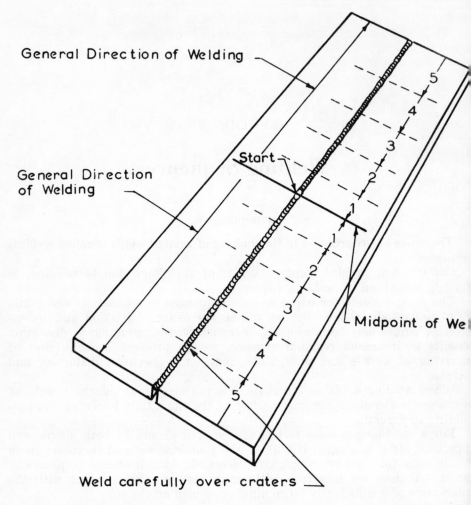

General Direction of Welding

General Direction
of Welding

Start

5
4
3
2
1
1
2
3
4
5

Midpoint of We

Weld carefully over craters

Notes:

1) The symmetrical back-step welding sequence consists of the application of the back-step method of Fig. 4_54 starting from the midpoint of the joint and progressing symmetrically toward the ends.

2) Each one of the increments (1, 2, 3, 4, 5, etc.) is, in general, the length of weld deposited by one electrode.

FIG. 5-1.   Symmetrical backstep welding sequence.

The effect of welding sequence is more fully realized when the members f the joint have no external constraint. When the joint members are not ree to move, the effect of the welding sequence on shrinkage is dependent pon the nature of the external constraint.

Several types of sequences may be used in making a manual welded oint, depending on the welding direction. The following sequences are nore commonly adopted:

a) *Continuous sequence.* This is a longitudinal sequence consisting of asses which are made continuously from one end of the joint to the other. t is used almost exclusively in automatic welding.

b) *Back-step sequence.* This is a longitudinal sequence consisting of veld bead increments which are deposited in the direction opposite to the

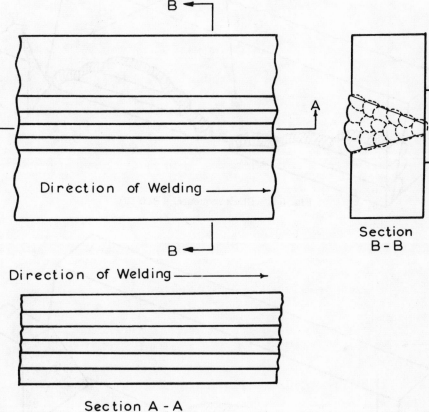

B

A

Direction of Welding ⟶

Section B-B

B

Direction of Welding ⟶

Section A - A

Note:

Every bead progresses in the direction of welding without interruption except for the beginning and ending of the deposition of each electrode.

Fig. 5-2. Built-up sequence for multi-pass welded joints.

progress of the weld. This sequence, illustrated in Fig. 4-54, is effective in reducing shrinkage.

c) *Symmetrical back-step sequence.* This is the sequence where welding proceeds longitudinally from the center towards both ends of the joint using the back-step sequence. An illustration of this sequence is given in Fig. 5-1. This sequence is very effective in minimizing the effect of shrinkage.

For multi-pass welded joints, there are some special welding sequences and the most commonly used are indicated below:

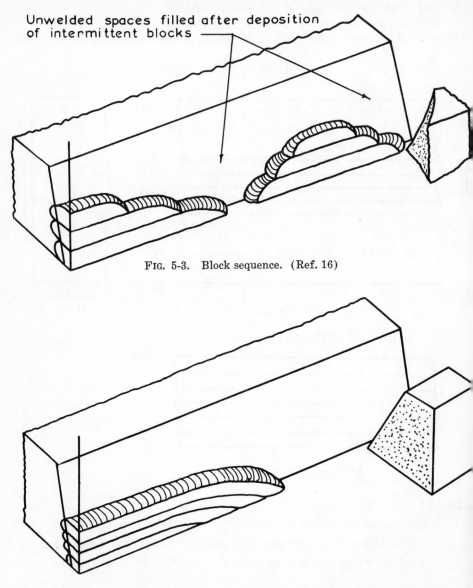

FIG. 5-3.   Block sequence.   (Ref. 16)

FIG. 5-4.   Cascade sequence.   (Ref. 16)

1) *Built-up sequence.* This sequence is the continuous sequence of (a) applied to a multi-pass welded joint. An illustration of a welded joint made using this sequence is shown in Fig. 5-2.

2) *Block sequence.* This is a sequence resulting from a combination of longitudinal and built-up sequences for a continuous multi-pass weld. As illustrated in Fig. 5-3, a series of separate blocks of weld material is completely or partially built up in cross section before the material between these blocks is deposited.

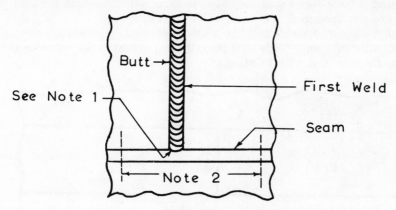

Notes:

1) Finish full and gouge out to restore groove shape.

2) Second weld to be carried straight through for seam.

a) Correct sequence

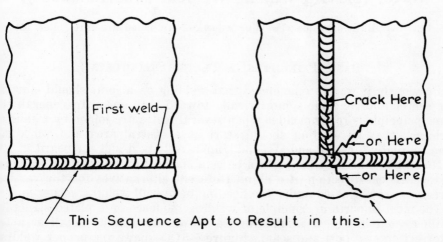

b) Incorrect sequence

FIG. 5-5. Welding detail at a tee intersection. (Ref. 16)

3) *Cascade sequence.* This is a combined longitudinal and built-up sequence consisting of weld beads which are deposited in overlapping layers. This is illustrated in Fig. 5-4. In manual welding, a back-step sequence is normally used in depositing the successive layers.

Experience and experimentation have shown that, in general, the block and cascade sequences minimize shrinkage in multi-pass welded joints.

Experience also indicates that whenever possible manual welding should start at the center of the joint and continue symmetrically toward both ends using a back-step sequence. This is especially desirable for long joints which are not free to move.

Finally, once the welding of a joint is started, it should be completed without interruptions. This is especially important when work is done in cold weather or in drafty locations.

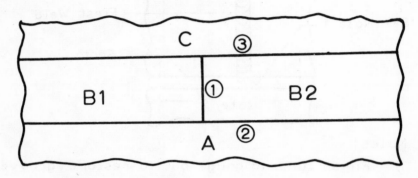

① Weld butt complete.
② Weld inboard seam complete.
③ Weld outboard seam complete.
Note: ② and ③ may be welded simultaneously.

FIG. 5-6. Basic principle of welding sequence for a plated structure. (Ref. 16)

BASIC PRINCIPLES IN PLATED STRUCTURES

Previously it was recommended that welding on a joint should start at the center and continue symmetrically toward both ends. In general, the same principle is recommended when several plates are joined by means of welding; that is, welding should start at a central area and work out longitudinally forward and aft, and transversely port and starboard.

No single general principle can be established for the welding sequence in the vertical direction of a ship. Different alternatives for the vertical direction are discussed under the heading of overall welding sequence.

The most important principle of welding sequence on a plated structure is illustrated in Fig. 5-5. This figure shows the welding detail at a tee intersection of a butt and seam. Figure 5-5(a) shows the proper welding sequence which allows the second weld to be made with the least amount of restraint across the joint. The sequence shown in Fig. 5-5(b) is incor ect because the restraint caused by the first weld and the termination of he butt in a tight corner may result in a potential source of cracking, as lustrated in the figure. When this basic principle is applied to a plated tructure, the welding sequence becomes as indicated in Fig. 5-6 which hows a butt bounded by two seams. In Fig. 5-7 the application of the ame basic principle to a multiple plate structure is illustrated. This figure uggests that the sequence may be extended almost without limit and that everal welding operations can be carried out simultaneously without disegarding the basic principle. Therefore, a reasonably large number of hen can be assigned to the welding of the plated structure if required y production schedule. Figure 5-7 represents a typical shell bottom with

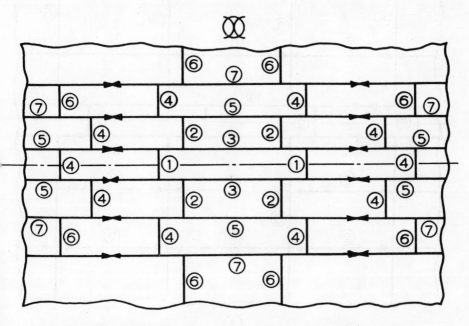

Note: Typical shell bottom with shifted butts.

FIG. 5-7. Correct welding sequence in multiple plate structure. (Ref. 16)

hifted butts. When only the keel butts are shifted, as shown in Fig. 5-8, much simpler welding sequence may be adopted. In this structure any umber of outboard seams can be welded independently, as long as a roper sequence is followed for the welding of the butted plates (i.e., butts nd seams in this case) and the edge of the keel plate.

SEQUENCE IN PLATES WITH ATTACHMENTS

When referring to the basic principles of welding sequence in plated tructures, no mention was made of the problem concerning the attachment f frames, stiffeners, bulkheads, etc., to the plating. The joining of these tructural members to the plating has to be considered in establishing the velding sequence of the plating. In general, to allow for unrestricted plate

shrinkage, these attachments should be left unwelded across the open butt
and seams until the plating is completely welded. Figure 5-9 shows the
same basic sequence of Fig. 5-6, except that the former includes the
welding of frames and girders in addition to the plating. The welding
sequence of Fig. 5-9 is the one recommended and commonly adopted for
plates with attachments.

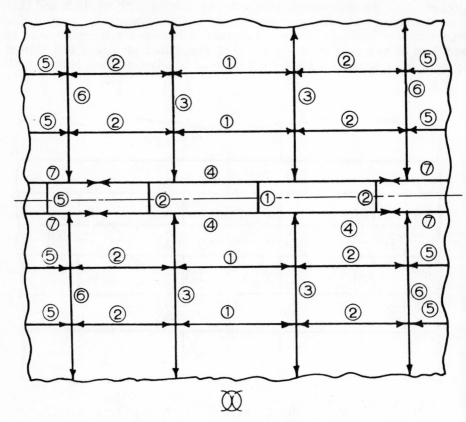

Note: Typical shell bottom with only keel butts
      shifted.

FIG. 5-8.   Correct welding sequence in multiple plate structure.

There are some alternatives to the welding sequence of Fig. 5-9 which
may be adopted when they fulfill production or schedule requirements more
satisfactorily. When dealing with small plates, the welding sequence of
Fig. 5-10 may be more practical since it avoids cutting up the welding of
attachments into relatively short lengths of weld. This sequence consists
in completing the welding of plating, as indicated in Fig. 5-6, and then
welding the attachments to the plating. This scheme usually is not satisfactory since it does not permit proper control over shape and dimensions.
In simple structures, however, weld shrinkage may be predicted and work
planned to result in proper shape.

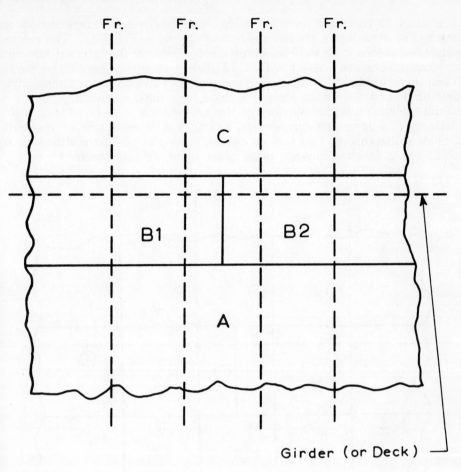

Girder (or Deck)

Notes:
1) Weld frames and girder (or deck) to plates
   to within about 12 in. of all unwelded butts
   and seams.
2) Weld butt complete.
3) Weld unwelded portion of girder (or deck)
   in way of butt.
4) Weld inboard seam complete.
5) Weld unwelded portion of frames in way of seam.
6) Weld outboard seam complete.
7) Weld unwelded portion of frames.

FIG. 5-9.   Correct welding sequence with plate attachments. (Ref. 16)

A panel or assembly may be welded completely and independently as long as the boundaries are not welded, as shown in Fig. 5-11. The recommended sequence is to weld all seams first. Then all the internal framing or attachments are welded within 12 inches of the edges of the panel. When these welding operations are completed in two adjacent panels, they may be joined together. Once the boundary butts between panels are completed, the unwelded portions of the attachments may be welded to the plating. The unwelded "crossovers," 12 inches at each side of the butt, provide a distance of two feet of unrestricted plating in the direction in which the greatest shrinkage takes place upon welding the butt.

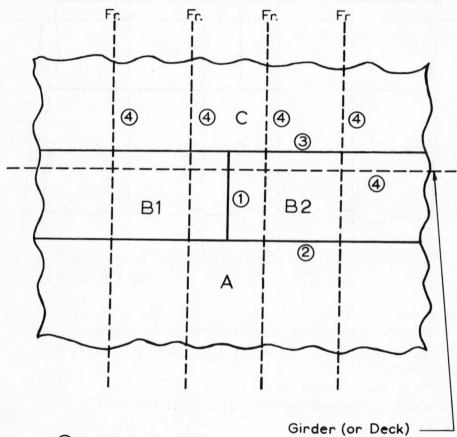

① Weld butt complete.

② Weld inboard seam complete.

③ Weld outboard seam complete.

④ Weld frames and girder (or deck) complete.

Note: ② and ③ may be welded simultaneously.

FIG. 5-10.   Alternative welding sequence with plate attachments when plate sizes are small.

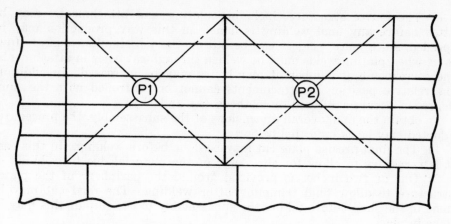

Notes:

1) Weld seams in panels P1 and P2.
2) Weld all framing to within 12 in. of
   panel edges.
3) Treat panels as individual plates in
   overall sequence.

FIG. 5-11.   Proper sequence for welding side shell in panels. (Ref. 16)

WELDING SEQUENCE IN SUBASSEMBLIES

The basic principles of welding sequence for plated structures were discussed in the previous subsections. In general, the same principles are observed in the welding of subassemblies. However, since comparatively little restraint is present in fabricating subassemblies and because the material can be positioned to suit production requirements, more alternatives are available as far as welding sequence is concerned.

In the fabrication of subassemblies, plates are generally laid on skids or platens and clamped or dogged down to prevent distortion, generally without interfering with shrinkage.

Welding sequences of plated subassemblies with respect to stiffeners are listed below:

a) The plates are laid down with the stiffener side up, which is also in this case the weld face side. After welding the plates, the stiffeners and frames are fitted and welded. When welding is complete on this side, the structure is turned over and chipped and welded on the opposite or smooth side.

b) The plate butts and seams are completely welded on both sides before the attachments are fitted and welded to the plating. This insures more accurate dimensions for the subassembly. However, auxiliary temporary stiffening may have to be provided when turning over the plated panel in which the butts and seams have been welded on one side only. Failure to do this may result in cracking of the incomplete welds.

c) The entire structure, including plating and attachments, may be fitted before any final welding is done. In this way production may be speeded, since more welders can be put on the job simultaneously. However, when plating welds must be welded through rat holes in attachments the corresponding number of man-hours may be increased. In addition the relative position of attachments cannot be controlled with the same degree of accuracy offered by methods (a) and (b).

To obtain the final overall dimensions of the subassembly, the procedure adopted may be as indicated below:

1) The final precise plate cut may be done before welding. In this case it is necessary to allow for shrinkage of the material due to welding, or

2) One or two inches is provided around the periphery of the plated structure to allow final trimming after welding. The final cut may be done in the shop before taking the subassembly to the ship or this may be done in place.

In general, it is good practice to have any erection butt with only one of the plates uncut. One plate edge should be shop prepared for weld, and the one with best access for final cutting should be cut at erection.

The choice of overall welding sequence and trimming procedure of plated subassemblies depends on a number of factors, among which the following may be included: Shipyard facilities and production methods, type of construction of the structure and its location on the ship.

OVERALL WELDING SEQUENCE

In the erection of a ship, the overall welding sequence in general is similar to that recommended for plated structures. Welding is started at the centerline of the bottom amidships and progresses symmetrically forward and aft and to port and starboard. In the vertical plane, the general direction of welding may be from the bottom up around the bilges and thence up the side plating. This general overall welding sequence is illustrated in Fig. 5-12.

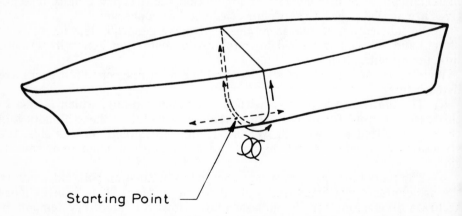

Starting Point

FIG. 5-12.   General overall welding sequence in the erection of the ship.

When welding in the vertical plane follows the direction indicated above, it means that the lower seams of the side plating will be welded before the upper ones, namely, the deck seams and the connection at the gunwale. This tends to shorten the upper portion of the hull girder and, as a result, the ship may rise from the blocks at both ends, as shown in Fig. 5-13.

To prevent the ship's ends from rising off the blocks due to shrinkage of the welded seams, the following methods will prove useful:

a) The side and deck plating is built in independent panels, as those of Fig. 5-11. The panels are then welded to each other at the gunwale and to the bilge strake. *See* Fig. 5-14.

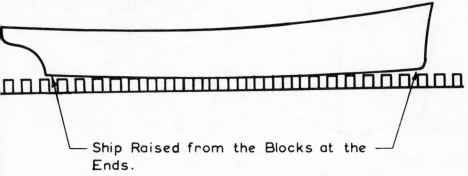

Ship Raised from the Blocks at the Ends.

FIG. 5-13.   Tendency of the ship to raise from the blocks when using welding sequence of Fig. 5-12.

b) Starting at the quarter points, or closer to midships, the upper deck plating, together with the sheer strakes and the ship bottom plating, including the bilge strakes, are welded as separate units before the side plating between the tank top and upper deck is welded. The welding sequence for the side plating may be so planned that the last joints to be finished are those at or near mid-depth. *See* Fig. 5-15.

c) A convenient overall welding sequence is that of keeping the bilges open and the gunwale unwelded. The bottom, side plating and upper deck plating may be treated as separate panels, and welding of these panels may be carried out independently to suit erection and production requirements. The ship box girder is progressively assembled with the lower and upper flanges kept unattached to the two side webs, represented by the port and starboard side plating. When welding in two contiguous panels is finished, these can in turn be welded to each other, as shown in Fig. 5-16.

d) The overall welding sequence offering the greatest flexibility in erection and production is the one that provides open vertical joints extending girthwise all around the hull. In this method the hull may be considered as made up of several transverse subassemblies which are butted together after all welding in the individual sections has been completed. To realize the fullest advantage, all plate attachments, such as girders and stiffeners, must be welded to the plating before the sections are joined. The joining of the independent transverse sections requires .careful shipfitting and suitable provision has to be made to join stringers and other longitudinal

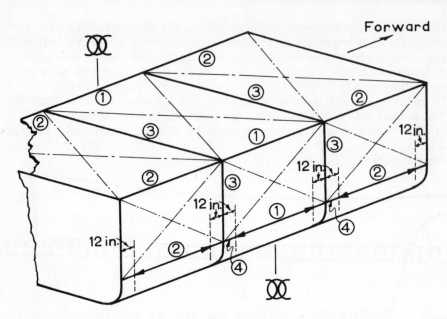

Notes:

    a) Ship bottom including bilge strakes welded complete before joining side and deck plating panels.

    b) The rest of ship erection to progress symmetrically forward and aft following the general procedure illustrated in the figure.

① Weld seams between midship side plating panel, deck panel, and bottom assembly.

② Weld seams between side plating panels forward and aft of midship side plating panel and corresponding deck panels and bottom assembly. Leave seam between side plating panel and bottom assembly unwelded for about 12 in. at each side of the butts.

③ Weld butts between midship panels and those located forward and aft.

④ Weld unwelded portions of bilge seams.

FIG. 5-14.   Overall welding sequence to avoid raising of the ship ends.   Alternative A.

members. This overall sequence is the logical choice when ships as a whole are built in more than one section to suit available facilities and also when dealing with ship conversion and jumboizing. Figure 5-17 shows the general principle of this overall welding sequence.

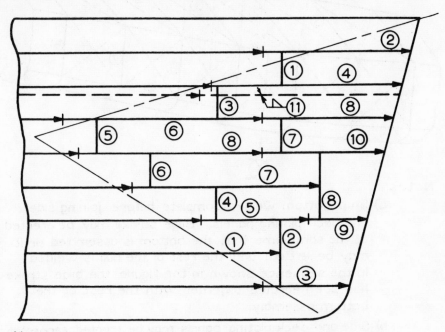

Notes:

I) Ship bottom including bilge strakes, and upper deck plating together with sheer strakes, welded complete before starting the sequence illustrated in this figure.

II) Today most bow and stern sections are sub-assembled and in these extreme portions of the ends of the ship the overall sequence illustrated here does not necessarily apply.

FIG. 5-15.   Overall welding sequence of the ship's ends to keep these from rising off the blocks.

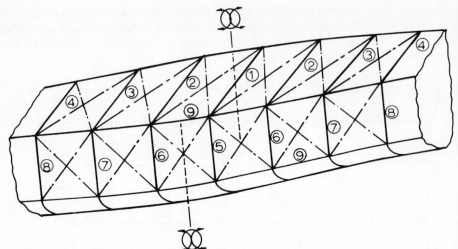

Notes:

a) Ship bottom welded complete before joining side and deck plating panels. Bilge strake may be erected at the same time that the bottom is assembled or it may be left out until the rest of the hull is welded. In the sequence shown in the figure the bilge strake has been erected together with the rest of the bottom assembly.

b) Side and deck plating panels may be treated separately and welded independently of each other in the shop or at the building way. These panels have to be built complete including plate attachments.

①through④ Weld deck plating panels to each other.

⑤through⑧ Weld side plating panels to each other. Welding of the deck panels to each other may precede the welding of these panels to each other or viceversa.

⑨ Weld seams at the gunwale and at the bilges.

FIG. 5-16.   Overall welding sequence to avoid rising of the ship ends. Alternative C.

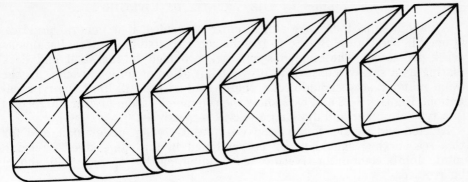

a) Transverse subassemblies before being joined
to each other.

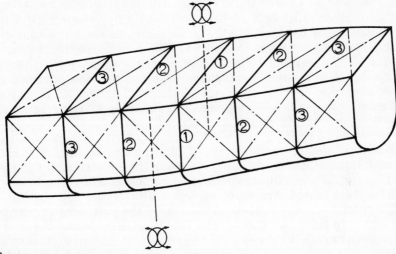

Notes:
① Weld together the first two transverse subassemblies
closest to midship.
②③ etc.
Join by butt welding additional transverse subassemblies to
the two of step① by successive symmetrical steps (forward
and aft) as indicated in the figure.

b) Transverse subassemblies attached at the
girthwise butt joints.

FIG. 5-17.   Overall welding sequence to avoid rising of the ship ends. Alternative D.

SEQUENCE IN THE VICINITY OF RIVETING

Although ships today are almost entirely welded, it is general practice, at least in the United States, to include some riveted longitudinal seams as crack arrestors. The riveted seams are provided in the shell and deck plating as a safety measure to prevent initiation of major cracks. In the event major cracks should occur, the riveted seams will limit their propagation. Figures 5-18 and 5-19 show the common location of crack arrestors in a typical tanker and dry cargo vessel, respectively.

Riveted and welded joints behave differently when under load, and for this reason they should never be combined in the same stress-carrying joint. Joints combining riveting and welding, as that of Fig. 5-20, should be avoided.

As a general rule, wherever a structure is both partially riveted and welded, any welding in the vicinity of the riveted joints should be done before the rivets are driven. This is to avoid restraint while making the welded joint and to ensure tight rivets. The usual procedure is to weld immediately after finish-bolting and follow this by riveting (if slip has occurred because of welding, it may be necessary to ream the holes before riveting). Commonly, this is the most practical and economical procedure. When, for some exceptional circumstance, it is necessary to make welds across riveted seams already completed, this can be done provided rivets for a distance of six inches each side of the weld are tested for tightness after welding. Recommended methods of combining riveting and welding in ship structures are illustrated in Figs. 5-21 and 5-23.

Combinations of riveting and welding in ship structures require careful consideration of details at the points of crossing and transition of the two means of joining. Care is necessary to ensure both sound and tight structures. Descriptions and illustrations of some details are given below:

a) When in a plated structure the seams are riveted and the butts are welded, a special situation arises at the end of the butt weld in way of the riveted seam. In some cases, no special provision is made and the butt weld is continued through to its end. This results in the two strakes being welded together at the seam lap, as shown in Fig. 5-24. This procedure has been followed in a number of ships and no fractures or other apparent difficulties have been reported as a result. However, this solution seems to change the inherent structural characteristic of the riveted seam.

If keeping the true nature of the riveted seam is desirable, a backing member must be inserted to keep welds clear of the laps. In general, following the recommended practice for welding sequence in the vicinity of riveted joints, the laps are first fitted and bolted. To do this properly, only a thin backing metal sheet can be inserted at the lap in way of the butt. At times a copper sheet is preferred, because after the butt weld is completed, the lap may be pried apart, the insert removed and riveting may be carried out in the usual manner. If the copper shim is small and thin, the copper will tend to melt and alloy with the weld. The result is a weld metal which is hard and brittle. When erection and bolting allows

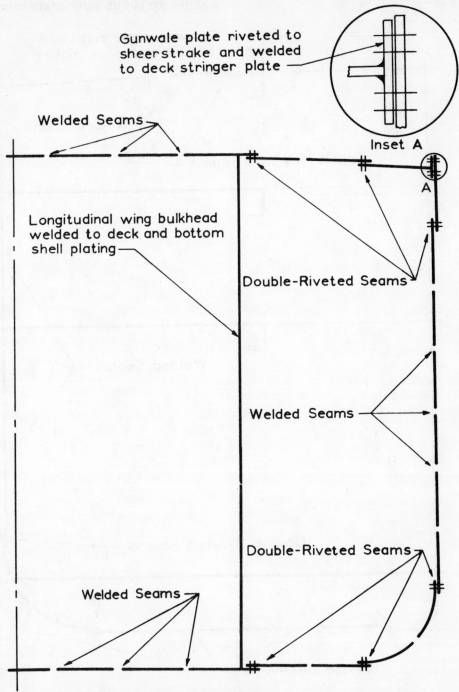

Gunwale plate riveted to sheerstrake and welded to deck stringer plate

Inset A

Welded Seams

Longitudinal wing bulkhead welded to deck and bottom shell plating

Double-Riveted Seams

A

Welded Seams

Double-Riveted Seams

Welded Seams

Note: For number and location of crack arrestors see current A.B.S. rules.

FIG. 5-18.   Tanker's transverse section showing riveted seams (crack arrestors).

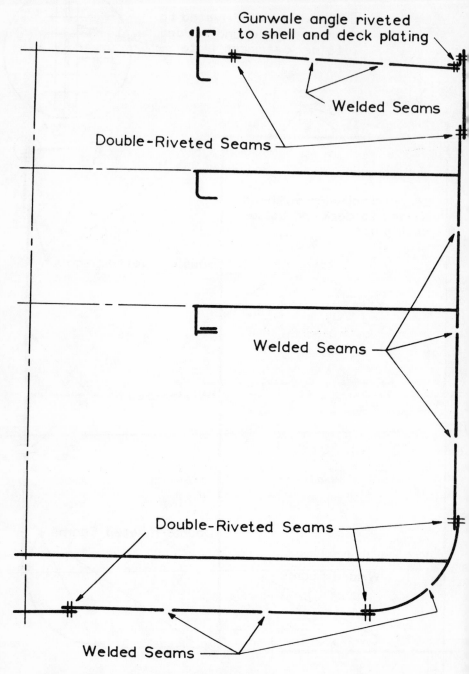

Gunwale angle riveted
to shell and deck plating

Welded Seams

Double-Riveted Seams

Welded Seams

Double-Riveted Seams

Welded Seams

Note: For number and location of crack arrestors
see current A.B.S. rules.

FIG. 5-19.   Transverse section of a cargo vessel showing
riveted seams (crack arrestors).

a thicker copper shim, melting of the insert may be avoided. However, copper seems to repel the weld metal and undesirable, though not critical, porosity in the deposited metal close to the copper shim may result. Figure 5-25 illustrates the use of a copper shim and weld defects likely to occur. If a steel shim about 1/16-inch thick is inserted, it will keep the weld from fusing into the supporting plate. Since the backing is then of the same material as the weld, no alloying takes place. In this case, the shim cannot be retrieved and the edge has to be caulked over it carefully, otherwise poor tightness may result. The use of steel shims is illustrated in Fig. 5-26.

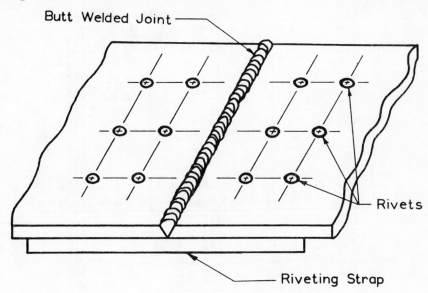

Note: This combination to be avoided.
Use rivet or butt weld alone.

FIG. 5-20. Bad example of combination riveting and welding.

b) In a plated structure with riveted seams and welded butts, another special situation may arise when the butt is in an inner strake. To have a satisfactory weld throughout the thickness of the plate, including the ends of the butts in way of the laps, two solutions are available. One solution is to groove the plates so all the welding is done on the reverse side (except for the backing weld clear of the laps). Another solution is that of grooving the butt joint in the usual way between the seams and to reverse the groove just in way of the laps. Both methods are illustrated in Fig. 5-27.

c) As mentioned before, most welded ships are built with several riveted seams, called crack arrestors. These seams are riveted amidships for about half to six-tenths the length of the ship and are changed to regular welded seams at the ends where the level of longitudinal stress is considerably reduced.

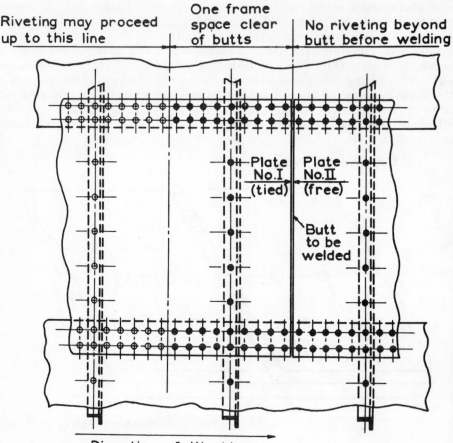

Direction of Working

Notes:
1) —⊕—⊕— This riveting may be done before welding vertical butt.
2) —◆-◆—This riveting has to be done after welding vertical butt.
3) Sometimes member No. II is displaced so that holes are unfair by the amount of the contraction expected in the weld. When this is done it is expected that after the weld has cooled the holes will be fair and riveting may proceed. However, more commonly, holes are sub-punched and, then, reamed after welding is completed.
4) Service bolts should be 1/8 in. smaller than rivets, spaced not less than 12 in. apart to allow movement of member No. II. Add bolts to close plate for riveting after completion of welding.

FIG. 5-21.   Correct method of combining riveted seams and welded butts. (Ref. 23)

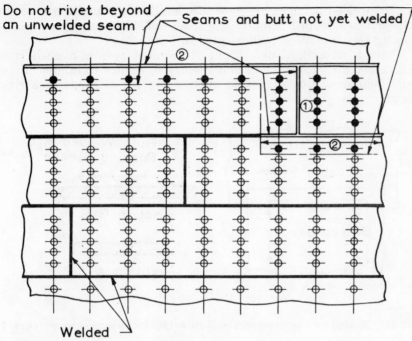

Do not rivet beyond an unwelded seam

Seams and butt not yet welded

Welded

Notes:

1) —⊕——⊕— This riveting may be done before welding seams and butt marked ② and ①.

2) —◆——◆— This riveting has to be done after welding seams and butt marked ② and ①.

3) Weld ① before welding ②

FIG. 5-22.   Correct welding sequence with welded seams and butts with frames riveted. (Ref. 27)

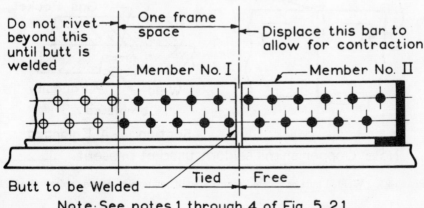

Do not rivet beyond this until butt is welded

One frame space

Displace this bar to allow for contraction

Member No. I

Member No. II

Butt to be Welded

Tied   Free

Note: See notes 1 through 4 of Fig. 5-21.

FIG. 5-23.   Welding sequence for riveted stringer angle with welded butts. (Ref. 23)

Since the welded portions are generally abutted, a transition is required from the riveted lapped joint to the flush-welded seam. A satisfactory solution for this transition is illustrated in Fig. 5-28.

d) Where a watertight or oiltight attachment crosses a shell riveted seam, a special structural detail is necessary to ensure tightness. Figures 5-29 and 5-30 show two suggested alternatives for oil-stops at a riveted shell seam.

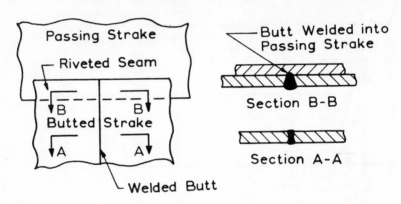

FIG. 5-24.   Welded butt at riveted seam. Butt welded into passing strake. (Ref. 24)

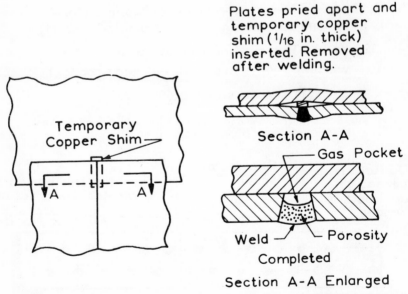

Note: Copper shims seldom used at present.

FIG. 5-25.   Welded butt at riveted seam. Use of temporary copper shim. (Ref. 21)

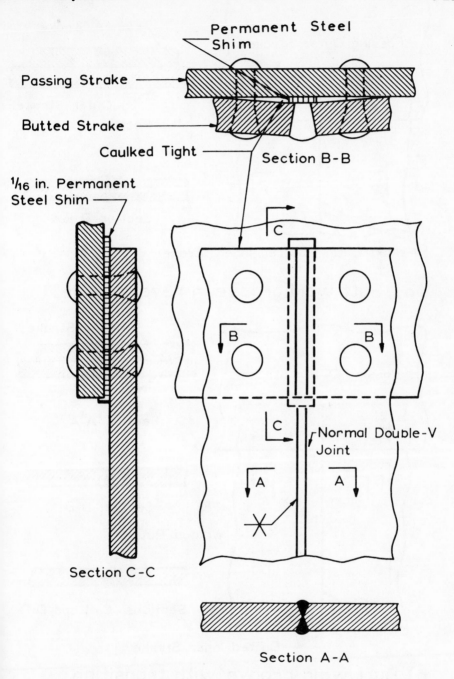

FIG. 5-26. Welded butt at riveted seams. Permanent steel shim inserted between strakes. (Ref. 21)

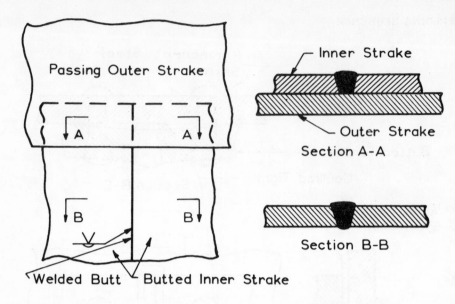

a) Butt weld groove in reverse side.

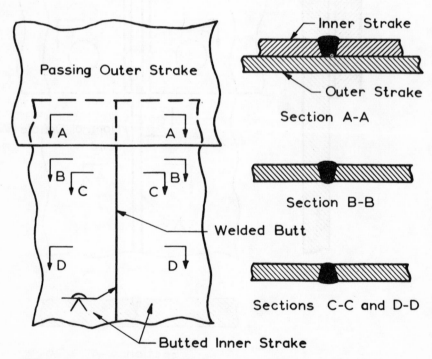

b) Butt weld groove with transition in way of the lap.

Fig. 5-27. Welded butt in inner strake between two riveted seams.

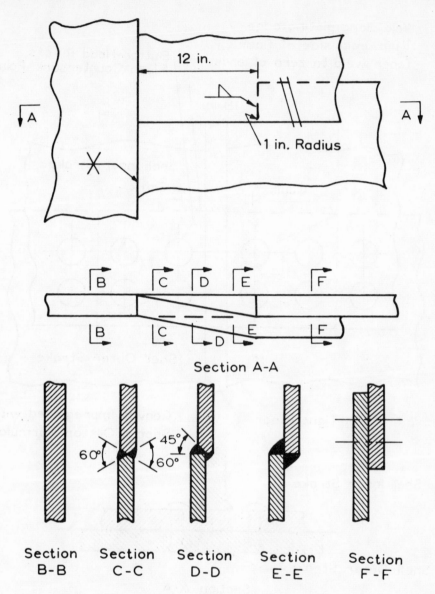

12 in.

A

1 in. Radius

A

B   C   D   E   F

Section A-A

B   C   D   E   F

60°   45°
       60°

Section   Section   Section   Section   Section
B-B   C-C   D-D   E-E   F-F

FIG. 5-28.   Transition of riveted seam to welded seam.

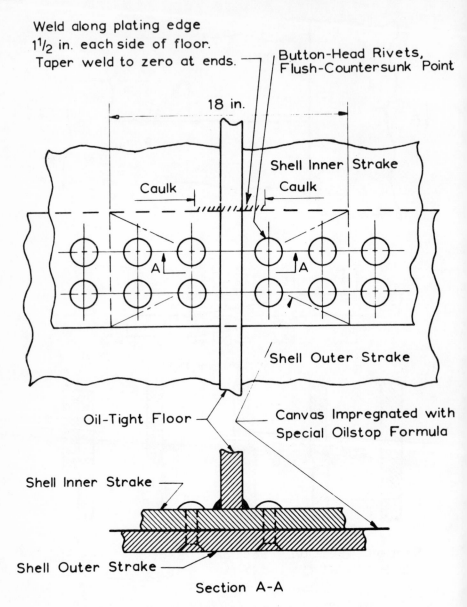

FIG. 5-29. Suggested oil-stop for riveted shell seam.

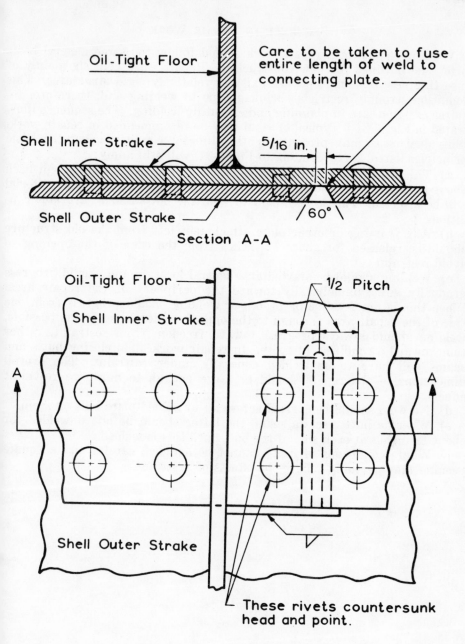

FIG. 5-30. Suggested welded oil-stop for riveted shell seam.

SEQUENCE IN REPAIR WORK

Welding sequence in repair work should follow the same general basic principles outlined for new construction. Repair work consists mainly of inserting new material between existing relatively rigid structures. This condition strongly restricts shrinkage due to welding and, therefore, requires extreme care in planning and executing welding. The sequence illustrated in Fig. 5-31 is typical of what may be recommended in repair work. Individual cases may present slightly different conditions, but the basic principles listed, corresponding to Fig. 5-31, will still apply:

a) The seams in the remaining structure of the ship should be cut back about 12 inches from the periphery of the opening where the new material will be inserted. This is necessary to weld the butts under favorable conditions.

b) Any framing or other plate attachment left from the old structure should be released for about 12 inches from the edge of the opening to avoid restraint.

c) Welding should be started at a central location and should progress gradually and symmetrically toward the periphery of the repair area. When this is not feasible or practical, welding should progress from one side of the repair area through to the opposite side. In so far as possible, welding should always progress toward freedom from restraint, rather than toward a condition of fixity. In repair work, final closing butts and seams will have to be welded generally under restraint. The overall dimensions of the repair should be large enough to minimize restraint effects.

d) No weld should be carried across an unwelded plate butt or seam.

e) Where a butt meets a seam, the latter should be left unwelded for about 12 inches at each side of the butt until this is welded.

f) Where conditions of fixity cannot be avoided, careful and adequate peening may partially relieve the effects of restraint.

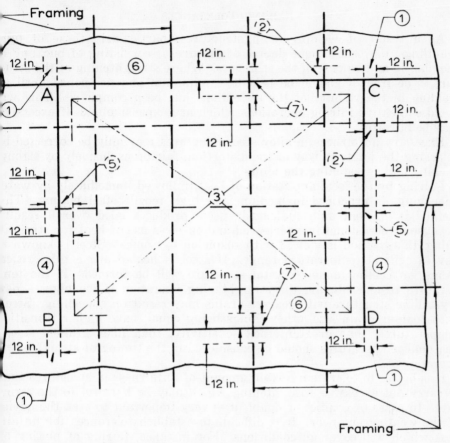

Notes:

  ① Cut back seams in existing material about 12 in. to free the structure for welding of vertical butts.

  ② Release any framing in the existing structure for about 12 in. clear of the opening to minimize restraint. (This operation has been indicated at two spots in the figure.)

  ③ Weld framing to within 12 in. of all unwelded butts and seams.

  ④ Weld vertical butts complete.

  ⑤ Weld unwelded framing in way of vertical butts (weld frame butts first).

  ⑥ Weld horizontal seams.

  ⑦ Weld unwelded framing in way of horizontal seams (weld frame butts first).

Fɪɢ. 5-31.   Typical welding sequence in repair work.

FAIRING TOLERANCES

As a result of welding, ship structures, particularly those of ligh scantlings, may show some degree of unfairness consisting of buckling i the plating and bowing of the stiffeners. Where straightening of the struc ture is desired, it should be held to a minimum and postponed until a welding in the vicinity of the distortions has been completed. This wi avoid successive fairing operations which are expensive and, if excessive may be harmful.

Excessive unfairness in alloy steel structures may only be corrected b releasing the joints in way of the distortion, fairing exclusively by strong backing and refastening the joints.

Fairing by the local application of heat, followed immediately by wate quenching, is practiced in medium and high tensile steel plating. Thi method is efficient and, judiciously used, produces good overall results Because of occasional inexperienced and careless use of heat for straight ening, this method is viewed with suspicion by some. (Steel is known t have a critical temperature range. If steel is heated above this critica range, on cooling a new crystal structure will be formed. If the tem perature reached during the straightening operation is too high, a ne crystalline structure with coarser grains may result on quenching. Stee with coarser grain size, other things being equal, have higher transitio temperatures, thus greater crack sensitivity, than finer grained steel. Seasonal temperatures should be considered in the timing of straightenin operations.

It is better to tolerate a certain amount of unfairness in structures than to carry out excessive straightening which may be harmful to the struc ture. In cases of conflict or doubt, it is very important to seek the advic of the welding engineer. It is difficult to establish tolerances for unfair ness which will cover all conditions. For instance, fairing of plating o decks which are to be covered with an underlay under deck covering, an of bulkheads which are to be lined with metal, insulation or plastic board may be relaxed. Judgment is necessary in cutting and rewelding unfai structure, as such repairs do not necessarily increase soundness thoug they will improve appearance. In many cases the requirements reflect th preferences of one individual who may be the inspector, supervisor o shipowner.

SUMMARY

The order of events in the welding of structures is a very importan factor in the soundness and reliability of ships. A properly determine order, called welding sequence, should minimize shrinkage stresses an harmful distortion. To achieve these objectives, each successive welde part should be allowed maximum freedom to move during welding an subsequent cooling throughout the joining operation.

In general, the two following basic principles should be observed:

a) Start welding from a central position and progress symmetricall in all directions relative to the starting point.

b) Weld first those joints which will tend to contract most, or weld firs attachments which will not restrain points of maximum contraction.

Each individual joint should be successively welded following a specific welding sequence. This may vary depending on the type, location and cross-section of the joint. Pages 5-3—5-6 give information and include illustrations of the most common welding sequences used in welded joints.

The most important principle of welding sequences on a plated structure is always to avoid making any weld across an unwelded plate joint in adjoining members. This and other basic principles in the welding of plated structures are explained and illustrated on pages 5-6—5-8.

Nearly all ship structures are a combination of plating and reinforcing attached members, such as frames, stiffeners, girders, bulkheads, etc. These attachments complicate welding sequences, since their joining to the plating and to each other must be considered. This problem is analyzed and elucidated with the help of several figures on pages 5-9—5-11.

Welding sequence in subassemblies is discussed and illustrated on pages 5-11–5-12. Different alternatives for the welded fabrication of subassemblies are also analyzed.

Pages 5-12–5-17 deal with the overall welding sequence in ship construction. This sequence considers the effect of welding in the three dimensions of the ship.

Composite riveted and welded joints in a welded structure present special problems due to difference in load carrying capacity across the joint. This could result in undersize welds taking the major share of the load and lead to failure. Such joints should be avoided. In addition, wherever tightness is important, great care should be taken in the design and fabrication of adjacent riveted and welded structural details. Welding adjacent to driven rivets will develop unsoundness in such riveting. Several riveted seams are used in most welded ships to serve as crack arrestors. Problems related to the combination of riveting and welding are analyzed and illustrated on pages 5-18–5-29.

The effect of shrinkage may be particularly harmful in repair work. This is especially true when new material has to be inserted between relatively rigid existing material in the structure. Welding sequence principles for welded repair work are presented and illustrated on pages 5-30—5-31.

Since shrinkage in welding will result in a certain amount of distortion in the structures, this problem is discussed on page 5-32.

SECTION VI

Various Details
in Ship Steel Structures

INTRODUCTION

The intent of this section is to discuss several details, not considered elsewhere in this publication, which are known to have caused failures in ship structures.

In discussing these failures, the practical reasons for their occurrence are given. In general these reasons will be recognized as consistent with those presented in previous sections in greater detail. Aside from steel sensitivity, operating temperature, and cyclic stressing, the cracking failures dealt with in this section result from the presence of notches, stress concentration and the necessary magnitude of localized three-dimensional tension stress at the detail. Recommended good practices which might avoid such failures are presented also.

In general, the following practices are emphasized:

a) Avoid *hard spots** in highly stressed members.

b) Since stress concentration is unavoidable in discontinuous connections, provide the means to reduce this effect and eliminate notches by the use of generous fairing radii, doublers, etc., where stress concentration may be critical.

c) Provide for easy, smooth flow of stresses from one member to another, avoiding discontinuous or tortuous paths.

d) Avoid attachments to highly stressed members where the geometry may introduce notches or defects conducive to possibility of failure.

e) Reduce the congestion of welds, especially in highly stressed members and in areas of stress concentration. These lead to an accumulation of shrinkage stresses and overlapping of heat-affected zones in stress fields which may already be high and sometimes complex.

---

* A hard spot is a region of localized rigidity in a structural member otherwise flexible or less rigid.

6-1

Some general structural details which are commonly accepted as satisfactory are illustrated and explained.

LONGITUDINALS AT INTERSECTIONS

In Section I, it was mentioned that the longitudinal framing acts generally as members fully effective in longitudinal strength; for this reason it is necesary that their continuity be ensured, particularly for 40 per cent to 60 per cent of the ship's length amidships. This continuity requirement is extremely important for deck and bottom longitudinals because their contribution to the section modulus of the hull girder is substantial. To obtain continuity the connection of longitudinals to transverse bulkheads is a structural detail that has to be designed properly and executed carefully.

In the past, the structural detail of the attachment of the longitudinals to the transverse bulkheads has been the source of considerable trouble for designers, builders and operators. Tankers in particular have been plagued with these difficulties due to adoption of details simple for fabrication but complex relative to notches (and state of stress). This condition resulted in structures susceptible to break-up when primary structural notches, such as butt weld voids, initiated a crack in way of transverse bulkheads.

With the introduction of welding in tanker construction, a connection between transverse bulkheads and longitudinals was sought, having continuous member through the bulkhead with the following characteristics:

a) Sufficient cross-sectional area to preserve longitudinal strength.

b) Proper shape to avoid excessive interference with the normal flexibility of the bulkhead.

Figure 6-1 shows a connection between a transverse bulkhead and a longitudinal as used in the original design of the T2 tanker. It consisted of heavy plate bracket extending continuously through the bulkhead, the cross sectional area of the plate being equal to that of the longitudinal. The length of the faying surface between the bracket and the longitudinal allowed a sufficient amount of welding to develop the full strength of the latter. This type of connection involved secondary notches* where the longitudinals ended abruptly, such as points H in Fig. 6-1. In addition, the working of the plating flexing with the ship in a seaway produced, at times, a fatigue crack due to weld undercutting at the longitudinal discontinuity. Since the weld undercutting occurs in the weld heat-affected zone, a primary crack may be developed in the bottom plating which undergoes severe stresses in a tanker. Such a crack would lead to a major tanker failure comparable to one originating in a defective butt weld adjacent to transverse bulkheads.

---

* A secondary notch is a notch not in a single plate plane. While generally not conducive to crack initiation, such a notch will become a primary notch leading to vessel failure under certain conditions, such as: if a crack occurs in an adjacent defective butt weld which initiates it, then, due to stress concentration and dynamic effect, the secondary notch will initiate additional cracks in the locality. Thus, local crack arrest protection is nullified, since under such circumstances, the seam, while able to stop initial cracking, is unable to stop additional cracks originating at secondary notches beyond the seam.

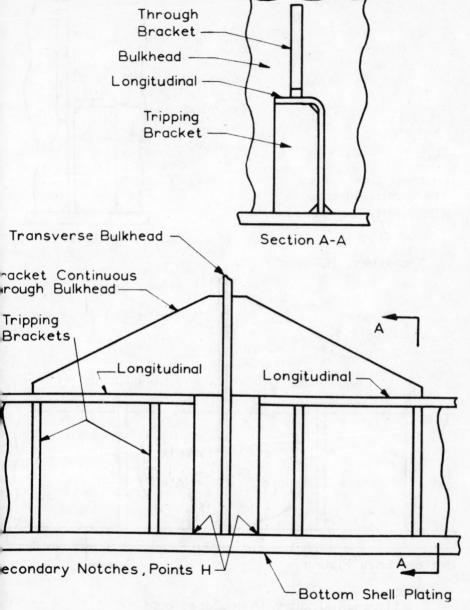

FIG. 6-1.   Connection between a transverse bulkhead and longitudinals
in the original T2 tanker design.

To spread the load over a larger area and avoid discontinuity notch
fect, the ends of the longitudinals are scalloped in the modified connection
esign of Figs. 6-2 and 6-3. This modification increases *energy absorption*
*fracture** by tenfold over the unscalloped detail. This type of scalloped

---

* The energy absorption to fracture is the amount of work input necessary to produce
acture in a structure.

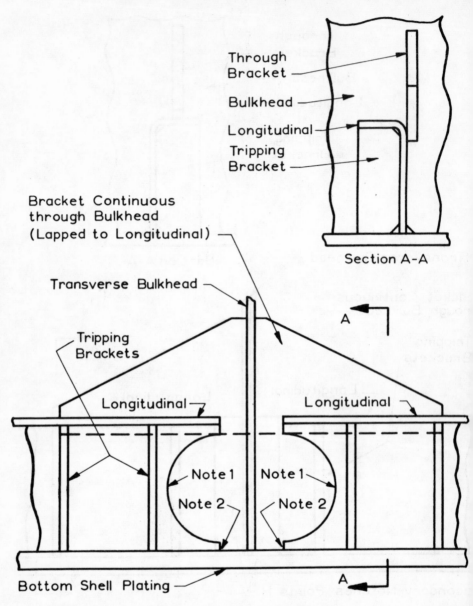

Through Bracket

Bulkhead

Longitudinal

Tripping Bracket

Section A-A

Bracket Continuous through Bulkhead (Lapped to Longitudinal)

Transverse Bulkhead

Tripping Brackets

A

Longitudinal

Longitudinal

Note 1   Note 1

Note 2   Note 2

A

Bottom Shell Plating

Notes:
1.) Longitudinals with scalloped ends.
2.) Stress at these points relieved because of scalloped ends.
3) The lap welded connection requires an exactness of alignment of longitudinals which sometimes is difficult to obtain.

FIG. 6-2.   Connection between a transverse bulkhead and longitudinal with scalloped ends. Lapped bracket.

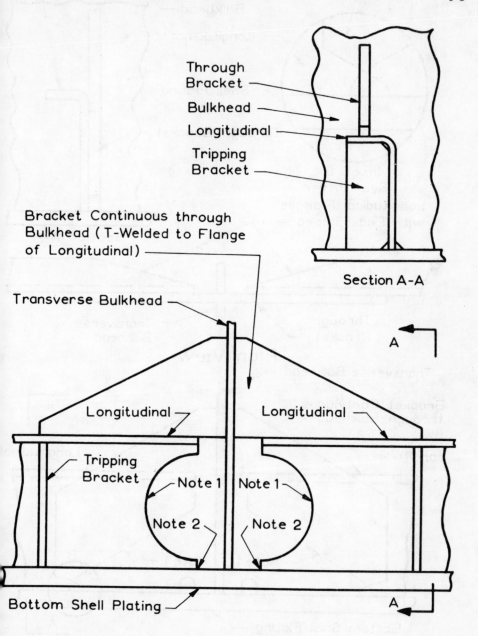

Through Bracket

Bulkhead

Longitudinal

Tripping Bracket

Bracket Continuous through Bulkhead (T-Welded to Flange of Longitudinal)

Section A-A

Transverse Bulkhead

A

Longitudinal

Longitudinal

Tripping Bracket

Note 1

Note 1

Note 2

Note 2

Bottom Shell Plating

A

Notes:
1.) Longitudinals with scalloped ends.
2.) Stress at these points relieved because of scalloped ends.

FIG. 6-3.   Connection between a transverse bulkhead and longitudinal with scalloped ends. Bracket T-welded to flange of longitudinal.

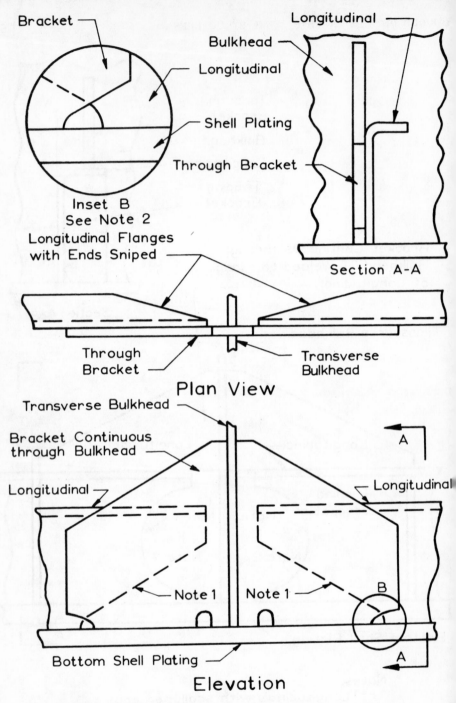

Inset B
See Note 2

Section A-A

Plan View

Elevation

Notes:
  1) Longitudinal web sniped at ends.

  2) Inset B shows an alternative used
     sometimes in this type of connection.

FIG. 6-4. Connection of longitudinal to transverse bulkhead with trough bracket
lapped to longitudinal with snipped ends.

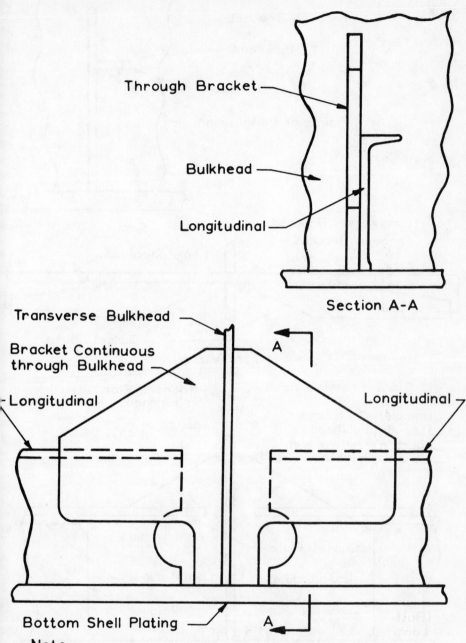

Through Bracket

Bulkhead

Longitudinal

Section A-A

Transverse Bulkhead

Bracket Continuous
through Bulkhead

Longitudinal

Longitudinal

A

A

Bottom Shell Plating

Note:
   To avoid secondary notches, the longitudinal has
   scalloped ends and the through bracket has
   reduced rigidity at the connection with the shell
   plating.

FIG. 6-5.   Connection of longitudinal to transverse bulkhead with through bracket
            lapped to longitudinal with scalloped ends.

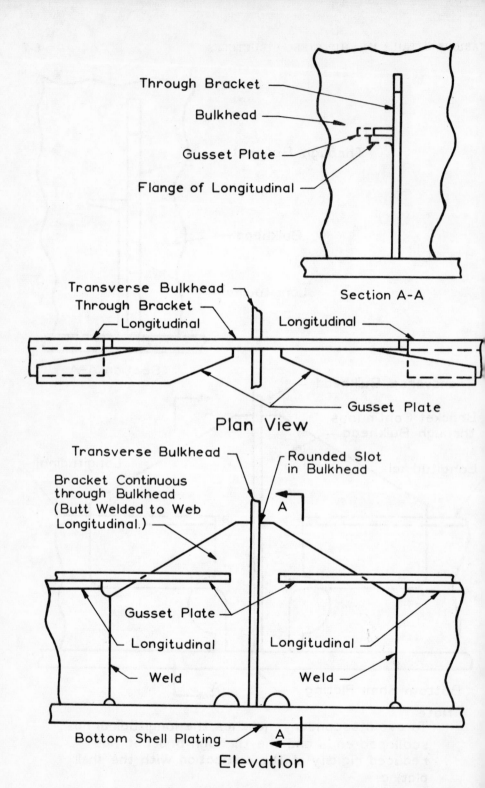

FIG. 6-6. Connection of longitudinal to transverse bulkhead with through bracket butt welded to web longitudinal.

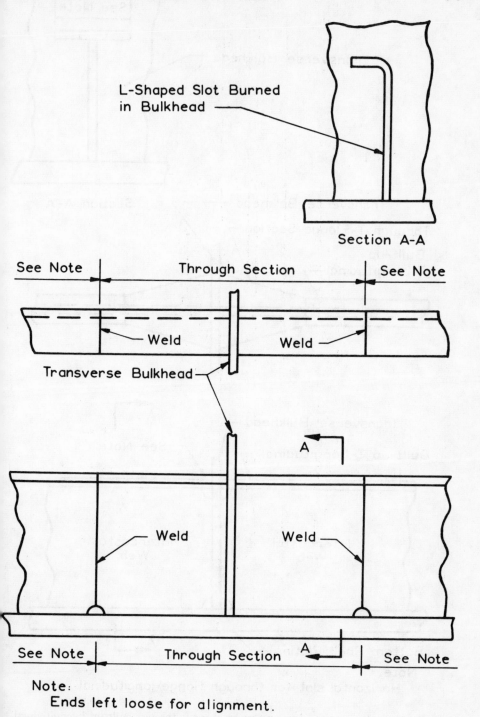

Section A-A

Note:
Ends left loose for alignment.

FIG. 6-7. Connection of transverse bulkhead and through L-shaped longitudinal.

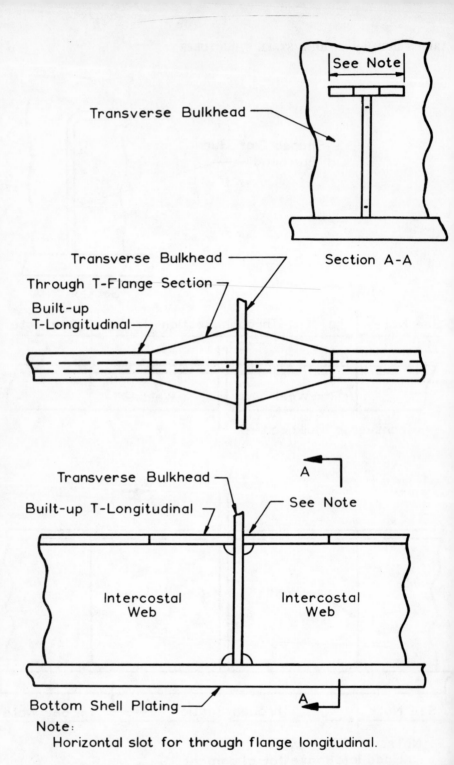

FIG. 6-8. Connection of transverse bulkhead to through built-up T-longitudinal.

6-10

connection has performed satisfactorily in limited service. The heavy plate continuous bracket through the bulkhead is essentially the same as that of Fig. 6-1. This bracket may be lapped to the web of the longitudinal, Fig. 6-2, or T-welded to its flange, Fig. 6-3.

Probably there is more variety in the connection of longitudinals to transverse bulkheads than in any other structural detail in welded ships. Other modern satisfactory connections of longitudinals to a transverse bulkhead are illustrated in Figs. 6-4 through 6-8. Figures 6-4 and 6-5 show two connections with lapped-through bracket which are relatively simple

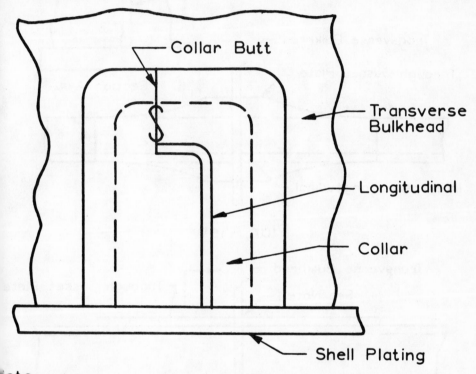

FIG. 6-9.   Collar plates at the intersection of longitudinal with transverse bulkhead.

to fit. Figure 6-6, which is a connection with butted-through bracket, requires careful fitting at the butt joint of the web of the longitudinal. In Figs. 6-7 and 6-8, two connections are shown where the longitudinals are carried through the transverse bulkhead to obtain more satisfactory continuity. The connections of Figs. 6-7 and 6-8 have been proposed or used in large tankers. The substantial size of the longitudinals permits acceptable access for welding all around at their intersection with the transverse bulkhead. These connections require either a closely fitted slot in the bulkhead with the bulkhead plating welded directly to the longitudinal all

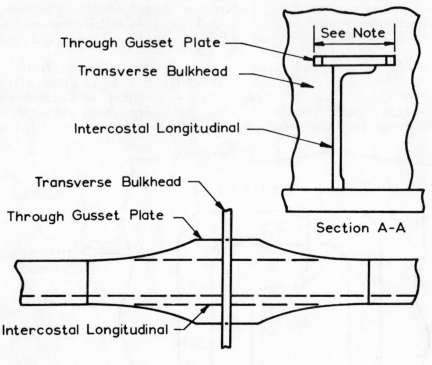

Through Gusset Plate

Transverse Bulkhead

Intercostal Longitudinal

Section A-A

Transverse Bulkhead

Through Gusset Plate

Intercostal Longitudinal

Plan View

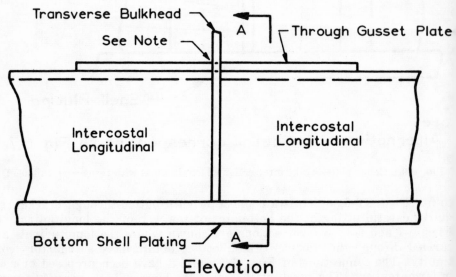

Transverse Bulkhead

See Note

Through Gusset Plate

Intercostal
Longitudinal

Intercostal
Longitudinal

Bottom Shell Plating

Elevation

Note:
Horizontal slot for through gusset plate.

FIG. 6-10.   Connection of intercostal longitudinals to transverse bulkhead.

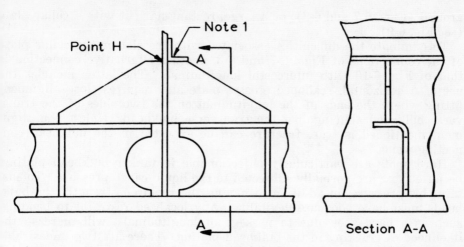

a) Continuous angle to lessen hard spot effect.

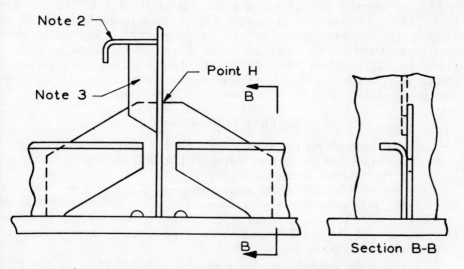

b) Chock to lessen hard spot effect.

Notes:
1) Continuous angle attached to the bulkhead at the top of the through bracket to lessen the effect of hard spot at point H.

2) Lowest horizontal stiffener on bulkhead.

3) Chock lapped to through bracket reduces effect of hard spot at point H.

Fig. 6-11. Ways to minimize hard spots at the intersection of longitudinals with a transverse bulkhead.

around (Figs. 6-7 and 6-8), or a large, rectangular cut with a collar plate (*see* Fig. 6-9).

To eliminate the difficulties associated with the slot or the collar plate of the connections of Figs. 6-7 and 6-8, another alternative connection is that of Fig. 6-10 with intercostal longitudinals. The latter includes the use of a horizontal, scalloped, gusset plate and requires close alignment fitting where the ends of the longitudinal on the two sides of the transverse bulkhead abut against the transverse bulkhead. Unless the alignment mentioned is true, fracture can be expected in the bulkhead connecting welds.

Hard spots are particularly objectionable in tanker bulkhead plating because these are normally subjected to the liquid cargo pressure. To sustain this pressure, in addition to having the required strength, the bulkheads must have adequate flexibility. Any localized restraint to bending such as a hard spot, due to passage of longitudinals, will increase the likelihood of cracking in the bulkhead plating. There are two undesirable consequences of cracking in bulkheads, namely, cargo contamination and an increased possibility of further bulkhead failure. Figure 6-11 shows hard spots formed in transverse bulkheads at the top of the through heavy, plate brackets used to connect longitudinals through the bulkheads (points H). To lessen the effect of these hard spots, a continuous angle may be attached to the bulkhead at the top of the through bracket, as shown in Fig. 6-11(a), or a chock, consisting of a flat plate lapped to the through bracket and abutted against the lowest horizontal stiffener may be fitted to the bulkhead, as shown in Fig. 6-11(b).

BRACKET CONNECTIONS

Bracketed connections are used a great deal in ship structures.

A typical bracketed connection is that of Fig. 6-12 between a frame and beam in a transversely framed ship.

Tests carried out with a full-scale specimen of a structure similar to that of Fig. 6-12 have indicated a substantial stress concentration factor at points P. The measured stress at that location, both for the flanges of the framing and the bracket, was about three times as large as the corresponding calculated value. (Ref. 24.)

To evaluate the influence of the geometry at a corner joint, the three shapes shown in Fig. 6-13 were tested using the photoelasticity method (Ref. 24.) The model having the two legs intersecting at 90°, Fig. 6-13(b) showed a maximum stress concentration factor of approximately two and two-thirds at the inside corner. The maximum stress concentration factor for a model with a 45° knee, Fig. 6-13(a), was approximately one and two-thirds at the toes of the knee. The model with a circular knee, Fig 6-13(c), did not show any appreciable stress concentration. These models were made of flat plate, and therefore the tests do not represent conditions actually found in ship structures. However, the test results indicate the relative merits of the three shapes illustrated with respect to stress concentration.

The flanged, circular, portal knee of Fig. 6-14 showed, in tests, a stress concentration factor of only one and one-third at the flange, with reference to the stress measured in the straight portion of the inner flange (such as points A). (Ref. 24.)

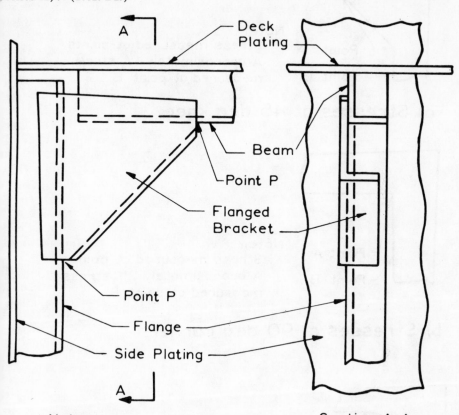

Note: Section A-A
   Stresses measured in tests with a full-scale
   specimen in both the flanges of the framing
   and the bracket at points P equal to about
   three times the corresponding calculated
   value.

FIG. 6-12.   Typical frame and beam bracketed connection. (Ref. 24)

The fact that a flanged, circular, portal knee reduces the stress concentration at the corner joint to a practically negligible value is generally well known by those concerned with the design and construction of ships. There are other factors, such as ease of construction and lower cost, however, which make the typical triangular bracket the preferred choice for most connections between two structural members intersecting at 90°, such as frames and beams.

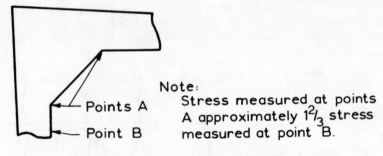

Note:
Stress measured at points
A approximately $1\frac{2}{3}$ stress
measured at point B.

a) Stresses at 45 deg. knee.

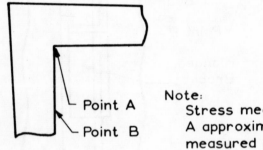

Note:
Stress measured at point
A approximately $2\frac{2}{3}$ stress
measured at point B.

b) Stresses at 90 deg. corner.

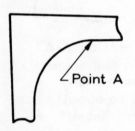

Note:
Stresses at circular knee
not greater than stress at
other points such as point A.

c) Stresses at circular knee.

General Note:
Stresses measured photoelastically at the joint
of two structural members at an angle of 90
deg. with each other.

FIG. 6-13. Geometry and stresses at a corner joint. (Ref. 24)

The stress concentration factor associated with bracketed structural connections has been reviewed. It is obvious that this factor should be kept low if stresses are to be kept within reasonable limits. A more important consideration in the detail design of brackets, however, is that of avoiding *hard spots*. If a relatively rigid bracket is attached to a low-rigidity member, a hard spot is formed wherever they come together at a sharp-cornered intersection. This situation may become serious if the bracketed structure is heavily loaded, as the hard spot is a potential source of fracture.

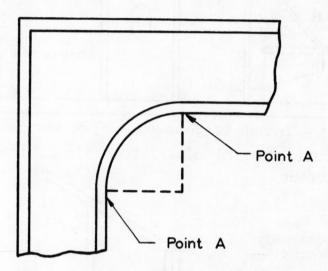

Note:
Maximum stress measured on flange of circular knee approximately equal to $1\frac{1}{3}$ stress measured at points such as A.

FIG. 6-14.   Flanged circular portal knee.   (Ref. 24)

Figure 6-15 illustrates a bracket detail which caused cracks in longitudinals in T2 tankers. This bracket was used to connect the end of a bottom longitudinal with the web of stiffeners on transverse bulkheads. A hard spot was obtained at point H of Fig. 6-15(a) which led to the fracture at the toe of the bracket. This situation was corrected by scalloping the bracket, as shown in Fig. 6-15(b), called a "soft toe" effect.

A hard spot is illustrated in point H of Fig. 6-16(a) where the toe of a large tripping bracket intersects the bulkhead plating. This may lead to fracture of the plating, especially if the bulkhead is frequently under heavy pressure loading as in the case of tankers. Figure 6-16(b) indicates how the detail may be improved by inserting a scalloped or tapered tee bar to distribute the load over a larger area. An alternative solution is shown in Fig. 6-16(c) where a continuous header is used to distribute the load in the bulkhead plating.

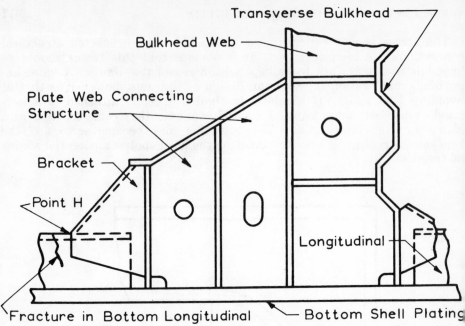

a) Arrangement of bottom structure of T2 tanker.

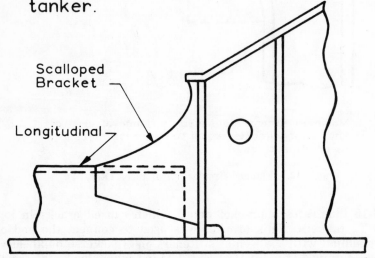

b) Same as a) but with scalloped bracket.

Note:
   The hard spot at point H which led to the fracture in the longitudinal shown in (a) can be minimized by scalloping the bracket as illustrated in (b).

FIG. 6-15.   Hard spot at a bracketed connection of a longitudinal. (Ref. 25)

6-18

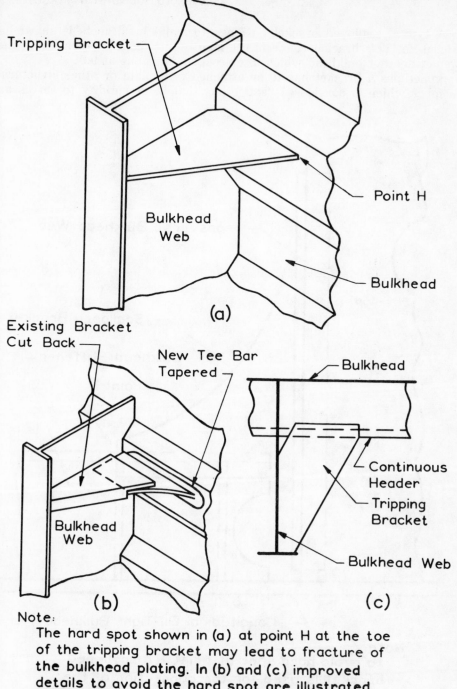

Note:
The hard spot shown in (a) at point H at the toe of the tripping bracket may lead to fracture of the bulkhead plating. In (b) and (c) improved details to avoid the hard spot are illustrated. Both details consist in increasing locally the rigidity of the soft member (in this case the bulkhead plating).

FIG. 6-16.   Tripping bracket causing a hard spot.   (Ref. 26)

A typical scalloped bracket designed to avoid hard spots is shown in Fig. 6-17. This bracket connects the longitudinal of a bulkhead with the web of another bulkhead which intersects the first one at 90°.

Sometimes a bracket has to be attached to a plate or other structural member which is considered "soft", i.e., that lacks rigidity to act as an

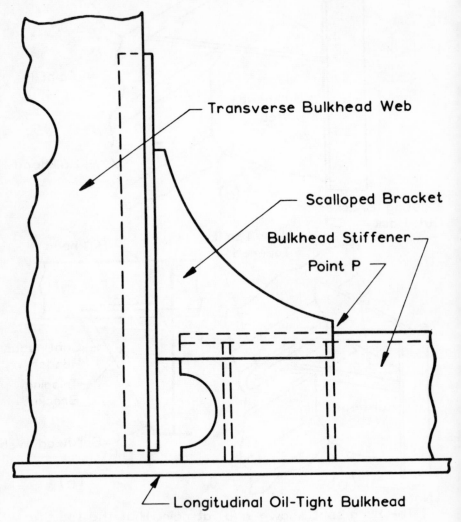

Transverse Bulkhead Web

Scalloped Bracket

Bulkhead Stiffener

Point P

Longitudinal Oil-Tight Bulkhead

Note:
To avoid hard spot at point P a scalloped bracket is used for the connection of the stiffener of the longitudinal bulkhead to the web of the transverse bulkhead.

FIG. 6-17.   Typical scalloped bracket to avoid hard spots.

adequate support. In such a case, if the bracket has a flange, this should not be welded to the connecting member as, otherwise, a hard spot will result in the soft structure. When a substantial load is applied to the structure, as the ship works at sea, cracks may develop at the junction. If the bracket flange is to be welded to the soft structure, the flange should

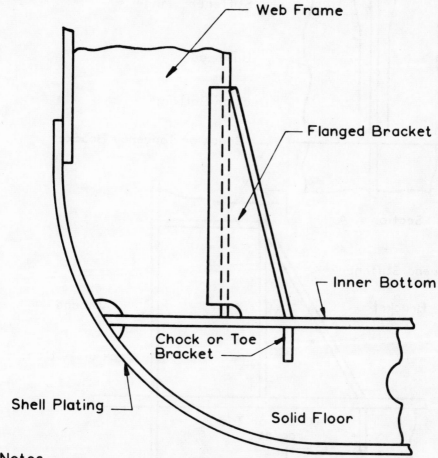

Web Frame

Flanged Bracket

Inner Bottom

Chock or Toe Bracket

Shell Plating

Solid Floor

Notes:
1) A chock is located under the toe of the bracket to avoid a hard spot in the inner bottom plating where the bracket flange is welded to it.

2) The flange should not be welded to the inner bottom unless a chock is used. If no chock is used then the bracket flange should be sniped clear of the plating to avoid a hard spot.

FIG. 6-18.   Typical chock at the toe of a bracket to avoid hard spots.

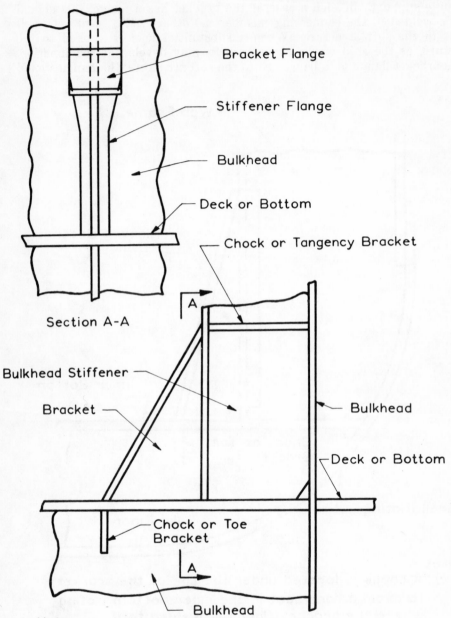

Bracket Flange

Stiffener Flange

Bulkhead

Deck or Bottom

Chock or Tangency Bracket

Section A-A

Bulkhead Stiffener

Bracket

Bulkhead

Deck or Bottom

A

Chock or Toe Bracket

A

Bulkhead

Note:
The chocks shown in the figure are used to back up the bracket flange and avoid hard spots in the plating.

FIG. 6-19. Typical detail for stiffener bracket in a warship.

be backed up by a chock or toe bracket, as shown in Fig. 6-18. This figure illustrates the bracketed connection between a web frame and the inner bottom of a merchant ship.

Chocks or toe brackets are frequently used in bracketed structures of warships. This is necessary because these structures are generally heavily loaded in seeking minimum scantlings. Figure 6-19 shows a typical detail for a stiffener bracket in a warship.

TROUBLESOME INTERSECTIONS

The point at which two or more structural members intersect generally requires special attention, as it is a potential source of trouble in ship structures. These intersecting members may be coplanar or in different planes.

When one of the intersecting members is loaded, it deflects, and the intersecting member (due to attachment) must be able to deflect if trouble is to be avoided. It is important that the deflection and concurrent stressing of the intersecting member take place in a smooth, continuous, uniform manner. When this process is interrupted by local points of rigidity, local notches and their stress concentrations can be effective and the resultant condition may be one leading to failure. The effect of these local points or *hard spots* may be minimized by proper detail design and construction.

Unless design care is observed, cracks may develop in plating, stiffeners or welding joints at or in the vicinity of the intersections.

The intersection of the corrugated bulkheads in tankers requires careful detail design and construction. To simplify construction, the longitudinal corrugated bulkheads of the T2 tankers were cut off square and a built-up I-section (cruciform) was inserted to carry the longitudinal bulkhead across the transverse bulkhead. The interrupted, corrugated, longitudinal bulkhead was welded to the flanges of the I-section, while the transverse bulkhead landed at and was welded to the web of this section. This type of construction is illustrated in Fig. 6-20.

The objectionable feature of the structure shown in Fig. 6-20 is that none of the material of the longitudinal bulkhead lines up with the web of the built-up I-section, except for a small area where the diagonal part of the corrugated plate crosses the web (points P in Fig. 6-20). As a consequence, there is a tendency for the longitudinal stresses carried by the fore and aft bulkhead to "crowd" through the common point P at the crossing. This lack of continuity has resulted in frequent cracking at that point. To ease this situation, structures of this type have been fitted with a pair of "bridging" brackets at the point where the objectionable stress concentration was attained. These brackets, shown in Fig. 6-20, somewhat improve continuity at this critical location. Full-scale structural tests have shown that the load concentration at points P is practically eliminated by means of the bridging brackets.

Figure 6-21(a) illustrates a hard spot, point H developed at the intersection of plated, structural, longitudinally-discontinuous members. When the ship is stressed in a seaway, the contiguous members tend to move slightly with respect to each other. Relative motion between the parts is

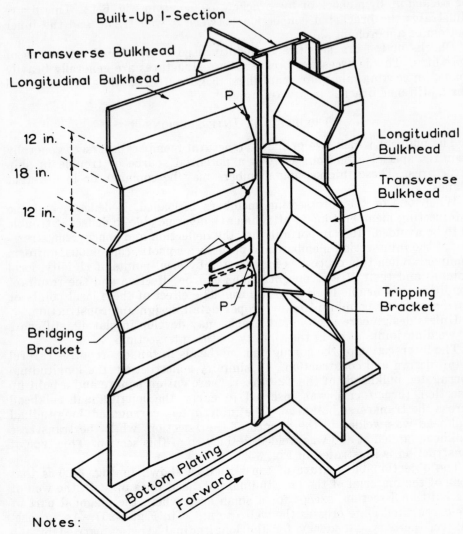

Notes:

1) This is an example of faulty design originated by the desire to simplify construction without due regard for the need of preserving longitudinal continuity at the intersection.

2) Bridging brackets used to ease stress concentration at points P resulting from discontinuity of the longitudinal material. To simplify the drawing only one pair of brackets is shown in the figure.

FIG. 6-20.   Bulkhead intersection of T2 tanker.

prevented at point H due to single point attachment between longitudinal bulkhead and the deck. This point attempts to establish stress continuity between the two members and this can lead to almost immediate failure. As a result, cracks may develop, as illustrated in Fig. 6-21(a). To improve this situation, a pair of brackets, as shown in Fig. 6-21(b), may be used.

VARIOUS CRITICAL VESSEL DETAILS
(not previously covered in text)

1) *Bilge Keels.* Unsatisfactory details in bilge keels have led to many fractures in bilge strakes. Since the bilge strake is a primary hull girder component, special care is required in the detail design and construction of bilge keels.

The depth of the bilge keels is limited by docking considerations. They are designed so their farthest point from the hull envelope in a transverse plane is at a safe distance from the corner determined by the vertical line of the ship's side and deadrise line extended, as shown in Fig. 6-22. Since, in spite of this precaution, occasionally bilge keels are damaged, it is desirable to design them so they will tear from the ship without causing undue harm to the hull envelope.

If the bilge keel ends in a notch discontinuity as in Fig. 6-23(a), a major crack may start at this point as a result of the notch, the stress concentration and the relatively large bending stresses in the vicinity. This condition is corrected by providing a long tapered ending of the bilge keel which lands on a local doubler over a web frame, as illustrated in Fig. 6-23(b). This arrangement eliminates the notch effect, minimizes stress concentration and provides adequate support for the bilge keel ending. Narrow bilge keels, about 18 in. and below, usually consist of a single plate, as shown in Figs. 6-24(a) and 6-24(b). Deeper bilge keels, up to about 4 ft are built up of two plates, as shown in Fig. 6-24(c). Both in riveted and welded construction, the attachment to the hull envelope is so designed that in case of damage the bilge keel may be torn away with minimum injury to the shell plating.

Riveted construction requires an angle to connect the bilge keel to the shell plating, as shown in Fig. 6-24. The practice mentioned above is easily complied with by making the riveted joint between the angle and the shell plating substantially stronger than the riveted joint between the angle and the bilge keel (so the rivets in the shell are not loosened, resulting in leakage).

Figure 6-25 shows a detail of the attachment to the shell plating of a single-plate, welded, bilge keel. The serrated connection results in a relatively weak attachment to the shell plating.

2) *Ends of Deckhouses and Superstructures.* As explained in Section I, the ends of long deckhouses and superstructures require special consideration because they involve stress concentration and undesirable lateral loading in a high stress field. The classification societies require that the thickness of the stringer plate and sheer strake be substantially increased at the ends of these erections due to the severe stress condition involved.

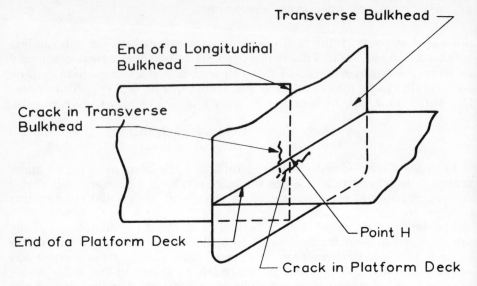

a) Hard spot H at intersection.

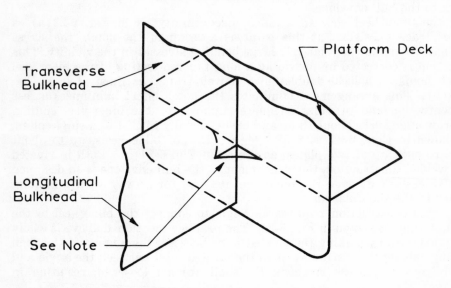

b) Intersection brackets to avoid hard spot.

Note:
To ease hard spot a pair of brackets attached to longitudinal bulkhead in the plane of the platform may be used, as shown above, or a pair of brackets located in the plane of the longitudinal bulkhead may be attached to platform deck.

FIG. 6-21. Intersection of structural members at a point. (Ref. 21)

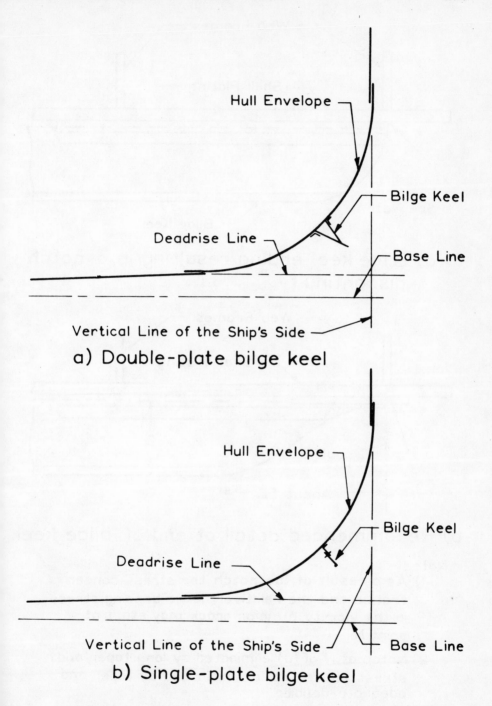

Hull Envelope

Bilge Keel

Deadrise Line

Base Line

Vertical Line of the Ship's Side

a) Double-plate bilge keel

Hull Envelope

Bilge Keel

Deadrise Line

Vertical Line of the Ship's Side

Base Line

b) Single-plate bilge keel

FIG. 6-22.   Location of bilge keels relative to hull envelope.

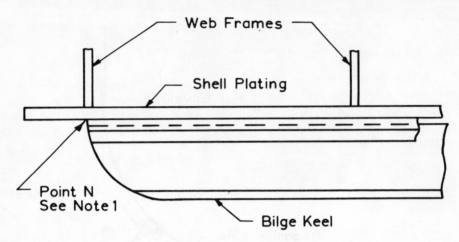

a) Bilge keel ending resulting in a notch discontinuity.

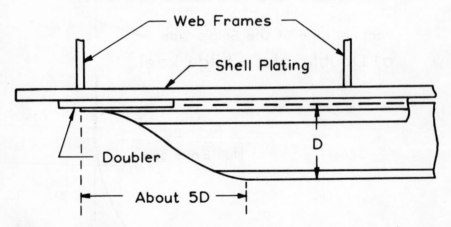

b) Recommended detail at end of bilge keel.

Notes:

1) As a result of the notch, the stress concentration and the relatively large bending stress in the vicinity, a major crack may start at point **N**.

2) Notch at N of (a) eliminated by long taper, and stress concentration minimized by taper and adequate doubler.

FIG. 6-23. Welded bilge keel ending.

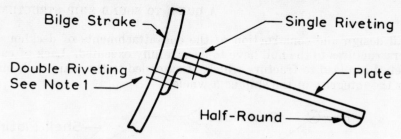

a) Single-plate riveted construction

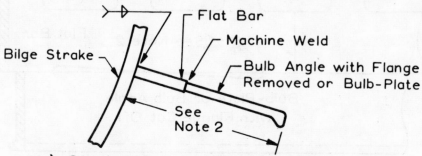

b) Single-plate welded construction

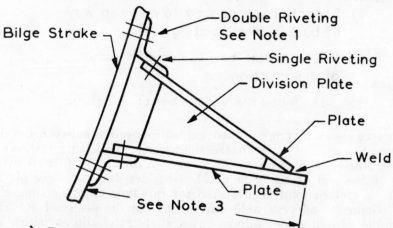

c) Double-plate combined riveted and welded construction

Notes:

1) This riveted joint made stronger than the riveted joint between the angle and the bilge keel to minimize injury to the shell plating if the bilge keel is torn away accidentally.

2) Depth 10 to 18 in. according to size of ship.

3) Depth up to 4 ft according to size of ship.

FIG. 6-24. Types of bilge keels.

The detail design and construction of the end attachments of deckhouses and superstructures to the hull have to be carefully executed. Lack of care in this detail can lead to fracture which, if extended to the main hull, may endanger the integrity of the ship as a whole.

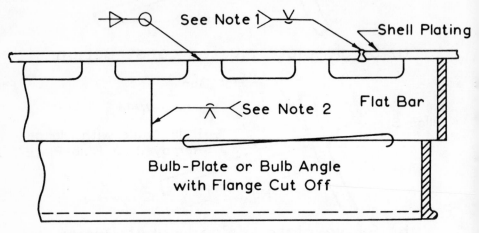

Notes:
   1) Serrations arranged to come in way of butt in shell plating.

   2) Butts in flat bar to come in way of a serration.

FIG. 6-25.   Welded bilge keel attachment to shell plating.

Figure 6-26 shows a recommended welded connection between the deck plating and the ends of a deckhouse sides. This arrangement allows an alleviating stress distribution at the sudden discontinuity formed by the junction of the end of the long deckhouse sides and the deck plating. Frequently a riveted joint is preferred for this type of connection, since riveting eliminates adverse weld effects and can be designed for rivet failure in lieu of hull girder failure. Also, slight rivet slip at critical end regions of house side plating allows some attenuation of stress concentration resulting in structural benefit without failure.

The connection of the end of a superstructure to the side plating requires special attention to detail, especially in the case of welded construction. Figure 6-27 shows a recommended design for this connection. Extra care should be exercised in avoiding any notches in free plate edges in the vicinity of this junction. Furthermore, the point of tangency of the superstructure side plating and sheer strake should be ground smooth, as indicated in Fig. 6-27.

3) *Sheer Strake.* The sheer strake is an important component of the main ship girder and is a highly stressed structural member. Extreme care should be exercised to avoid any notch, opening, or the attachment of any

fitting to this strake, particularly on its free edge. Necessary openings in this strake, such as side ports, should be kept clear of other hull discontinuities, adequately reinforced, and have corners rounded to at least one-eighth the vertical dimension of the opening.

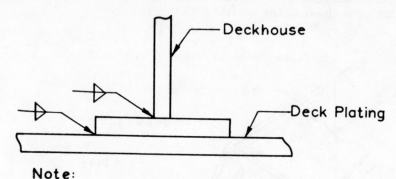

Note:

This is a recommended welded connection between the deck plating and the ends of a deckhouse.

FIG. 6-26.   Deckhouse connection to deck.

Figure 6-28 shows a sheer strake cut with square corners for an accommodation ladder in the early "Liberty" ships. This cut was responsible for a number of major failures. In such existing ships the cut was extended and rounded corners were introduced. No further trouble was experienced as a result of the cut. In later "Liberty" ships the cut was eliminated. Cuts of this type, even with generously radiused corners, should be avoided in the sheer strake.

In ships where the sheer strake is extended above the top of the deck stringer, scuppers are desirable to drain water from the deck. Figure 6-29(b) shows a typical type of deck scupper. Scupper holes in the sheer strake, as illustrated in Fig. 6-29(a), are to be avoided because they involve stress raisers adjacent to a free plate edge, in an already highly stressed member.

The attachment of any unfaired or massive fitting to the sheer strake must be avoided to prevent structural discontinuity and resultant notches susceptible to cracking from being introduced into this highly stressed strake. Figure 6-30 shows two acceptable methods of attaching a welded chock foundation on deck without producing sheer strake or stringer plate notches. (*Note:* When a massive fitting such as a chock foundation is welded direct to the deck, this is sometimes referred to as a *hard spot* in a direct stress field. However, this type of construction and those involving similar features are no longer permitted.)

Figure 6-31 illustrates an actual example of fractured sheer strake and deck stringer caused by the fracture of the defective butt weld in a half-round rubbing piece attached to the sheer strake.

4) *Bulwarks.* In Section I we discussed the properties of the ship when considered as a box girder. It was mentioned that material placed at a great distance from the neutral axis, which contributed to the longitudinal strength of the vessel, is subjected to relatively greater longitudinal stress than material closer to the neutral axis.

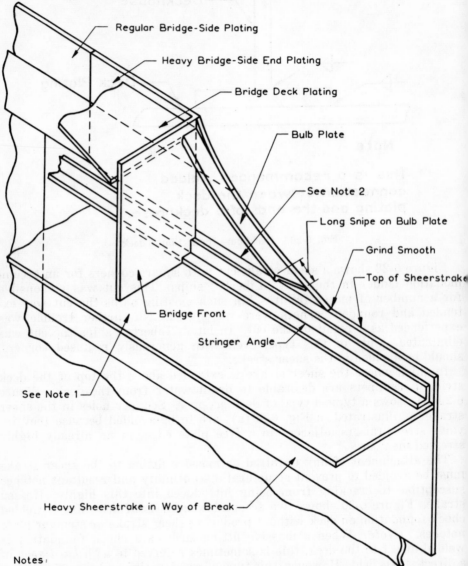

Notes:

1) Upper deck stringer plate thickness increased in way of break.

2) Sometimes this welded seam is stopped clear of the transition region. Also, a riveted connection between the house side plating and sheerstrake is desirable.

FIG. 6-27.   Connection of the end of superstructure to side plating. (Ref. 21)

If members of secondary structural importance which are located at a great distance from the neutral axis, such as the bulwark, are rigidly connected to the ship girder, they become fully effective in longitudinal bending and subject to high stress. This, in conjunction with notches such as defective cap-rail butts, has led to fractures in the bulwark, which have progressed into the hull envelope and resulted in major casualties.

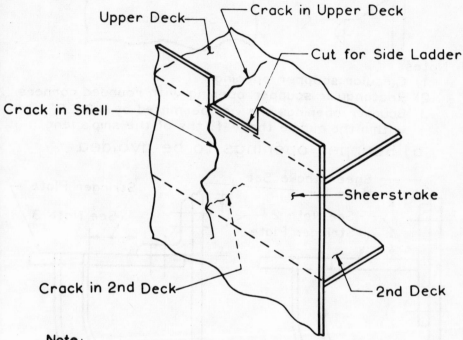

Note:

In the early "Liberty" ships this cut in the sheerstrake was made with square corners. This resulted in a number of major failures. When these corners were rounded and notches eliminated no more trouble was experienced with them. However, such cuts should be eliminated.

Fig. 6-28. Sheer strake cut for accommodation ladder in "Liberty" ships. (Ref. 21)

Figure 6-32 illustrates two recommended types of bulwark. The loose or floating bulwark of Fig. 6-32(a) is typical of welded construction. The 6-in. gap between the free edge of the sheer strake and the bottom of the bulwark plate gives a passage equivalent to that required for freeing ports. Since the bulwark plate is completely separated from the sheer strake, there is no possibility of it working as a longitudinally effective structure.

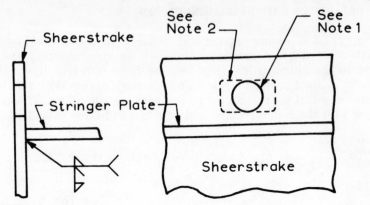

Notes:
1) Circular scupper opening.
2) Rectangular scupper opening with rounded corners.
3) Scupper openings are not permitted by U.S.C.G. within the middle three-fifths of the ship's length.

a) Scupper openings to be avoided.

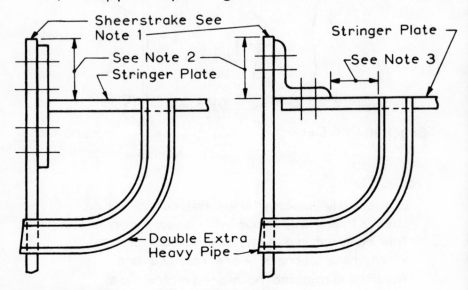

Notes:
1) Keep top smooth and free of notches.
2) This height to be a minimum.
3) One inch minimum for caulking.
4) Make both scupper holes normal to plating and grind smooth; finish with 100 per cent penetration weld.

b) Satisfactory deck scuppers.

FIG. 6-29. Strength-deck scuppers.

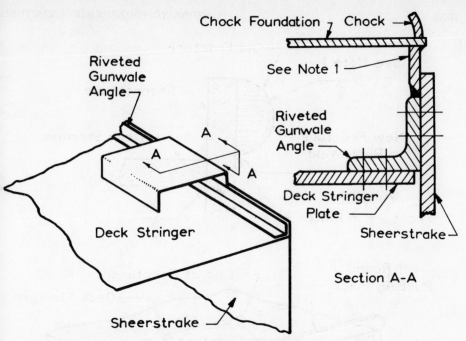

Chock Foundation — Chock →

See Note 1 —

Riveted Gunwale Angle —

Deck Stringer Plate —

Sheerstrake —

Section A-A

Riveted Gunwale Angle —

A

A

A

Deck Stringer

Sheerstrake —

a) Saddle type welded chock foundation

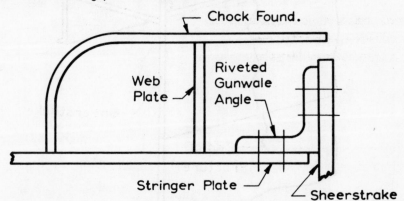

— Chock Found.

Web Plate —

Riveted Gunwale Angle —

Stringer Plate —

— Sheerstrake

b) Cantilever type welded chock foundation

Notes:

1) Flat-bar welded to gunwale angle before latter is put in place. Flat bar not attached to sheerstrake. (A temporary copper shim may be used to avoid welding through sheerstrake.)

2) An alternate method of supporting the chock foundation (chock not shown in this figure) is that of using transverse webs attached only to the stringer plate.

FIG. 6-30.   Recommended ways to attach a deck chock.

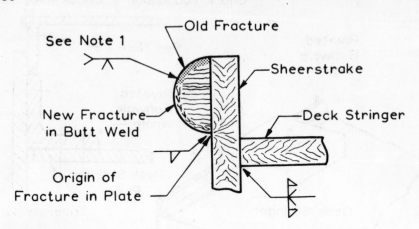

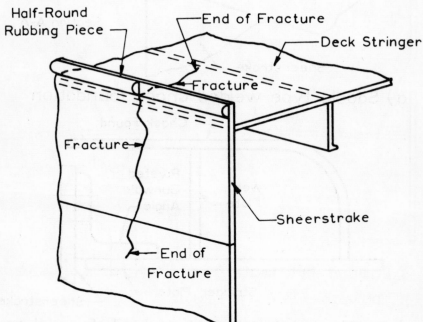

Notes:
1) The half-round was not grooved to full depth for this butt joint.
2) Fracture originated at a small defect in a member of no structural importance, i.e., a half-round rubbing piece.
3) Plates at fracture show herring-bone structure typical of brittle fracture.
4) The detail design of this rubbing piece is unacceptable.

FIG. 6-31.   Failure caused by welded attachment to sheer strake. (Ref. 27) 'he attached type of bulwark shown in Fig. 6-32(b) is acceptable because 1e riveted connection (single row) serves as a crack arrestor for cracks riginating in the bulwark.

Trouble has been experienced in some ships where the bulwark has been ttached directly by welding to the bridge house. A deckhouse, especially high one, unlike the bulwark, will not follow closely the longitudinal

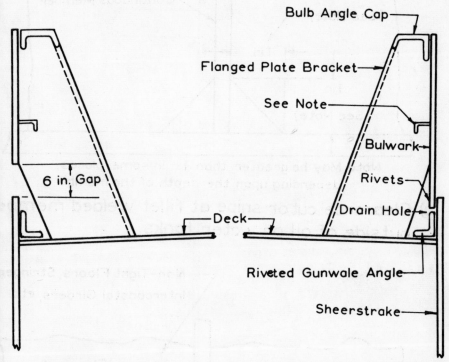

a) Loose or floating bulwark

b) Attached bulwark

Note: Intercostal stiffener angle used where extra strength is needed, such as near bow.

FIG. 6-32. Recommended types of bulwark. (Ref. 21)

eflection of the ship's girder. In addition, if the bulwark is not in line rith the side plating of the superstructure, a certain amount of joint ccentricity is introduced. Both these items can intensify longitudinal ulwark stresses. Under such circumstances, normal weld connections an become potential crack sources, if the connection between the deck-ouse and the bulwark is relatively rigid. Therefore, the junction of ulwark with bridge houses should receive the special attention of the

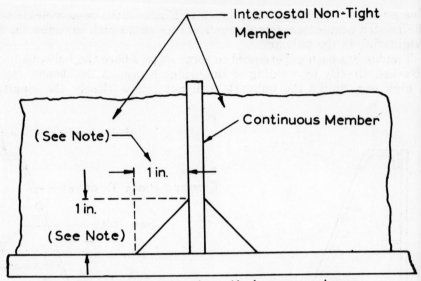

Intercostal Non-Tight Member

Continuous Member

(See Note)

1 in.

1 in.

(See Note)

Note: May be greater than 1 in. in some places,
depending upon the depth of the member.

a) Clearance cut or snipe at fillet welded membe[r]
outside of oil or water tanks.

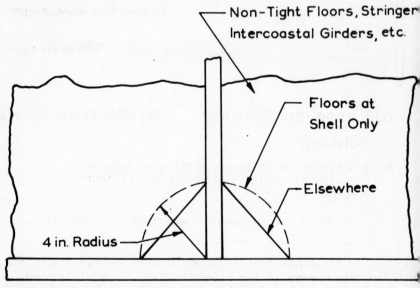

Non-Tight Floors, Stringer[s]
Intercoastal Girders, etc.

Floors at Shell Only

Elsewhere

4 in. Radius

b) Drain holes and clearance cut.

FIG. 6-33.   Drain holes and clearance cuts.

ngineering Department. Under certain circumstances, it may be better
o discontinue the bulwark at the bridge than to join the two. In such a
ase, the discontinued bulwark must receive special design consideration.

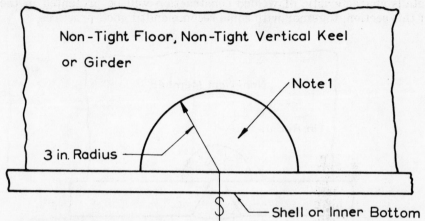

a) Drain hole and clearance cut in oil and water tanks.

Note 1: Cut at non-tight floor in way of shell or inner bottom, or cut at non-tight vertical keel, or girder at shell only.

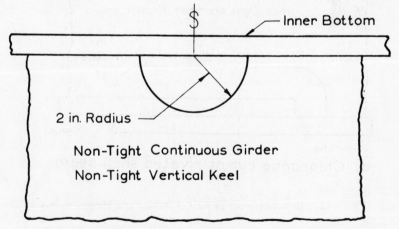

b) Air hole and clearance cut in oil and water tanks.

FIG. 6-34.   Drain holes, air holes and clearance cuts in oil and water tanks.

GENERAL DETAILS

In welded construction, minor structural details may be of great importance. To obtain a sound ship, an adequate standard of workmanship
should be maintained in executing these details. Some general structural
details characteristic of welded construction will be presented in the rest
of this section, together with some recommended good practices.

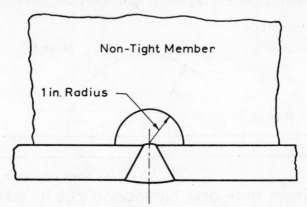

a) Clearance cut at welded butt and seam outside of oil or water tank.

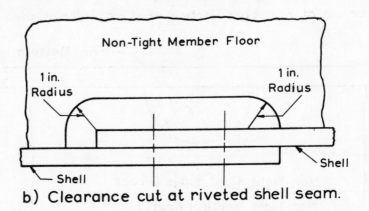

b) Clearance cut at riveted shell seam.

FIG. 6-35.   Clearance cuts in way of welded and riveted seams.

1) *Clearance Cuts, Cut-Outs, Drain Holes, etc.* In welded construction
involving joints in plating disposed at right angles to each other, these
details, sometimes called *rat holes*, or *mouse holes*, are often necessary for
the following purposes:

a) To weld butts without welding into impossible corners created by
contiguous structure.

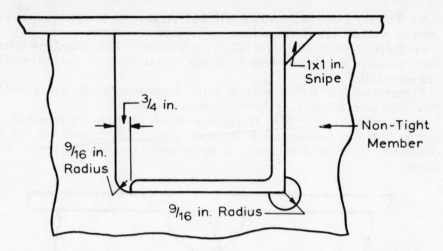

a) Cut-out for beams at non-tight members

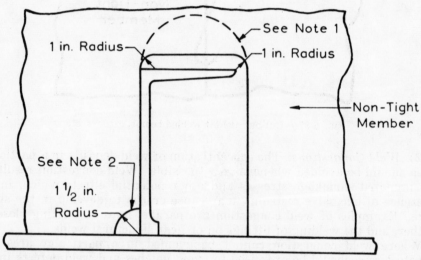

Notes:

1) Alternative shape of cut-out if pierced member is deep enough.

2) May use snipe instead.

b) Cut-out for longitudinal at non-tight members

General Note:
Measurements shown on the figures are not binding and are given for illustration purposes only.

Fig. 6-36. Cut-outs for simple passage of beams and longitudinals.

b) To carry on continuous welds and be able to complete such weld soundly without interference from contiguous structures.

c) To permit simplified, yet effective, passage of light members throug more massive members where tightness and additional weld strength i non-essential.

Figures 6-33 to 6-37 illustrate some recommended typical details o clearance cuts, cut-outs, drain holes and air holes.

If rat holes are necessary at locations where tightness is required, the can be closed by welding after the weld of the crossing member has bee completed, provided the closure is not effected by deposited weld meta alone.

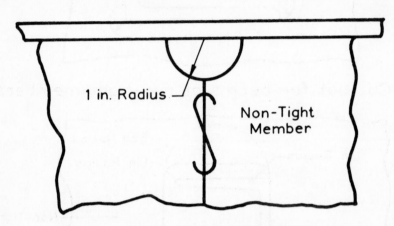

1 in. Radius

Non-Tight Member

Fig. 6-37.   Cut-out at butt welded beams, girders, etc.

2) *Weld Congestions.* The concentration of weld deposits in a particula area should be avoided whenever it is possible. Weld congestion results i accumulated shrinkage stresses and other potential effects which, in tl presence of excessive restraint, may cause cracks to develop in the stru ture. Examples of weld congestion are parallel lines of welding close t gether, and the welding of fittings on or near structural welds.

Where weld congestion cannot be avoided in a particular area, tl greatest care should be exercised to avoid notches and weld defects in tl immediate vicinity.

Figures 6-38 and 6-39 illustrate two cases where the combination weld congestion and restraint was responsible for cracks in the structur

3) *Alignment of Structure.* When structural members on one side a plate, such as intercostals, brackets or bulkheads, are essentially con tinuous with other members on the other side of the plate, it is very im portant to have them carefully aligned with each other.

The lack of alignment between structural members which are designe to insure direct, smooth transition of stress between the two may resu in structural failure due to joint eccentricity. Such eccentricity produc notch behavior not otherwise present.

Figure 6-40 illustrates ideal and also faulty alignment of structur members.

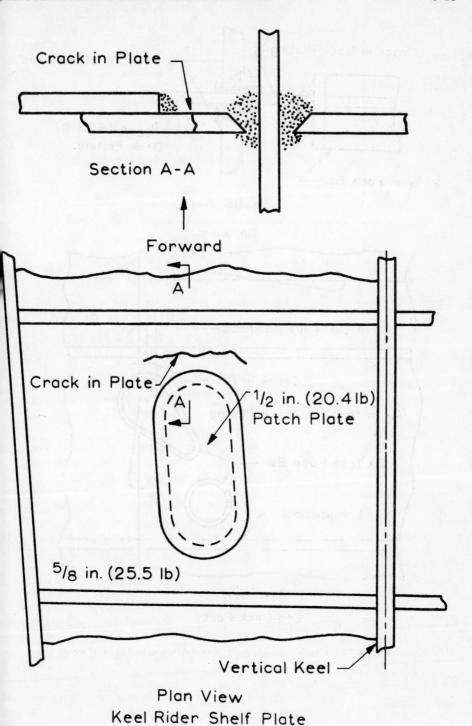

Crack in Plate

Section A-A

Forward

A

Crack in Plate

A

$1/2$ in. (20.4 lb) Patch Plate

$5/8$ in. (25.5 lb)

Vertical Keel

Plan View
Keel Rider Shelf Plate

FIG. 6-38. Crack through restricted area between welds.

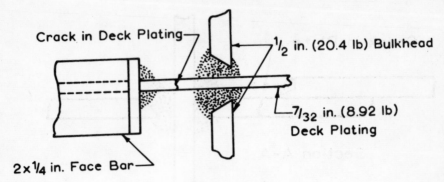

Crack in Deck Plating

½ in. (20.4 lb) Bulkhead

7/32 in. (8.92 lb) Deck Plating

2 x ¼ in. Face Bar

Section A-A

Forward

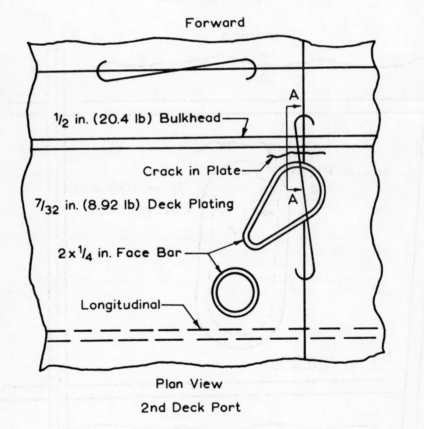

½ in. (20.4 lb) Bulkhead

Crack in Plate

7/32 in. (8.92 lb) Deck Plating

2 x ¼ in. Face Bar

Longitudinal

Plan View

2nd Deck Port

FIG. 6-39.   Crack through deck in restricted area between welds.

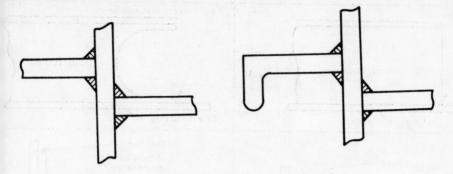

a) Faulty condition of alignment

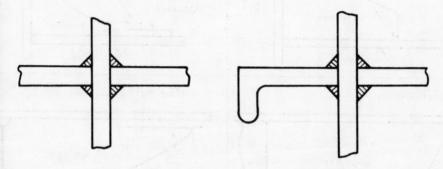

b) Ideal condition of alignment

Note: Sometimes a small amount of misalignment
      in lower stressed structure is permitted.
      The magnitude of this allowance may depend
      upon the nature and location of the structure.

FIG. 6-40.   Alignment of structural members.

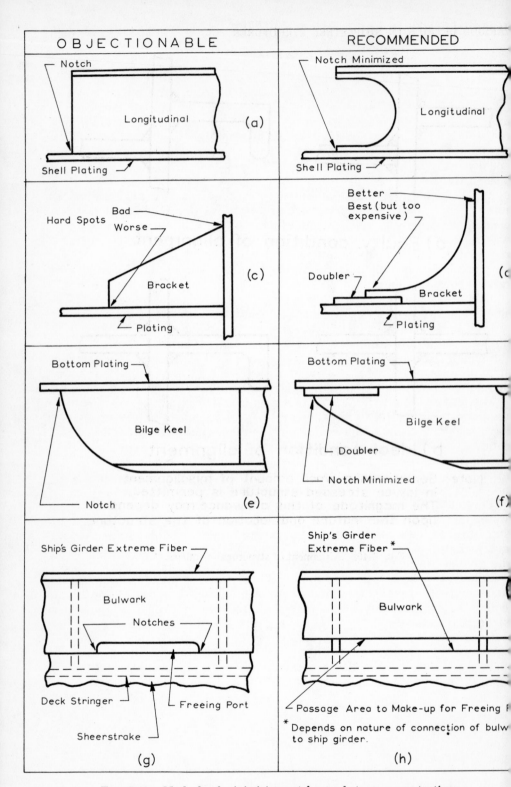

FIG. 6-41. Methods of minimizing notches and stress concentrations.

SUMMARY

Riveting, as a means of joining structural parts, has the inherent property of alleviating stress concentration and thereby reducing its effect in nitiating failure. This is a result of the ability of riveted members to undergo minor displacements with respect to each other, and to allow a redistribution of stress. Also, the state of stress in the plating around the rivets involved in the transmission of load from one member to another is not generally conducive to the type of failure (cracking) which occurs in welded ships.

In the first ships where welding was used extensively as a method of joining, there was a tendency to adapt structures designed for riveting to welded construction. As a result of fabrication and service cracking, it was soon realized that the design and fabrication of welded structures required a new approach and special consideration of certain critical structural details which were not particularly susceptible to failure in riveted construction.

This section includes reference to structural details selected to emphasize some of the most important principles applying to welded construction.

Figure 6-41 is an illustrated summary of the means of eliminating notches and of minimizing adverse effects of stress concentrations.

Some of the problems due to the intersection of longitudinals with other structural members are discussed on pages 6-2–6-14. Typical recommended details at these intersections are illustrated and described.

The use of brackets at the junction of various structural members requires special attention to structural detail. Incorrect details frequently have been the cause of local structural failures originating at bracketed connections. This is explained and illustrated on pages 6-14—6-23.

The intersection of plated components of ship structures, especially the intersection of bulkheads with other bulkheads and decks, present special problems which are illustrated and discussed on pages 6-23—6-25.

There are a number of miscellaneous details in ship structures which, when incorrectly designed or fabricated, have been the cause of many structural failures, some of them of major character. Some of these details are included on pages 6-25—6-39. Recommended practices in the proper design and fabrication of these details are presented also.

Finally, on pages 6-40–6-46 some general recommended welding details and practices are discussed and illustrated. These include the use of rat holes, the avoidance of weld congestion, and use of proper alignment of structural members.

SECTION VII

Miscellaneous Structural Data

TABLE 7-1. Squares, cubes, square roots, cube roots, circumferences and areas of circles. (Ref. 28)

Number N	Square N^2	Cube N^3	Square Root $\sqrt{N}$	Cube $\sqrt[3]{N}$	Circle. (N=D =diam) Circum. $\pi \times D$	Circle. (N=D =diam) Area $\dfrac{\pi \times D^2}{4}$
0.1	0.01	0.001	0.316	0.464	0.3142	0.00785
0.2	0.04	0.008	0.447	0.585	0.6283	0.03142
0.3	0.09	0.027	0.548	0.669	0.9425	0.07069
0.4	0.16	0.064	0.632	0.737	1.2566	0.12566
0.5	0.25	0.125	0.707	0.794	1.5708	0.19635
0.6	0.36	0.216	0.775	0.843	1.8850	0.28274
0.7	0.49	0.343	0.837	0.888	2.1991	0.38485
0.8	0.64	0.512	0.894	0.928	2.5133	0.50266
0.9	0.81	0.729	0.949	0.965	2.8274	0.63617
1.0	1.00	1.000	1.000	1.000	3.1416	0.78540
1.5	2.25	3.375	1.225	1.145	4.712	1.7671
2.0	4.00	8.000	1.414	1.260	6.283	3.1416
2.5	6.25	15.625	1.581	1.357	7.854	4.9087
3.0	9.00	27.000	1.732	1.442	9.425	7.0686
3.5	12.25	42.875	1.871	1.518	10.996	9.6211
4.0	16.00	64.000	2.000	1.587	12.566	12.5664
4.5	20.25	91.125	2.121	1.651	14.137	15.9043
5.0	25.00	125.000	2.236	1.710	15.708	19.6350
5.5	30.25	166.38	2.345	1.765	17.279	23.76
6.0	36.00	216.00	2.450	1.817	18.850	28.27
6.5	42.25	274.63	2.550	1.866	20.420	33.18
7.0	49.00	343.00	2.646	1.913	21.991	38.48
7.5	56.25	421.88	2.739	1.957	23.562	44.18
8.0	64.00	512.00	2.828	2.000	25.133	50.27
8.5	72.25	614.13	2.915	2.041	26.704	56.75
9.0	81.00	729.00	3.000	2.080	28.274	63.62
9.5	90.25	857.38	3.082	2.118	29.845	70.88
10.0	100.00	1000.00	3.162	2.154	31.416	78.54
10.5	110.25	1157.63	3.240	2.190	32.987	86.59
11.0	121.00	1331.00	3.317	2.224	34.56	95.03
11.5	132.25	1521	3.391	2.257	36.13	103.9
12.0	144.00	1728	3.464	2.289	37.70	113.1
12.5	156.25	1953	3.536	2.321	39.27	122.7
13.0	169.0	2197	3.606	2.351	40.84	132.7
13.5	182.3	2460	3.674	2.381	42.41	143.1
14.0	196.0	2744	3.742	2.410	43.98	153.9
14.5	210.3	3049	3.808	2.438	45.55	165.1
15.0	225.0	3375	3.873	2.466	47.12	176.7
15.5	240.3	3724	3.937	2.493	48.69	188.7
16.0	256.0	4096	4.000	2.520	50.27	201.1
16.5	272.3	4492	4.062	2.546	51.84	213.8
17.0	289.0	4913	4.123	2.571	53.41	227.0
17.5	306.3	5359	4.183	2.596	54.98	240.5
18.0	324.0	5832	4.243	2.621	56.55	254.5
18.5	342.3	6332	4.301	2.645	58.12	268.8
19.0	361.0	6859	4.359	2.668	59.69	283.5
19.5	380.3	7415	4.416	2.692	61.26	298.6

TABLE 7-1 (cont.)

Number N	Square N^2	Cube N^3	Square Root $\sqrt{N}$	Cube $\sqrt[3]{N}$	Circle. (N=D =diam)	
					Circum. $\pi \times D$	Area $\dfrac{\pi \times D^2}{4}$
20.0	400.0	8000	4.472	2.714	62.83	314.2
20.5	420.3	8615	4.528	2.737	64.40	330.1
21.0	441.0	9261	4.583	2.759	65.97	346.4
21.5	462.3	9938	4.637	2.781	67.54	363.1
22.0	484.0	10648	4.690	2.802	69.12	380.1
22.5	506.3	11391	4.743	2.823	70.69	397.6
23.0	529.0	12167	4.796	2.844	72.26	415.5
23.5	552.3	12978	4.848	2.864	73.83	433.7
24.0	576.0	13824	4.899	2.884	75.40	452.4
24.5	600.3	14706	4.950	2.904	76.97	471.4
25.0	625.0	15625	5.000	2.924	78.54	490.9
25.5	650.3	16581	5.050	2.943	80.11	510.7
26.0	676.0	17576	5.099	2.962	81.68	530.9
26.5	702.3	18610	5.148	2.981	83.25	551.5
27.0	729.0	19683	5.196	3.000	84.82	572.6
27.5	756.3	20797	5.244	3.018	86.39	594.0
28.0	784.0	21952	5.292	3.037	87.96	615.8
28.5	812.3	23149	5.339	3.055	89.54	637.9
29.0	841.0	24389	5.385	3.072	91.11	660.5
29.5	870.3	25672	5.431	3.090	92.68	683.5
30.0	900.0	27000	5.477	3.107	94.25	706.9
30.5	930.3	28373	5.523	3.124	95.82	730.6
31.0	961.0	29791	5.568	3.141	97.39	754.8
31.5	992.3	31256	5.612	3.158	98.96	779.3
32.0	1024	32768	5.657	3.175	100.5	804.2
32.5	1056	34328	5.701	3.191	102.1	829.6
33.0	1089	35937	5.745	3.208	103.7	855.3
33.5	1122	37595	5.788	3.224	105.2	881.4
34.0	1156	39304	5.831	3.240	106.8	907.9
34.5	1190	41064	5.874	3.255	108.4	934.8
35.0	1225	42875	5.916	3.271	110.0	962.1
35.5	1260	44739	5.958	3.287	111.5	989.8
36.0	1296	46656	6.000	3.302	113.1	1018
36.5	1332	48627	6.042	3.317	114.7	1046
37.0	1369	50653	6.083	3.332	116.2	1075
37.5	1406	52734	6.124	3.347	117.8	1104
38.0	1444	54872	6.164	3.362	119.4	1134
38.5	1482	57067	6.205	3.377	121.0	1164
39.0	1521	59319	6.245	3.391	122.5	1195
39.5	1560	61630	6.285	3.406	124.1	1225
40.0	1600	64000	6.325	3.420	125.7	1257
40.5	1640	66430	6.364	3.434	127.2	1288
41.0	1681	68921	6.403	3.448	128.8	1320
41.5	1722	71473	6.442	3.462	130.4	1353
42.0	1764	74088	6.481	3.476	131.9	1385
42.5	1806	76766	6.519	3.409	133.5	1419
43.0	1849	79507	6.557	3.503	135.1	1452
43.5	1892	82313	6.595	3.517	136.7	1486
44.0	1936	85184	6.633	3.530	138.2	1521
44.5	1980	88121	6.671	3.544	139.8	1555

TABLE 7-1 (cont.)

Number N	Square N²	Cube N³	Square Root √N	Cube ³√N	Circle. (N=D =diam) Circum. π x D	Circle. (N=D =diam) Area π x D²/4
45.0	2025	91125	6.708	3.557	141.4	1590
45.5	2070	94196	6.745	3.570	142.9	1626
46.0	2116	97336	6.782	3.583	144.5	1662
46.5	2162	100545	6.819	3.596	146.1	1698
47.0	2209	103823	6.856	3.609	147.6	1735
47.5	2256	107172	6.892	3.622	149.2	1772
48.0	2304	110592	6.928	3.634	150.8	1810
48.5	2352	114084	6.964	3.647	152.4	1847
49.0	2401	117649	7.000	3.659	153.9	1886
49.5	2450	121287	7.036	3.672	155.5	1924
50.0	2500	125000	7.071	3.684	157.1	1963
50.5	2550	128788	7.106	3.696	158.7	2003
51.0	2601	132651	7.141	3.708	160.2	2043
51.5	2652	136591	7.176	3.721	161.8	2083
52.0	2704	140608	7.211	3.733	163.4	2124
52.5	2756	144703	7.246	3.744	164.9	2165
53.0	2809	148877	7.280	3.756	166.5	2206
53.5	2862	153130	7.314	3.768	168.1	2248
54.0	2916	157464	7.348	3.780	169.7	2290
54.5	2970	161879	7.382	3.791	171.2	2333
55.0	3025	166375	7.416	3.803	172.8	2376
55.5	3080	170954	7.450	3.814	174.4	2419
56.0	3136	175616	7.483	3.826	175.9	2463
56.5	3192	180362	7.517	3.837	177.5	2507
57.0	3249	185193	7.550	3.849	179.1	2552
57.5	3306	190109	7.583	3.860	180.6	2597
58.0	3364	195112	7.616	3.871	182.2	2642
58.5	3422	200202	7.649	3.882	183.8	2688
59.0	3481	205379	7.681	3.893	185.4	2734
59.5	3540	210645	7.714	3.904	186.9	2781
60.0	3600	216000	7.746	3.915	188.5	2827
60.5	3660	221445	7.778	3.926	190.1	2875
61.0	3721	226981	7.810	3.936	191.6	2922
61.5	3782	232608	7.842	3.947	193.2	2971
62.0	3844	238328	7.874	3.958	194.8	3019
62.5	3906	244141	7.906	3.968	196.3	3068
63.0	3969	250047	7.937	3.979	197.9	3117
63.5	4032	256048	7.969	3.990	199.5	3167
64.0	4096	262144	8.000	4.000	201.1	3217
64.5	4160	268336	8.031	4.010	202.6	3267
65.0	4225	274625	8.062	4.021	204.2	3318
65.5	4290	281011	8.093	4.031	205.8	3370
66.0	4356	287496	8.124	4.041	207.3	3421
66.5	4422	294080	8.155	4.051	208.9	3473
67.0	4489	300763	8.185	4.062	210.5	3526
67.5	4556	307547	8.216	4.072	212.1	3578
68.0	4624	314432	8.246	4.082	213.6	3632
68.5	4692	321419	8.276	4.092	215.2	3685
69.0	4761	328509	8.307	4.102	216.8	3739
69.5	4830	335702	8.337	4.111	218.3	3794

TABLE 7-1 (cont.)

Number N	Square N^2	Cube N^3	Square Root $\sqrt{N}$	Cube $\sqrt[3]{N}$	Circle. (N=D =diam) Circum. $\pi \times D$	Circle. (N=D =diam) Area $\frac{\pi \times D^2}{4}$
70.0	4900	343000	8.367	4.121	219.9	3848
70.5	4970	350403	8.396	4.131	221.5	3904
71.0	5041	357911	8.426	4.141	223.1	3959
71.5	5112	365525	8.456	4.151	224.6	4015
72.0	5184	373248	8.485	4.160	226.2	4072
72.5	5256	381078	8.515	4.170	227.8	4128
73.0	5329	389017	8.544	4.179	229.3	4185
73.5	5402	397065	8.573	4.189	230.9	4243
74.0	5476	405224	8.602	4.198	232.5	4301
74.5	5550	413494	8.631	4.208	234.0	4359
75.0	5625	421875	8.660	4.217	235.6	4418
75.5	5700	430369	8.689	4.227	237.2	4477
76.0	5776	438976	8.718	4.236	238.8	4536
76.5	5852	447697	8.746	4.245	240.3	4596
77.0	5929	456533	8.775	4.254	241.9	4657
77.5	6006	465484	8.803	4.264	243.5	4717
78.0	6084	474552	8.832	4.273	245.0	4778
78.5	6162	483737	8.860	4.282	246.6	4840
79.0	6241	493039	8.888	4.291	248.2	4902
79.5	6320	502460	8.916	4.300	249.8	4964
80.0	6400	512000	8.944	4.309	251.3	5027
80.5	6480	521660	8.972	4.318	252.9	5090
81.0	6561	531441	9.000	4.327	254.5	5153
81.5	6642	541343	9.028	4.336	256.0	5217
82.0	6724	551368	9.055	4.344	257.6	5281
82.5	6806	561516	9.083	4.353	259.2	5346
83.0	6889	571787	9.110	4.362	260.8	5411
83.5	6972	582183	9.138	4.371	262.3	5476
84.0	7056	592704	9.165	4.380	263.9	5542
84.5	7140	603351	9.192	4.388	265.5	5608
85.0	7225	614125	9.220	4.397	267.0	5675
85.5	7310	625026	9.247	4.405	268.6	5741
86.0	7396	636056	9.274	4.414	270.2	5809
86.5	7482	647215	9.301	4.423	271.7	5877
87.0	7569	658503	9.327	4.431	273.3	5945
87.5	7656	669922	9.354	4.440	274.9	6013
88.0	7744	681472	9.381	4.448	276.5	6082
88.5	7832	693154	9.407	4.456	278.0	6151
89.0	7921	704969	9.434	4.465	279.6	6221
89.5	8010	716917	9.460	4.473	281.2	6291
90.0	8100	729000	9.487	4.481	282.7	6362
90.5	8190	741218	9.513	4.490	284.3	6433
91.0	8281	753571	9.539	4.498	285.9	6504
91.5	8372	766061	9.566	4.506	287.5	6576
92.0	8464	778688	9.592	4.514	289.0	6648
92.5	8556	791453	9.618	4.523	290.6	6720
93.0	8649	804357	9.644	4.531	292.2	6793
93.5	8742	817400	9.670	4.539	293.7	6866
94.0	8836	830584	9.695	4.547	295.3	6940
94.5	8930	843909	9.721	4.555	296.9	7014

TABLE 7-1 (cont.)

Number N	Square N^2	Cube N^3	Square Root $\sqrt{N}$	Cube $\sqrt[3]{N}$	Circle. (N=D =diam)	
					Circum. $\pi \times D$	Area $\dfrac{\pi \times D^2}{4}$
95.0	9025	857375	9.747	4.563	298.5	7088
95.5	9120	870984	9.772	4.571	300.0	7163
96.0	9216	884736	9.798	4.579	301.6	7238
96.5	9312	898632	9.823	4.587	303.2	7314
97.0	9409	912673	9.849	4.595	304.7	7390
97.5	9506	926859	9.874	4.603	306.3	7466
98.0	9604	941192	9.899	4.610	307.9	7543
98.5	9702	955672	9.925	4.618	309.4	7620
99.0	9801	970299	9.950	4.626	311.0	7598
99.5	9900	985075	9.975	4.634	312.6	7776
100.0	10000	1000000	10.000	4.642	314.2	7854

TABLE 7-2. Fractions and decimal equivalents. (Ref. 29)

	1/64	.015625		33/64	.515625
	1/32	.03125		17/32	.53125
	3/64	.046875		35/64	.546875
	1/16	.0625		9/16	.5625
	5/64	.078125		37/64	.578125
	3/32	.09375		19/32	.59375
	7/64	.109375		39/64	.609375
1/8		.125	5/8		.625
	9/64	.140625		41/64	.640625
	5/32	.15625		21/32	.65625
	11/64	.171875		43/64	.671875
	3/16	.1875		11/16	.6875
	13/64	.203125		45/64	.703125
	7/32	.21875		23/32	.71875
	15/64	.234375		47/64	.734375
1/4		.25	3/4		.75
	17/64	.265625		49/64	.765625
	9/32	.28125		25/32	.78125
	19/64	.296875		51/64	.796875
	5/16	.3125		13/16	.8125
	21/64	.328125		53/64	.828125
	11/32	.34375		27/32	.84375
	23/64	.359375		55/64	.859375
3/8		.375	7/8		.875
	25/64	.390625		57/64	.890625
	13/32	.40625		29/32	.90625
	27/64	.421875		59/64	.921875
	7/16	.4375		15/16	.9375
	29/64	.453125		61/64	.953125
	15/32	.46875		31/32	.96875
	31/64	.484375		63/64	.984375
1/2		.5	1		1.

TABLE 7-3. Conversion of inches (in.) into decimals of a foot (ft). (Ref. 29)

Inches		Decimal of a Foot	Inches		Decimal of a Foot
	1/16	.005208		1/16	.255208
	1/8	.010416		1/8	.260416
	3/16	.015625		3/16	.265625
	1/4	.020833		1/4	.270833
	5/16	.026042		5/16	.276042
	3/8	.031250		3/8	.281250
	7/16	.036458		7/16	.286458
0 in.	1/2	.041666	3 in.	1/2	.291666
	9/16	.046875	(.250)	9/16	.296875
	5/8	.052083	(ft)	5/8	.302083
	11/16	.057292		11/16	.307292
	3/4	.062500		3/4	.312500
	13/16	.067708		13/16	.317708
	7/8	.072916		7/8	.322916
	15/16	.078125		15/16	.328125
	1/16	.088542		1/16	.338542
	1/8	.093750		1/8	.343750
	3/16	.098958		3/16	.348958
	1/4	.104166		1/4	.354166
	5/16	.109375		5/16	.359375
	3/8	.114583		3/8	.364583
	7/16	.119792		7/16	.369792
1 in.	1/2	.125000	4 in.	1/2	.375000
(.083333)	9/16	.130208	(.33333)	9/16	.380208
(ft)	5/8	.135416	(ft)	5/8	.385416
	11/16	.140625		11/16	.390625
	3/4	.145833		3/4	.395833
	13/16	.151042		13/16	.401042
	7/8	.156250		7/8	.406250
	15/16	.161458		15/16	.411458
	1/16	.171875		1/16	.421875
	1/8	.177083		1/8	.427083
	3/16	.182292		3/16	.432292
	1/4	.187500		1/4	.437500
	5/16	.192708		5/16	.442708
	3/8	.197906		3/8	.447916
	7/16	.203175		7/16	.453125
2 in.	1/2	.208333	5 in.	1/2	.458333
(.166666)	9/16	.213542	(.416666)	9/16	.463542
(ft)	5/8	.218750	(ft)	5/8	.468750
	11/16	.223958		11/16	.473958
	3/4	.229166		3/4	.479166
	13/16	.234375		13/16	.484375
	7/8	.239583		7/8	.489583
	15/16	.244792		15/16	.494792

TABLE 7-3 (cont.)

Inches		Decimal of a Foot	Inches		Decimal of a Foot
	1/16	.505208		1/16	.755208
	1/8	.510416		1/8	.760416
	3/16	.515625		3/16	.765625
	1/4	.520833		1/4	.770833
	5/16	.526042		5/16	.776042
	3/8	.531250		3/8	.781250
	7/16	.536458		7/16	.786458
6 in.	1/2	.541666	9 in.	1/2	.791666
(.50)	9/16	.546875	(.750)	9/16	.796875
(ft)	5/8	.552083	(ft)	5/8	.802083
	11/16	.557292		11/16	.807292
	3/4	.562500		3/4	.812500
	13/16	.567708		13/16	.817708
	7/8	.572916		7/8	.822916
	15/16	.578125		15/16	.828125
	1/16	.588542		1/16	.838542
	1/8	.593750		1/8	.843750
	3/16	.598958		3/16	.848958
	1/4	.604166		1/4	.854166
	5/16	.609375		5/16	.859375
	3/8	.614583		3/8	.864583
	7/16	.619792		7/16	.869792
7 in.	1/2	.625000	10 in.	1/2	.875000
(.583333)	9/16	.630208	(.833333)	9/16	.880208
(ft)	5/8	.635416	(ft)	5/8	.885416
	11/16	.640625		11/16	.890625
	3/4	.645833		3/4	.895833
	13/16	.651042		13/16	.901042
	7/8	.656250		7/8	.906250
	15/16	.661458		15/16	.911458
	1/16	.671875		1/16	.921875
	1/8	.677083		1/8	.927083
	3/16	.682292		3/16	.932292
	1/4	.687500		1/4	.937500
	5/16	.692708		5/16	.942708
	3/8	.697916		3/8	.947916
	7/16	.703125		7/16	.953125
8 in.	1/2	.708323	11 in.	1/2	.958333
(.66666)	9/16	.713542	(.916666)	9/16	.963542
(ft)	5/8	.718750	(ft)	5/8	.968750
	11/16	.723958		11/16	.973958
	3/4	.729166		3/4	.979166
	13/16	.734375		13/16	.984375
	7/8	.739583		7/8	.989583
	15/16	.744792		15/16	.994792

TABLE 7-4. Weight and gage of steel plates.

U. S. Standard Gage No.	Thickness Decimals Inches	Thickness Fractions Inches	Weight (lb per sq ft)
30	.0120		0.500
28	.0149	About 1/64	0.625
26	.0179		0.750
24	.0239		1.000
22	.0299	About 1/32	1.250
20	.0359		1.500
18	.0478	About 3/64	2.000
16	.0598	About 1/16	2.550
14	.0747	About 5/64	3.125
12	.1046	About 7/64	4.375
11	.1196	About 1/8	5.000
10	.1345		5.625
9	.1495	About 5/32	6.250
8	.1644		6.875
7	.1793	About 3/16	7.500
6	.1943		8.125
5	.2092	About 7/32	8.750
4	.2242		9.375
3	.2391	About 1/4	10.000

TABLE 7-5. Weight of steel plates and corresponding rivet diameters.

Thickness Decimals (in.)	Thickness Fractions (in.)	Weight (lb per sq ft)	Rivet Diam. (in.)
.02		0.816	
.04		1.632	
.06		2.448	
.0625	1/16	2.550	
.08		3.264	
.10		4.080	
.12		4.896	
.125	1/8	5.100	
.14		5.712	
.16		6.528	
.18		7.344	1/2

TABLE 7-5 (cont.)

| Thickness | | Weight (lb per sq ft) | Rivet Diam. (in.) |
Decimals (in.)	Fractions (in.)		
.1875	3/16	7.650	1/2
.20		8.16	1/2
.22		8.98	1/2
.24		9.79	1/2 5/8
.25	1/4	10.20	5/8
.26		10.61	5/8
.28		11.42	5/8
.30		12.24	5/8
.3125	5/16	12.75	5/8
.32		13.06	5/8
.34		13.87	5/8
.36		14.69	3/4 5/8
.3750	3/8	15.30	3/4
.38		15.50	3/4
.40		16.32	3/4
.42		17.14	3/4
.4375	7/16	17.85	3/4
.44		17.95	3/4
.46		18.77	3/4
.48		19.58	3/4
.50	1/2	20.40	3/4
.52		21.22	7/8
.54		22.03	7/8
.56		22.85	7/8
.5625	9/16	22.95	7/8
.58		23.66	7/8
.60		24.48	7/8
.62		25.30	7/8
.625	5/8	25.50	7/8
.64		26.11	7/8
.66		26.93	7/8
.68		27.74	7/8
.6875	11/16	28.05	7/8
.70		28.56	7/8

TABLE 7-5 (cont.)

Thickness		Weight (lb per sq ft)	Rivet Diam. (in.)
Decimals (in.)	Fractions (in.)		
.72		29.38	1
.74		30.19	1
.75	3/4	30.60	1
.76		31.01	1
.78		31.82	1
.80		32.64	1
.8125	13/16	33.15	1
.82		33.46	1
.84		34.27	1
.86		35.09	1
.875	7/8	35.70	1
.88		35.90	1
.90		36.72	1
.92		37.54	1
.9375	15/16	38.25	1
.94		38.35	1-1/8
.96		39.17	1-1/8
.98		39.98	1-1/8
1.00	1	40.80	1-1/8
1.0625	1-1/16	43.35	1-1/8
1.125	1-1/8	45.90	1-1/8
1.1875	1-3/16	48.45	1-1/4
1.250	1-1/4	51.00	1-1/4
1.3125	1-5/16	53.55	
1.375	1-3/8	56.10	
1.4375	1-7/16	58.65	
1.50	1-1/2	61.20	
1.625	1-5/8	66.30	
1.75	1-3/4	71.40	
1.875	1-7/8	76.50	
2.00	2	81.60	

TABLE 7-6. Weight of steel angles in pounds per lineal foot.

Sum of Flanges in.	Thickness in inches										
	1/8	3/16	1/4	5/16	3/8	7/16	1/2	9/16	5/8	3/4	1
2	0.80	1.16	1.49	....	....	....	....	....	....	....	....
2-1/2	1.01	1.48	1.92	2.33	....	....	....	....	....	....	....
3	1.23	1.80	2.34	2.86	3.35	....	....	....	....	....	....
3-1/2	1.44	2.12	2.77	3.39	3.99	4.6	....	....	....	....	....
4	1.65	2.44	3.19	3.92	4.7	5.3	6.0	....	....	....	....
4-1/2	1.86	2.75	3.62	4.5	5.3	6.1	6.8	....	....	....	....
5	2.08	3.07	4.1	5.0	5.9	6.8	7.7	....	....	....	....
5-1/2	2.28	3.39	4.5	5.6	6.6	7.6	8.5	9.5	....	....	....
6	2.50	3.71	4.9	6.1	7.2	8.3	9.4	10.4	11.5	....	....
6-1/2	....	4.1	5.4	6.6	7.9	9.1	10.2	11.4	12.5	....	....
7	....	4.4	5.8	7.2	8.5	9.8	11.1	12.4	13.6	16.0	....
7-1/2	....	...	6.2	7.7	9.1	10.6	11.9	13.3	14.7	17.3	....
8	....	...	6.6	8.2	9.8	11.3	12.8	14.3	15.7	18.5	....
8-1/2	....	...	...	8.7	10.4	12.0	13.6	15.2	16.8	19.8	....
9	....	...	...	9.3	11.0	12.8	14.5	16.2	17.8	21.1	....
9-1/2	....	...	...	9.8	11.7	13.5	15.3	17.1	18.9	22.4	28.9
10	....	...	...	10.3	12.3	14.3	16.2	18.1	20.0	23.6	30.6
10-1/2	....	...	...	10.9	13.0	15.0	17.0	19.1	21.0	24.9	32.3
11	....	...	...	11.5	13.6	15.7	17.8	20.0	22.1	26.2	34.0
11-1/2	....	...	...	12.0	14.2	16.5	18.7	21.0	23.2	27.5	35.7
12	....	...	...	12.5	14.9	17.2	19.6	21.9	24.2	28.7	37.4
14	....	...	...	....	....	20.2	23.0	25.7	28.5	33.8	44.2
16	....	...	...	....	....	....	26.4	29.6	32.7	38.9	51.0

Example. For a 4×3×3/8 in. angle, the sum of the flanges is four plus three equal to seven (4 + 3 = 7). Enter table at left (first column) on line corresponding to seven (7), and under heading of 3/8 in. the weight is determined to be 8.5 lb per lineal foot.

TABLE 7-7. Weight of steel channels cut to angles.

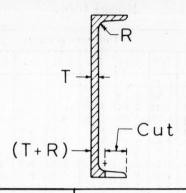

| Size of Original Channel (in.×in.×lb per ft length) | Web Thickness (in.) | Flange | | Weight of Angle (lb per ft length) |
		Width of Flange Cutting (in.)	Average Thickness (in.)	
18 × 4 × 58.0	.70	3	.625	51.6
18 × 4 × 51.9	.60	2-7/8	.625	45.8
18 × 4 × 45.8	.50	2-7/8	.625	39.7
18 × 4 × 42.7	.45	2-15/16	.625	36.5
15 × 3-3/8 × 50.0	.716	2-1/2	.650	44.5
15 × 3-3/8 × 40.0	.520	2-7/16	.650	34.6
15 × 3-3/8 × 33.9	.400	2-7/16	.650	28.5
13 × 4 × 50.0	.787	3	.610	43.8
13 × 4 × 40.0	.560	3	.610	33.8
13 × 4 × 35.0	.477	3-1/8	.610	28.5
13 × 4 × 31.8	.375	3-1/8	.610	25.3
12 × 4 × 50.0	.835	2-7/8	.700	43.2
12 × 4 × 45.0	.700	2-13/16	.700	38.3
12 × 4 × 40.0	.590	2-3/4	.700	33.5
12 × 4 × 35.0	.467	2-3/4	.700	28.5
12 × 3-1/2 × 37.0	.600	2-1/2	.600	32.1
12 × 3-1/2 × 32.9	.500	2-1/2	.600	28.0
12 × 3-1/2 × 30.9	.450	2-9/16	.600	25.7
10 × 4 × 41.1	.794	2-15/16	.575	35.4
10 × 4 × 33.6	.575	3	.575	27.8
10 × 4 × 28.5	.425	3	.575	22.7
10 × 3-1/2 × 28.3	.475	2-7/16	.575	23.5
10 × 3-1/2 × 24.9	.375	2-7/16	.575	20.1
10 × 3-1/2 × 25.3	.425	2-9/16	.50	20.9
10 × 3-1/2 × 21.9	.325	2-11/16	.50	17.4

TABLE 7-8. Weight of steel I-beams cut to T-beams.

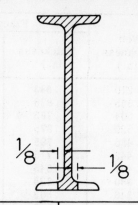

| Size of Original I-Beam (in.×in.×lb per ft of length) | Web Thickness (in.) | Flange | | Weight of T (lb per ft of length) |
		Thickness (in.)	Width of T Toe (in.)	
6 × 4 × 16	.26	.404	.51	11.2
6 × 4 × 12	.23	.279	.48	8.7
6 × 4 × 8.5	.17	.194	.42	6.2
8 × 6-1/2 × 28	.285	.463	.535	18.54
8 × 6-1/2 × 24	.245	.398	.495	15.88
8 × 5-1/4 × 20	.248	.378	.498	13.86
8 × 5-1/4 × 17	.230	.308	.48	12.01
8 × 4 × 15	.245	.314	.495	11.3
8 × 4 × 13	.230	.254	.48	10.0
8 × 4 × 10	.17	.204	.42	7.6
10 × 8 × 39	.318	.528	.568	25.7
10 × 5-3/4 × 29	.289	.500	.539	20.06
10 × 5-3/4 × 25	.252	.430	.502	17.32
10 × 5-3/4 × 21	.240	.340	.49	14.91
10 × 4 × 19	.250	.394	.50	14.4
10 × 4 × 17	.240	.329	.49	13.0
10 × 4 × 15	.230	.269	.48	11.7
10 × 4 × 11.5	.180	.204	.43	9.1
12 × 8 × 50	.371	.641	.631	33.8
12 × 8 × 45	.336	.576	.586	30.4
12 × 8 × 40	.294	.516	.544	26.9
12 × 6-1/2 × 36	.305	.540	.555	24.97
12 × 6-1/2 × 31	.265	.465	.515	21.51
12 × 6-1/2 × 27	.240	.400	.49	18.85
12 × 4 × 22	.260	.424	.51	16.9
12 × 4 × 19	.240	.349	.49	14.9
12 × 4 × 165	.230	.269	.48	13.3
12 × 4 × 14	.200	.224	.45	11.4
14 × 8 × 53	.370	.658	.62	36.36
14 × 8 × 48	.339	.593	.589	32.97
14 × 8 × 43	.308	.528	.558	29.31
14 × 6-3/4 × 38	.313	.513	.563	27.14
14 × 6-3/4 × 34	.287	.453	.537	24.43

TABLE 7-8 (cont.)

| Size of Original I-Beam (in.×in.×lb per ft of length) | Web Thickness (in.) | Flange | | Weight of T (lb per ft of length) |
		Thickness (in.)	Width of T Toe (in.)	
14 × 6-3/4 × 30	.270	.383	.52	21.86
16 × 11-1/2 × 96	.535	.875	.785	63.97
16 × 11-1/2 × 88	.504	.795	.754	58.91
16 × 8-1/2 × 78	.529	.875	.779	54.7
16 × 8-1/2 × 71	.486	.795	.736	49.82
16 × 8-1/2 × 64	.443	.715	.693	44.94
16 × 8-1/2 × 58	.407	.645	.657	40.8
16 × 7 × 50	.380	.628	.63	36.22
16 × 7 × 45	.346	.563	.596	32.68
16 × 7 × 40	.307	.503	.557	29.00
16 × 7 × 36	.299	.428	.549	26.63
18 × 8-3/4 × 85	.526	.911	.776	58.93
18 × 8-3/4 × 77	.475	.831	.725	54.16
18 × 8-3/4 × 70	.438	.751	.688	49.32
18 × 8-3/4 × 64	.403	.686	.653	45.12
18 × 7-1/2 × 55	.416	.695	.666	40.28
18 × 7-1/2 × 50	.390	.630	.64	36.66
18 × 7-1/2 × 47	.358	.570	.608	34.77
21 × 13 × 112	.527	.865	.777	76.00
21 × 9 × 82	.499	.795	.749	59.7
21 × 8-1/4 × 62	.400	.615	.65	46.1
24 × 12 × 100	.468	.775	.718	69.7
24 × 9 × 76	.440	.682	.69	56.8

TABLE 7-9. Approximate weights of electrode and weld metal in fillet welds (heavily coated electrodes). (Ref. 16)

Type of Weld	Size of Fillet (in.)	Lb of Electrode Required per Linear ft of Weld*	Steel Deposited per Linear ft of Weld
Horizontal	1/8	0.048	0.027
	3/16	0.113	0.063
	1/4	0.189	0.106
	5/16	0.296	0.166
	3/8	0.427	0.239
	1/2	0.760	0.425
	5/8	1.185	0.663
	3/4	1.705	0.955
	1	3.030	1.698
Positioned (Flat)	1/4	0.212	0.119
	5/16	0.334	0.187
	3/8	0.486	0.272
	1/2	0.850	0.475
	5/8	1.275	0.713
	3/4	1.820	1.020
	1	3.210	1.800
Corner	1/8	0.07	0.041
	3/16	0.16	0.095
	1/4	0.30	0.167
	5/16	0.46	0.261
	3/8	0.67	0.378
	1/2	1.19	0.665
	5/8	1.86	1.043
	3/4	2.68	1.502
	1	4.77	2.670

* Includes stub end and spatter loss.

TABLE 7-10. Approximate weights of electrode and weld metal in square-groove butt joints with reinforcement (heavily coated electrode). (Ref. 16)

Weld Type	Joint Dimensions (in.)		Lb of Electrode Required for Linear ft. of Weld*	Steel Deposited per Linear ft of Weld (lb)
	Plate Thickness	Root Opening		
Welded Both Sides	1/8 to 1/4	0	0.21	0.119
	1/8 to 1,4	1/32	0.24	0.132
	3/16 to 3/8	1/32	0.36	0.199
	3/16 to 3/8	1/16	0.39	0.218
	1/4 to 7/16	1/16	0.47	0.261
	1/4 to 4/16	3/32	0.53	0.288
With Backing Strip	1/8 to 1/4	0	0.11	0.060
	1/8 to 1/4	1/16	0.15	0.086
	3/16 to 3/8	1/16	0.23	0.129
	3/16 to 3/8	1/32	0.27	0.149
	1/4 to 7/16	1/32	0.33	0.184
	1/4 to 7/16	1/8	0.38	0.210

* Includes stub end and spatter loss.

TABLE 7-11. Approximate weights of electrode and weld metal in V-groove butt joints with reinforcement (heavily coated electrode). (Ref. 16)

Weld Type	Joint Dimensions (in.)			Lb of Electrode Required for Linear ft of Weld*	Steel Deposited per Linear ft of Weld (lb)
	Plate Thickness	Throat Opening	Root Opening		
With Backing Strip	1/4	0.405	--	0.61	0.340
	5/16	0.476	--	0.81	0.452
	3/8	0.549	--	1.03	0.577
	1/2	0.693	--	1.58	0.882
	5/8	0.838	--	2.23	1.248
	3/4	0.982	--	3.00	1.675
	1	1.273	--	4.83	2.710
Welded Both Sides **	1/4	0.207	1/16	0.41	0.231
	5/16	0.311	3/32	0.62	0.346
	3/8	0.414	1/8	0.85	0.475
	1/2	0.558	1/8	1.45	0.811
	5/8	0.702	1/8	1.99	1.115
	3/4	0.847	1/8	2.66	1.490
	1	1.138	1/8	4.30	2.410

* Includes stub end and spatter loss.
** Root of weld back gouged and welded.

TABLE 7-12. Approximate weights of electrode and weld metal in double-V groove with reinforcement (heavily coated electrode). (Ref. 16)

Joint Dimensions (in.)		Lb of Electrode Required for Linear ft. of Weld*	Steel Deposited per Linear ft. of Weld (lb)
Plate Thickness	Throat Opening		
5/8	0.405	1.29	0.724
3/4	0.468	1.68	0.937
1	0.630	2.71	1.520
1-1/4	0.774	3.92	2.195
1-1/2	0.919	5.35	3.00
1-3/4	1.063	6.98	3.91
2	1.207	8.88	4.97
2-1/4	1.352	10.95	6.12
2-1/2	1.496	13.20	7.40
3	1.784	18.50	10.33
3-1/2	2.073	24.60	13.80
4	2.368	31.70	17.80

*Includes stub end and spatter loss.

Note: If root of top weld is back gouged and welded, add 0.10 lb to steel deposited (equivalent to approximately 0.18 lb of electrode).

TABLE 7-13. Riveting size and countersink standards.

Rivet Size (in.)	American Bureau of Shipping				Lloyd's Register		
	Plate Thickness T. (in.)	Countersink			Plate Thickness T. (in.)	Countersink	
		Angle	Depth (in.)			Angle	Depth
1/2	3 16 - 1/4	63°	T		---		
5/8	1 4 - 3 8	63°	T		to 3/8	60°	T
3/4	3 8 - 1 2	47°	T		3/8 - 1/2	60°	T
7/8	1 2 - 23/32	47°	52 min.		1/2 - 23/32	45°	.9T
7/8	---	---	---		---	---	---
1	23 32 - 15/16	39°	.72 "		23 32 - 15/16	45°	.9T
1-1/8	15 16 - 1-5/32	39°	.94 "		15/16 - 1-5/32	45°	.9T
1-1/4	1-5/32 - 1-9/32	39°	.94 "		1-5/32 - 1-9/32	45°	.9T

Rivet Size (in.)	Norwegian Veritas				U. S. Navy		
	Plate Thickness T. (in.)	Countersink			Plate Thickness T. (in.)	Countersink	
		Angle	Depth (in.)			Angle	Depth
1/2	to 1/4	60° min.	T		Note 1	60°	1/4 in.
5/8	1/4 - 3/8	47° "	T		Note 1	60°	5/16 in.
3/4	3/8 - 1/2	41° "	T		Note 1	60°	3/8 in.
7/8	1/2 - 19/32	36° "	T		Note 1	60°	7/16 in.
7/8	19/32 - 23/32	36° "	0.9T		---	---	---
1	23/32 - 15/16	33° "	0.9T		Note 1	60°	1/2 in.
1-1/8	15/16 - 1-5/32	31° "	0.9T		Note 1	60°	9/16 in.
1-1/4	1-5/32 - 1-9/32	31° "	0.9T		Note 1	60°	5/8 in.

Note 1: Thickness not specified.

TABLE 7-14. Length of cone head - countersunk point rivets for various grips.

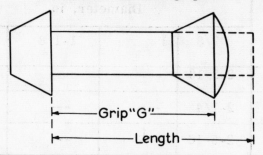

Grip "G"
Length

Grip "G"	Diameter, in.			
	1/2	5/8	3/4	7/8
3/8	1-1/16	---	---	---
7/16	1-1/8	---	---	---
1/2	1-3/16	1-5/16	---	---
9/16	---	1-7/16	---	---
5/8	---	1-1/2	---	---
11/16	---	1-9/16	---	---
3/4	---	1-5/8	1-5/8	---
13/16	---	---	1-11/16	---
7/8	---	---	1-3/4	---
15/16	---	---	1-13/16	---
1	---	---	1-15/16	1-15/16
1-1/16	---	---	---	2
1-1/8	---	---	---	2-1/16
1-3/16	---	---	---	2-1/8

TABLE 7-14 (cont.)

Grip "G"	Diameter, in.			
	7/8	1	1-1/8	1-1/4
1-1/4	2-3/16	---	---	---
1-5/16	2-1/4	---	---	---
1-3/8	2-5/16	---	---	---
1-7/16	2-3/8	2-1/2	---	---
1-1/2	---	2-11/16	---	---
1-5/8	---	2-13/16	---	---
1-3/4	---	2-7/8	---	---
1-7/8	---	3-1/16	3-1/4	---
2	---	---	3-7/16	---
2-1/8	---	---	3-5/8	---
2-1/4	---	---	3-13/16	3-11/16
2-3/8	---	---	---	3-3/4
2-1/2	---	---	---	3-7/8
2-9/16	---	---	---	4

Note: The length given above is just a guide. Small departures from the values given may be necessary to take care of different amounts of shank upset (because of punched-reamed, blown-reamed, or drilled holes), different amounts of material riveters require for cut-off in forming point (from zero to about D/2 in length), and profile of point as required by owners.

TABLE 7-15. Length of cone head - cone point rivets for various grips.

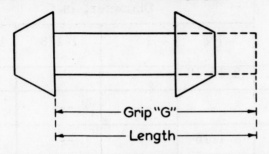

Grip "G"	Diameter, in.			
	1/2	5/8	3/4	7/8
3/8	1-1/4	---	---	---
7/16	1-5/16	---	---	---
1/2	1-3/8	1-3/8	---	---
9/16	---	1-7/16	---	---
5/8	---	1-1/2	---	---
11/16	---	1-9/16	---	---
3/4	---	1-5/8	1-7/8	---
13/16	---	---	2	---
7/8	---	---	2-1/16	---
15/16	---	---	2-1/8	---
1	---	---	2-1/4	2-5/8
1-1/16	---	---	---	2-3/4
1-1/8	---	---	---	2-13/16
1-3/16	---	---	---	2-7/8

TABLE 7-15 (cont.)

Grip "G"	Diameter, in.			
	7/8	1	1-1/8	1-1/4
1-1/4	2-15/16	---	---	---
1-15/16	3	---	---	---
1-3/8	3-1/16	---	---	---
1-7/16	3-1/8	3-1/16	---	---
1-1/2	---	3-1/8	---	---
1-5/8	---	3-1/4	---	---
1-3/4	---	3-3/8	---	---
1-7/8	---	3-1/2	3-5/8	---
2	---	---	3-3/4	---
2-1/8	---	---	3-15/16	---
2-1/4	---	---	4-1/16	4-3/16
2-3/8	---	---	---	4-5/16
2-1/2	---	---	---	4-7/16
2-9/16	---	---	---	4-1/2

Note: See note under Table 7-14.

TABLE 7-16. Length of countersunk head - countersunk point rivets for various grips.

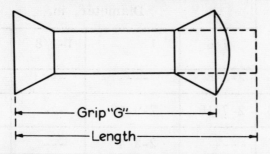

Grip "G"	Diameter, in.			
	1/2	5/8	3/4	7/8
1/2	1-1/4	1-7/16	---	---
9/16	---	1-1/2	---	---
5/8	---	1-9/16	---	---
11/16	---	1-5/8	---	---
3/4	---	1-11/16	1-11/16	---
13/16	---	---	1-3/4	---
7/8	---	---	1-13/16	---
15/16	---	---	1-7/8	---
1	---	---	2	2
1-1/16	---	---	---	2-1/16
1-1/8	---	---	---	2-1/8
1-3/16	---	---	---	2-3/16
1-1/4	---	---	---	2-1/4
1-5/16	---	---	---	2-5/16

TABLE 7-16 (cont.)

Grip "G"	Diameter, in.			
	7/8	1	1-1/8	1-1/4
1-3/8	2-3/8	---	---	---
1-7/16	2-7/16	2-9/16	---	---
1-1/2	---	2-3/4	---	---
1-5/8	---	2-15/16	---	---
1-3/4	---	3-1/8	---	---
1-7/8	---	3-3/16	3-3/8	---
2	---	---	3-1/2	---
2-1/8	---	---	3-3/4	---
2-1/4	---	---	3-15/16	3-3/4
2-3/8	---	---	---	3-7/8
2-1/2	---	---	---	4
2-9/16	---	---	---	4-1/8

Note: See note under Table 7-14.

TABLE 7-17. Rivet proportions.

Rivet Type	D	B	H	C or E
Swell Neck	1/2		1/4	9/16
	5/8		5/16	11/16
	3/4		3/8	13/16
	7/8		7/16	15/16
	1		1/2	1-1/16
	1-1/8		9/16	1-3/16
	1-1/4		5/8	1-5/16
Cone Head	1/2	7/8	3/8	15/32
	5/8	1-3/32	1/2	19/32
	3/4	1-5/16	5/8	45/64
	7/8	1-17/32	23/32	53/64
	1	1-3/4	13/16	15/16
	1-1/8	1-31/32	15/16	1-1/16
	1-1/4	2-3/16	1-1/32	1-11/64
Pan Head (Navy Standard)	1/2	3/4	19/64	1/2
	5/8	15/16	23/64	5/8
	3/4	1-1/8	7/16	3/4
	7/8	1-5/16	33/64	7/8
	1	1-1/2	37/64	1
	1-1/8	1-11/16	21/32	1-1/8
	1-1/4	1-7/8	47/64	1-1/4

TABLE 7-17 (cont.)

Rivet Type	D	B	H
Liverpool Head	1/2	1	5/32
	5/8	1-1/4	3/16
	3/4	1-1/2	7/32
	7/8	1-3/4	1/4
	1	2	9/32
	1-1/8	2-1/4	5/16
Note: Depth and angle of countersink to be in accordance with classification specification.	1-1/4	2-1/2	11/32
Button Head	1/2	25/32	5/16
	5/8	1	13/32
	3/4	1-3/16	31/64
	7/8	1-3/8	35/64
	1	1-19/32	41/64
	1-1/8	1-3/4	45/64
	1-1/4	2	51/64
Steeple Head	1/2	7/8	7/16
	5/8	1-3/32	35/64
	3/4	1-5/16	21/32
	7/8	1-17/32	49/64
	1	1-23/32	55/64
	1-1/8	1-15/16	31/32
	1-1/4	2-5/32	1-3/32

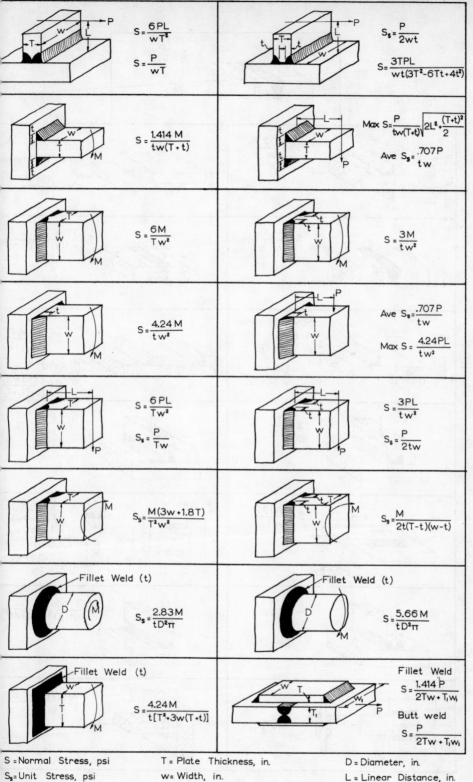

$$S = \frac{6PL}{wT^2}$$

$$S = \frac{P}{wT}$$

$$S_s = \frac{P}{2wt}$$

$$S = \frac{3TPL}{wt(3T^2 - 6Tt + 4t^2)}$$

$$S = \frac{1.414\,M}{tw(T+t)}$$

$$\text{Max } S_s = \frac{P}{tw(T+t)}\sqrt{2L^2 + \frac{(T+t)^2}{2}}$$

$$\text{Ave } S_s = \frac{.707P}{tw}$$

$$S = \frac{6M}{Tw^2}$$

$$S = \frac{3M}{tw^2}$$

$$S = \frac{4.24\,M}{tw^2}$$

$$\text{Ave } S_s = \frac{.707P}{tw}$$

$$\text{Max } S = \frac{4.24PL}{tw^2}$$

$$S = \frac{6PL}{Tw^2}$$

$$S_s = \frac{P}{Tw}$$

$$S = \frac{3PL}{tw^2}$$

$$S_s = \frac{P}{2tw}$$

$$S_s = \frac{M(3w + 1.8T)}{T^2 w^2}$$

$$S_s = \frac{M}{2t(T-t)(w-t)}$$

Fillet Weld (t)

$$S_s = \frac{2.83\,M}{tD^2\pi}$$

Fillet Weld (t)

$$S = \frac{5.66\,M}{tD^2\pi}$$

Fillet Weld (t)

$$S = \frac{4.24\,M}{t[T^2 + 3w(T+t)]}$$

Fillet Weld

$$S = \frac{1.414\,P}{2Tw + T_1 w_1}$$

Butt weld

$$S = \frac{P}{2Tw + T_1 w_1}$$

S = Normal Stress, psi   T = Plate Thickness, in.   D = Diameter, in.

S_s = Unit Stress, psi   w = Width, in.   L = Linear Distance, in.

M = Bending Moment, in.-lb.   P = External Load, lb.   t = Size of Weld, in.

FIG. 7-1. Weld stress formulas.

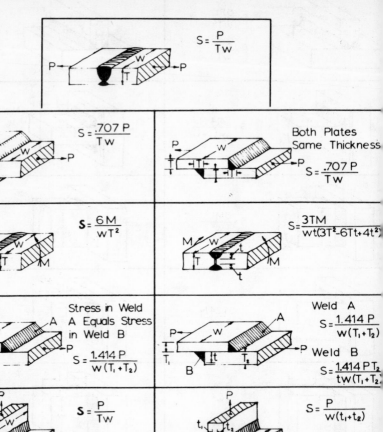

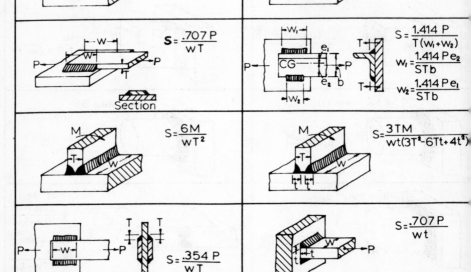

FIG. 7-1 (cont.)

Common Riveting Symbols and Abbreviations

a) General Abbreviations

S.	button head or point	pt.	point
	buttstrap	quad.	quadruple
n.	cone head	riv.	rivet
.	chain	s.	steeple head
;csk.	calked, calking	sgl.	single
l.	countersunk head or point	sm.	seam
.	double	stag.	staggered
	head	trb.	treble
	pan head	zz	zigzag

b) Tightness Abbreviations

.	airtight	O. T. F.	oiltight floor
.	flametight	O. T. M.	oiltight manhole
V.T.	non-watertight	W. T.	watertight
.	oiltight	W. T. B.	watertight bulkhead
.B.	oiltight bulkhead	W. T. F.	watertight floor
	W. T. M.		watertight manhole

c) Riveted Joint Abbreviations

L	single riveted butt lap	SRSBS	sgl. riv. sgl. butt strap
L	double riveted butt lap	DRSBS	dbl. riv. sgl. butt strap
L	treble riveted butt lap	TRSBS	trb. riv. sgl. butt strap
L	quadr. riveted butt lap	QRSBS	quad. riv. sgl. butt strap
S	sgl. riveted butt strap	SRDBS	sgl. riv. dbl. butt strap
S	dbl. riveted butt strap	DRDBS	dbl. riv. dbl. butt strap
S	trb. riveted butt strap	TRDBS	trb. riv. dbl. butt strap
S	quad. riveted butt strap	QRDBS	quad. riv. dbl. butt strap

d) Riveting Symbols

	single riveting	/////	quintuple riveting
	double riveting	//-//	dbl. -butt straps, dbl. riv.
	treble riveting	///-///	dbl. -butt straps, trb. riv.
	quadruple riveting	////-////	dbl. -butt straps, quad. riv.
	CN		chain riveting

Common Abbreviations on Ship's Structural Drawings

A	area	brz.	bronze
ab.; abov.	above	b.s.	both sides
A.B.S.	American Bureau of Shipping	B.S.	butt strap
abt.	about	Bt. Dk.	boat deck
a.c.; A.C.	alternating current	btk.	buttock
accom.	accomodation	B.V.	Bureau Veritas
adj.	adjustable	B.W.G.	Birmingham Wire Gage
A.E.	after end (rear or stern)	bwk.	bulwark
alt.	alteration		
alum.	aluminum	cal.	caliber
amm.; ammo.	ammunition	calc.	calculated
A.P.	after perpendicular; after peak; airport	cap.	capacity
		carp.	carpenter
app.	approved; appendix	C.B.	center of buoyancy; Carnegie Beam Section
approx.	approximate; approximately		
ard.	around	c to c; c/c	center to center
arrgt.	arrangement	cfm	cubic feet per minute
A.S.T.M.	American Society for Testing Materials	chg.	charge
		chk.plt.	checker plate
A.T.	airtight	C.I.	cast iron; corrugated iron
avg	average	cir	circular; circumference; circulating
aux.	auxiliary		
A.W.G.	American Wire Gage	₵ ; C.L.	centerline
		clk.	calked; calking
b	breadth (general)	cm	centimeter
B	breadth of ship; maximum breadth of ship or beam	coam.	coaming
		comp.	composition (brass or bronze)
b/b	back to back	compt.	compartment
B.A.	bulb angle	conn.	connection
bbl	barrel	const	constant
bd.	board	constr.	construction
B.E.	beveled edge	cont.	continuous
bel.	below	corr.	corrected
bet.	between	C.R.S.	cold rolled or corrosion resistant steel
bev.	bevel		
bhd.	bulkhead	C.S.	cast steel
bhp; B.H.P.	brake horsepower	csk.	countersink or countersunk
B.K.	bilge keel; bar keel	ctr.	center
bkt.	bracket	cu	cubic
₤ ; B.L.	baseline	cu ft	cubic feet
bldg.	building	cu in.	cubic inch
blk.	block; black	C.V.K.	center vertical keel
bm.	beam (structural member)	cyl	cylinder or cylindrical
B.M.	bolted manhole cover plate		
bosn.	boatswain	d	depth (general) diameter; draft of ship
bot.; bott.	bottom		
bdry.; bound.	boundary	D	depth of ship; down(ladder)
B.P.	between perpendiculars	D.B.	double bottom
br.	brass	dbl.	double
B.R.	boiler room	dblr.	doubler
Br.Dk.	bridge deck	d.c.; D.C.	deck covering; direct current
brg.	bearing	deg	degree

ept.	department	F.T.	flame or fume tight
et.	detail	F.T.D.	flame or fume tight door
ev.	developed	F.W.	fresh water; feed water
ia.;diam	diameter	fwd.	forward
iag.	diagonal		
iam	diameter	ga.	gage; gauge
im.	dimension	gal	gallon
isp.	displacement	gar.;garbd.	garboard
ist.	distance	galv.	galvanized
iv.	division; divided	gen.	generator
k.	deck	genl.	general
n.;dwn.	down	G.I.	galvanized iron
o	ditto	gird.	girder
r.	door	G.M.I.	glavanized malleable iron
rg.;dwg.	drawing	govt.	government
.W.	deadweight; drinking water		
.W.T.	deadweight	ht.;h	height
oz	dozen	H	draft, H-beam
		H.B.	half breadth
a.	each	hd.	head
.H.	extra heavy	hex.	hexagonal
lec	electric; electrical	h'h	heel to heel
l;elev.	elevation; elevator	hls	holes
.M.	expanded metal	H.M.S.	hull medium steel
mer.;emerg.	emergency	horiz.	horizontal
ncl.	enclosed	hp;H.P.	horsepower
ng.	engine; engineering	H.R.	half round
ngr.	engineer	H.R.S.	hot rolled steel
q	equal; equation	ht.	height
quip.	equipment	H.T.S.	high tensile steel; heat treated steel
quiv.	equivalent		
.R.	engine room	hvy.	heavy
.S.	extra strong		
sc.	escape	I	I(eye) beam
st.	estimated	I.B.	inner bottom
tc.	and so forth	ihp;I.H.P.	indicated horsepower
xist.	existing	I D	inside diameter
xp.	expanded; expansion	in.	inch; inches
xt.	external	inbd.	inboard
xt.	exterior; extend	incl.	including; included
		insp.	inspection; inspector
ab.	fabricated	inst.	instrument
.&A.	fore and aft	int.	internal
.B.	flat bar	interl.	intercostal
.B.K.	flat bar keel	inv.	inverted; invoiced
od.	freeboard	I.P.S.	iron pipe size
c'sle	forecastle		
.E.	forward end	jog.	joggle
.H.	flat head	jr.	junior
g.	figure		
.I.P.	fair in place	K	keel
.K.	flat keel	K.P.	kingpost
.L.	fixed light; floodable length		
lg.	flange	l	length (general)
r.	floor	L	length of ship
.O.	fuel oil	lb	pound
ord.	forward	L.B.P.	length between perpendicu-lars
ound.	foundation		
.P.	fore peak; forward perpen-dicular; flanged plate	lg.	long
		L.H.	left handed
r.	frame	lin.	lineal
r.sp.;F.S.	frame spacing; far side; forged steel	lkr.	locker
		L.L.W.L.	length on the load waterline
	feet; foot	L.O.	lubricating oil

L.O.A.	length overall		pc.	piece
long.	longitudinal		P.C	pitch circle
L.R.	Lloyd's Register		P.C.D.	pitch circle diameter
lt.	light		perf.	perforated
lvr.	lever; louvre		perp.	perpendicular
L.W.L.	load waterline		P.H.	pilothouse
			pl.	plan
m	meter		plat.	platform
mach.	machine		P̶ ; plt.	plate
mag.	magazine		pr.	pair
mar.	margin; marine		prelim.; prel.	preliminary
matl.	material		press.	pressure
max	maximum		prop.	propeller
mn. dk; M.D.	main deck		psi	pounds per square inc
mech.	mechanical		pt.	point
med.	medium		P S; P.& S.	port and starboard
met.	metal		P.W.	potable water
M.G.	machine gun; motor gener-			
	ator		qtrs.	quarters
M.H.	manhole			
M.I.	malleable iron		r	radius
min	minimum		rad.	radius; radiator
misc.	miscellaneous		rd.	round
mk.	mark		ref.	reference
M.L.	molded line; mold loft; mar-		req.	requisition; required
	gin line		red.	reduction
mld.	molded		reqd.	required
mm	millimeter		res.	reserve
m.m.	moment		R.F.W.	reserve feed water
M.P.	mid-perpendicular		rev.	reverse
M.S.	medium steel; machine		R.H.	right hand; round head
	steel; machine screw		riv.	rivet
M.S.; M S	motorship		rm.	room
M.V.	mushroom ventilator; motor		rpm; R.P.M.	revolutions per minut
	vessel		rt.	right
M/V	motor vessel			
			sect.	section
N.A.	naval architect; neutral axis		sep.	separate
nav.	navigating; navigation		sett.	settling
N.M.S.	non-magnetic steel		sgl.	single
no.	number		sh.	shape; sheer
nocsk.; nock.	no countersink		sht.	sheet
norm.	normal		shp; S.H.P.	shaft horsepower
N.& F.	near and far		sk.	sketch
N.S.	near side		sol.	solid
N.T.S.	not to scale		spa.	space; spaced
N.V.	Norwegian Veritas		spec.	specification; special
N.W.T.	non-watertight		sq	square
			S.S.; S S	steamship
O.A.	overall		st.	straight
O.B.	outboard		sta.	station
O D	outside diameter		stan.; stanch	stanchion
off.	office; officer		star.; stbd.	starboard
O.H.	oval head; open hearth		std.	standard
open.	opening		stiff.	stiffener
opp.	opposite		stl.	steel
ord.	ordinate		str.	stringer
O.S.	outside; outstanding; other		struct.	structural
	side		S.T.S.	special treatment stee
O.T.	oil tight		S.W.	salt water
O.T.H	oil tight hatch		symm.	symmetrical
pass.	passage; passenger		t	thickness
patt.	pattern		T	T-bar; top; tons

temp	template; temporary; temperature	vert.	vertical
		V.K.	vertical keel
T.F.O.	tons fuel oil	V.L.	vertical ladder
T.F.W.	tons fresh water	V.M.L.	vertical metal ladder
thd.	thread	vol.	volume
thk.	thick; thickness		
thru.	through	w; W	weight; weld
tk.	tank	wt.	weight
tol.	tolerance	W.Fl.; WF; W.F.	wide flange section
tot.	total	W.I.	wrought iron
trans.	transverse	W.L.	waterline
trk.	trunk	W.M.	wire mesh
T.S.	this side; turbine ship; twin screw	wt	weight
		W.S.	wrought steel
T.S.W.	tons salt water	W.T.	watertight
T.T.	tank top	W.T.D.	watertight door
		W.T.M.H.	watertight manhole
U	up (ladder)		
U.D.	upper deck	X.H.	extra heavy
U.S.S.	United States Ship; United States Standard	X.S.	extra strong
		X.X.H.	double extra heavy
U.S.Std.	United States Standard	X.X.S.	double extra strong
U.S.S.G.	United States Standard Gauge		
		yd	yard
V	vent; volume		
vent.	ventilator	Z	Z(zee) bar

References

1. Rossell, H. E. and Chapman, L. B., Principles of Naval Architecture, Vol. I, The Society of Naval Architects and Marine Engineers, New York, 1958.

2. Johnson, A. M., "The Overstressed Corner," Bureau of Ships Journal, June 1958.

3. Johnson, A. M., "The Overstressed Corner: Openings Adjacent to Abrupt Ending of Structure," Bureau of Ships Journal, December 1958.

4. Johnson, A. M., "The Stressed Corner," Bureau of Ships Journal, March 1958.

5. Vasarhelyi, D. and Hetchman, R. A., "Welded Reinforcement of Openings in Structural Steel Tension Members," Ship Structure Committee Report, Serial No. SSC—75, March 21, 1955.

6. Durelli, A. S., Phillips, E. A., and Tsao, C. H., Introduction to the Theoretical and Experimental Analysis of Stress and Strain, McGraw-Hill Book Company, Inc., New York, 1958.

7. Wahl, A. M., and Beeuwkes, "Stress Concentrations Produced by Holes and Notches," Transactions of the American Society of Mechanical Engineers, New York, August 1934.

8. Brock, J. S., "The Stresses around Square Holes with Rounded Corners," Journal of Ship Research, October 1938.

9. de Leires, H., and Dutilleul, H., "Sur L'Affaiblissement de la Résistance des Ponts de Navire dans la Region des Ouvertures et sur les Renforcements a y Apporter," Annuaire Bulletin-Association Technique Maritime et Aéronautique, France, 1953.

10. Kuntsmann, C. M., and Umberger, R. C., "The Stresses around Reinforced Square Openings with Rounded Corners in an Uniformly Loaded Plate," Webb Institute of Naval Architecture Thesis, June 1959.

11. Wright, E. A., Jonassen, F., and Acker, H. G., "Research Under the Ship Structure Committee," Transactions of the Society of Naval Architects and Marine Engineers, New York, November 1952.

12. Welding Research Council, Control of Steel Construction to Avoid Brittle Fracture, edited by Shank, M. E., New York, 1957.

13. De Garmo, E. P., "Tests of Various Designs of Welded Hatch Corners for Ships," Welding Research Supplement, American Welding Society, February 1948.

14. "Considerations of Welded Hatch Corner Design," Ship Structure Committee Report, Serial No. SSC—37, October 1, 1952.

15. Turnbull, J., "Hull Structures," Transactions of the Institution of Engineers and Shipbuilders in Scotland, Glasgow, Great Britian, December 1956.

16. American Welding Society, Welding Handbook, New York, N. Y., 4th edition.

17. Henry, O. H., and Claussen, G. E., Welding Metallurgy—Iron and Steel, American Welding Society, New York, N. Y., 2nd edition.

18. The Lincoln Electric Co., Procedure Handbook of Arc Welding Design and Practice, Cleveland, Ohio, 11th edition.

19. American Bureau of Shipping, Rules for Building and Classing Steel Vessels, New York, N. Y., 1961.

20. Osaka University, Technology Reports, Vol. 9, "Effect of Welding Conditions on the Shrinkage Distortion in Welded Structures," Part 2, Osaka, Japan, 1959.

21. Arnott, D., Design and Construction of Steel Merchant Ships, The Society of Naval Architects and Marine Engineers, New York, N. Y., 1955.

22. Kumose, T., Yoshida T., Abe T. and Onoue, H., "Prediction of Angular Distortion Caused by One-Pass Fillet Welding," Welding Journal, Vol. 33, pp. 945-956, 1954.

23. Admiralty Ship Welding Committee, "The Application of Electric Arc Welding to Ship Construction," His Majesty's Stationary Office, London, 1945.

24. Vedeler, J., "One Learns from Bitter Experience," International Shipbuilding Progress, Vol. 5, No. 42, February 1958.

25. Brown, D. P., "Structural Design and Details of Longitudinally Framed Tankers," Transactions of the Society of Naval Architects and Marine Engineers, New York, November 1949.

26. Tingey, R. H., "Tanker Design from the Operator's Viewpoint," Transactions of the Society of Naval Architects and Marine Engineers, New York, 1951.

27. Hodgson, J., "Brittle Fracture in Welded Ships," Transactions of the Institution of Naval Architects, London, 1958.

28. Schaler, L., Taschenbuch fur Schiffbauer, Bootbauer, Schiffzimmerer und Segelmacher, Richard Carl Schmidt & Co., Hamburg, West Germany, 1952.

29. Ryerson, J. T. & Son, Inc., Ryerson Data Book, 1958.

Index

Index

1